Great Hunting and Fishing Stories

SPORTS AFIELD: "Old Croc," by Jason Lucas; "The Stream," by Bill Wolf; "A Shift of the Wind," by Sigurd Olson; "Brindle Cow," by Bud Jackson; "We Get That Way," by Horace Lytle; "A Red Dog of Ireland," by Joe MacGaheran; "Wicomico Salmon," by F. Wallace Taber.

THE AMERICAN RIFLEMAN: "Reconversion of a Hunter," by Bert Popowski; "No Holes Barred," by Jim Berryman.

ALFRED A. KNOPF: "The W. D. A.," by John Alden Knight, previously published in his book "Woodcock."

G. P. PUTNAM'S SONS: "Great Day in the Morning," by Nash Buckingham, previously published in his book "Tattered Coat."

THE PUBLISHERS

Acknowledgments

We express appreciation to the original publishers listed below for permission to reprint the stories included in this anthology. The stories not listed here appear by permission of the individual authors.

COLLIER'S MAGAZINE: 1,000,000 B. C., by Frank Dufresne.

FIELD AND STREAM: "The Clearing Buck," by John S. Martin; "Bruisers of the Weed Beds," by Ben East; "The Stork and the Pintail," by Ira Bright; "Don't Tell Judy," by Clarke Venable; "Hand Line 'em for Fun," by Bill Ackerman; "Bear Valley Pay Day," by Ted Trueblood; "Way of the Wild Ones," by Frank Dufresne; "Fabulous Fish," by William J. Schaldach; "Scairty Cat," by David M. Newell; "The Rejuvenation of Greene," by Ira Bright; "Steve's Mixed Double," by Fred Copeland; "The Last Day," by Col. Harold P. Sheldon.

NATIONAL PARKS MAGAZINE: "The Wilderness," by Sigurd Olson.

NATURE MAGAZINE: "Odd Bedfellows," by Wilfred S. Bronson; "Leader of the Flock," by W. J. Schoonmaker.

OUTDOORS: "The Dodger," by Henry P. Davis; "Hail the Humber," by Lee Wulff; "Life among the Wood Ticks," by Gordon MacQuarrie; "With Woodcock," by Col. Harold P. Sheldon; "With Quail," by Nash Buckingham; "With Grouse," by Burton L. Spiller; "With Pheasants," by Ben East; "To Fish with Ghosts," by Lt. Clarence A. Schoenfield; "The Tail-Ender," by Henry P. Davis; "Pop Goes the Beagle," by Sgt. Tom Burrier; "Nantucket Blues," by Frank Vining Smith; "First Covey," by J. Austell Small.

OUTDOORSMAN: "The Expert Learns a Lesson," by Mabry I. Anderson; "Come On—Three," by Hank Bruns; " 'Pothole Guys, Friz Out,' " by Gordon MacQuarrie; "Cicero—the Bar Walker," by Charles E. Gillham.

GREAT
Hunting and Fishing
Stories

EDITED BY

J. HAMMOND BROWN

Grosset & Dunlap, Publishers

NEW YORK

Foreword

SPONSORED BY THE OUTDOOR WRITERS ASSOCIATION OF AMERICA, this collection of stories offers a picture of the current American scene in the realm of that recreational outdoors upon which an ever increasing number of us have come to rely as a palliative for our modern hectic manner of living.

Many of us get a thrill following a meandering mountain stream with rod and reel in hand; others prefer the tang that comes with fishing on salty waters. For some the dainty wand that is the flyrod is the key that opens the way to peace in the out-of-doors; others prefer the boat rod, even the lowly hand-line; and to the privileged few the real thrill comes in searching out leviathan in his ocean lair with instruments scaled to the effort.

Still others achieve the peak of enjoyment as they course Upland game fields in the companionship of a hunting dog; yet many prefer to still hunt, pitting their woodcraft against the cunning of the hunted. It may be Br'er Rabbit in the brier patch, Mister Bob White whistling in the field, a wedge of Canadian honkers winging down from Northern breeding grounds, a cock pheasant in a Dakota corn-field, a woodcock zig-zagging through a Vermont swale, a spike buck in the alders, a grouse, wild gobbler or the imported Hun of the great Northwestern hunting fields; each brings its own particular thrill to the hunter.

Then there is that army of nature lovers who seek contentment in the outdoors armed with neither rod nor gun, who wander beside still and turbulent waters, scale mountains and penetrate the wilder-ness for the sheer joy of communing with Nature and her children of the wilds.

To all of these this volume is dedicated and for all of these its stories have been collected that they may live again, each after his own fashion, days spent in the open.

These pages have also been designed for still another vast army of those who love the outdoors, who for one reason or another are denied actual participation, but who must gain their thrills through the eyes and the magic of the written word of others.

To each and every one of these, the angler, the hunter, the nature lover and the stay-at-home, these pages will bring many hours of enjoyment. In assembling these more than two score stories there was only one thought in mind, to bring to you as complete a picture as possible of the current American recreational outdoor scene.

In making this possible, the sponsors of this volume have had the cooperation of the publishers and editors of such National outdoor magazines as *Field and Stream*, *Nature Magazine*, *Outdoors*, *Out-doorsman* and *Sports Afield*. In fact the editors of these magazines, Hugh Grey, Richard Westwood, H. G. Tapply, Jim Mitchell and Ted Kesting selected from their respective magazines the reservoir of stories from which the final pages of this book emerged. To all of them, publishers and editors, due appreciation is hereby acknowledged.

Special acknowledgment and thanks are due to the publishers of *Collier's Magazine* for releasing Frank Dufresne's story "1,000,000 B.C."; to Alfred A. Knopf, publishers of the book "Woodcock" by John Alden Knight for permission to use one of its chapters; to Devereux Butcher, editor of the *National Parks Magazine* for the use of Sigurd Olson's story "The Wilderness"; to A. S. Barnes and Company, publishers of Col. Harold P. Sheldon's "Tranquillity" for permission to use his story "The Second Battle of Gettysburg" from this volume; to the publishers of The American Rifleman for permission to use Bert Popowski's story "Reconversion of a Hunter" and Jim Berryman's "No Holes Barred!"; and to G. P. Putnam's Sons, publishers of Nash Buckingham's "Tattered Coat" for the use of his story "Great Day in the Morning."

The sponsors of this volume also desire to thank all of those writers, whose names are elsewhere displayed, whose stories make this book possible. Their names compose a "Who's Who" of modern outdoor literature. Also equal thanks are due to the artists whose illustrations garnish the pages of this book. Through the medium of brush, etching tool, pen and pencil they have added greatly to this verbal portrayal of the recreational out-of-doors.

Just a few words in closing. This volume was conceived for your entertainment, therefore no preachments have found a place in its pages, and yet through each and every story you will find a pervading sense of good sportsmanship, a feeling that the creel and the game bag are always of secondary importance to the true outdoorsman, that the real thrill found in the outdoors, on the stream and in the field, is always in the chase and not in the kill.

And so its sponsors offer you this anthology in the hope that you and I and all of us will always so conduct ourselves when we partake of Nature's bounties that the outdoors indeed shall always be unlimited.

J. HAMMOND BROWN
Executive Director, OWAA

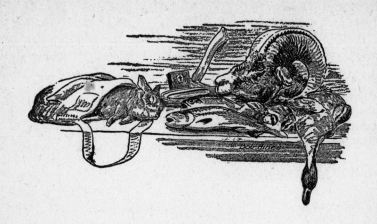

Contents

xi

xii Contents

xiv Contents

Great Hunting and Fishing Stories

A Tale of Fox-hunting in the Deep South

The Dodger

By HENRY P. DAVIS

A BULLFROG BELLOWED A THROATY CHALLENGE, TELEGRAPHING
to The Dodger's subconscious mind and ever-alert ears the fact
that evening shades were falling. The sturdy gray fox uncoiled himself from his comfortable curl. He rose, stretched, searched the sharp,
scented air of the autumn evening with his sensitive nose and gazed
with wary eyes at the valley below.

The peace and quietude of twilight promised an easy hunt for a
juicy meal. And The Dodger knew where it could be found. Meals
presented no great problem to him. Soon rabbits would be frolicking
in the moonlit spaces, fat frogs would be sending croaky serenades
along the bayou's edge. Field mice and cotton rats could be garnered
without too much trouble. Lush country and easy pickings!

Veteran of many a tilt with the hounds, wherein his fancy foot-

1

work had earned him the sobriquet "The Dodger," the big fox had grown a bit lazy of late. From his vantage point on the high hill he had watched the building of a new chicken house on Ellis Nelson's farm, had seen the fine young pullets become acclimated to their new surroundings and then be allowed the freedom of the Nelson acres. Easy pickings, indeed! It was a simple matter for him to sift down from his hillside lair, lie in wait along a hedgerow and pick off a plump pullet or fat hen returning home to roost.

He was smart enough not to confine his marauding to one farm, for he had felt the ire of many farmers in various forms—hounds, traps and guns. Had outwitted them all, except the one rifle bullet which had torn away the tip of one ear, and the confidence which comes with experience told him he could do it again. This evening he was hungry—and in the valley below a banquet table was laid. . . .

Young Tom Nelson was returning from the north forty with a load of corn. Lowering the bars of the home-lot, a snort from Nettie, the off-mare, brought him alert. Catching the line of the old mare's gaze, he saw it all. A loitering pullet; a flash of gray and red from the hedgerow; a smothered squawk—and The Dodger defiantly trotting toward the hills with his evening meal! Easy pickings, indeed.

"It was The Dodger! I know, dad," furious young Tommie informed his father. "He turned and practically laughed at me—then trotted away with that chicken as if the whole world belonged to him. I *know* it was The Dodger. I've seen him time and again. He's got a crop-ear."

"Unload your corn, son," replied Nelson. "I'm going to the store and 'phone The Judge. Maybe he'll bring his hounds out tonight."

"He'll never catch this old devil," grumbled Tommie.

No secrets could ever be hidden in a southern country store. Everything anyone says is heard by everyone else—and is a matter of general interest. News of the day, crop conditions, gossip of the community, are all subjects to be relayed, ofttimes shamelessly exaggerated. And when the store telephone is used there is an immediate hush. The user's end of the conversation becomes a personal matter to all sitters-around, who, naturally, strain their ears to hear what the party on the other end of the line has to say.

And so it was that those in Neal Harder's store that night knew that The Dodger, the crop-eared fox which denned on High Hill, had taken his tenth hen from Ellis Nelson's farm; that The Judge and

Cap'n Zack had been planning to hunt Rough-top Ridge south of town that night; that, in prospect of a tilt with The Dodger, they had changed their plans and would show up at Nelson's farm along about "good moon-up."

Of course, this meant a brief stop at Harder's store. To give horses and dogs a breathing spell, to buy a few apples, probably some cheese and crackers, and, if Harder gave a certain wink, to repair to his back room where flasks might be filled with a certain potent fluid known as "mountain dew," which possessed the properties of warding off colds and accounted for some of the mighty fox-horn blasts which rang through the early morning air—recalling the hounds from their futile pursuit of The Dodger.

As the small cavalcade topped the hill near Harder's store, the musical clink of curb-chains blending with the timed beat of well-shod hoofs, all ears came to attention. At the head of the column rode The Judge and Cap'n Zack, bodies comfortably swaying to the gliding gait of the best "walking-horses" in the county. Behind, tails aloft and red tongues lolling, trotted eight couples of foxhounds, matched for speed, application and endurance—but of varied voice in order to round out a choral effect.

Behind them rode Esau, the colored kennel man, making sure that all went well with the hounds. And, at a short distance to the rear, a small group of lovers of the chase, each of which had joined the procession as it had passed his farmhouse, jogged along in keen anticipation of a good night's sport.

Respects paid, and refreshments enjoyed by both men and beast, the party repaired to Nelson's farm, where more saddled horses were hitched to the picket-fence.

"I don't know where we'll jump him," said Ellis Nelson to The Judge. "But his trail should not be too cold and Tommie knows exactly where you can pick it up."

"Are you sure it's The Dodger?" asked Cap'n Zack.

"Tommie saw him plain as day," replied Nelson. "He's the big 'un with the crop-ear. Sure hope you catch him, for it looks like I won't have any chickens left soon."

"The night is a good one, the hounds are keen and we'll do our best," replied The Judge. "If he hasn't left the country, we'll give him a run for his money. Tommie, where did you see him last?"

"He popped out of the hedgerow right by that wild cherry tree, grabbed the pullet, trotted up the path and went through the little gap by that bunch of sassafras. I *know* it was The Dodger. I saw the whole thing. But you'll never catch him. He's too smart for any pack of hounds," the youngster grumbled.

"We'll see, sonny," smiled The Judge.

Telling Esau to keep the eager hounds in hand, The Judge and Cap'n Zack drew off to one side for a consultation and a look at the lay of the land. Both were master strategists in the hunting of either the gray or red fox. An occasional catch was, of course, to the liking of both, particularly if it was necessary to "blood" young hounds, but both had long since learned that the taking of a brush meant that that fox would never run again. And a good race meant more than a kill to each of the veterans.

But here was a different matter. This fox was not living off the countryside's bounteous offer of natural prey. Rather, he was becoming a serious menace to a good citizen's property—and his brush was demanded by no less a person than the serious-minded young scion of the household. Tonight they were hunting for sport—and something more.

The Judge called Esau to him. "Esau," he asked, "if you were The Dodger and were jumped out of a good warm bed and had to run for your life, where would you head for?"

The old negro scratched his graying poll, grinned and said: "Jedge, Ah ben thinkin' 'bout 'at same thing mahse'f. They all tells us this hyeah's a smaht fox. He's had a big belly-full of fine fat chickens. Mos' likely he's had a nap by now and ef he ain't disturbed he'll prob'bly sleep in till mornin'. He's loaded heavy an' he doan want no race. So ef we jump him—and he's got as much sense as they say he is—he's gonna make for 'at big thicket down yonder, wind in an' aroun' through them briers, cross 'at creek a time or two and then, ef he cain't shake 'em, high tail it for dry groun' in them high hills— an' take his chances.

"He's a smaht fox but he's a *gray* fox. He ain't gonna run outa the country like a red fox might do. An' he ain't gonna git too far away frum that chicken roost. Ef he ain' a ghost an'll stay on the groun' we'll hang his hide on Mistuh Nelson's barn tonight, provided," the old negro smiled knowingly, "we can out-run him an' out-smaht him."

The Judge and Cap'n Zack exchanged understanding glances. Dignity must be maintained—and Esau understood.

The trio returned to the waiting group, Esau, as usual, three paces to the rear. "Gentlemen," The Judge said, "we are out to catch The

Dodger tonight and to present his brush to Mr. Nelson. No hound has ever laid a tooth on him, but tonight we'll try to outwit him. Frankly, Cap'n Zack and I would like to see him live on and on—and match our hounds against him night after night. But he's proven himself to be an arrogant nuisance and we'll do our best to bring his career of thievery to an end. He has lived by his wits. Tonight we'll try tactics probably unfamiliar to him—and for which Cap'n Zack and I ask your pardon.

"Our consolation lies in the well-known fact," continued The Judge, "that a confirmed criminal must pay the penalty for his crimes."

Esau, in the background, gently rubbing the ear of a nervous young hound, mumbled under his breath, "Boss sho' makin' big talk tonight."

"We will work the hounds in relays tonight, putting in fresh hounds when the going gets too tough, and, if possible, taking up, for a rest, any tiring dog."

Reaching in his saddle-bags, The Judge produced a long leather leash and snapped it on the collar of a young hound coupled with white-black-and-tan Joe Wheeler, the veteran of the pack.

"Tommie," he said, "this young dog is your special charge for tonight. He's new to the pack, but he comes highly recommended and The Dodger will give him a test tonight. Stay close to Esau. He'll tell you what to do."

There was an audible gulp from Esau and he blurted out, "But, Jedge you ain' give me no instructions 'bout dis!"

"You'll get your instructions later," was the quiet reply.

"Gentlemen, we're going to try to pick up The Dodger's trail with three strike dogs, jump him and then point our tactics according to the turn of the tide. Tommie, look after that young dog. Esau, uncouple Joe Wheeler, Tip and Top. We'll await developments."

The three big hounds bounded away into the moonlit night. Presently the low rumbling roar of Joe Wheeler announced discovery of the trail. Tip and Top promptly chimed in. But there was a loss here and there. The entire pack was eager to go and difficult to restrain. But The Judge lifted his hand and said, "Let's wait until they jump him."

Black Esau whispered, "Jedge, 'at old fox done jumped hisself. Fust time Joe Wheeler opened he wuz on his way to duh thicket."

And Esau was right. The Dodger had enjoyed his chicken dinner. Had curled up and had a good nap, was settling down for the night when his crop-ear, always pointed up-wind, telegraphed "unusual noises in the valley below." The dog-fox lifted his head and listened. All was quiet. He licked his chops, curled up again and flicked his soft, bushy tail over his sensitive nose. Then the booming blare of Joe Wheeler's bass rang out—and The Dodger was on his way to the thicket.

Cap'n Zack and The Judge held another consultation. Then reached into their saddle-bags and withdrew a number of stout leashes.

"Gentlemen," said The Judge, "I'm sorry we can't give you a real race tonight, but we're out to *get* this fox—fair or foul. And it may be foul. With the help of some of you, Cap'n Zack will take part of the pack to the edge of the thicket, wait until you catch the line of the running dogs and try to pick up The Dodger's trail ahead of them. I will take the others and try to cut him off where Esau thinks he might pass. We'll get him *some way*."

When Cap'n Zack's party had passed out of hearing, The Judge turned to Esau and said, "Take Tommie and the young hound into the high country, wait till you hear the line of drive—then use your own judgment." To young Thomas Nelson, he said, "Son, you don't like The Dodger, do you?"

"No, sir," the boy replied, looking The Judge squarely in the eye. "He's an old devil—but I *do* like dogs. And this one's a dandy."

"Well, my boy," said The Judge, "if you like him you can have him—provided he catches The Dodger tonight. He's new in the pack and we haven't even given him a name yet. But I think he can show some of the old ones a thing or two. And, fair or foul, if he catches The Dodger tonight, he belongs to you."

"Geeee," breathed Tommie, and then, "C'mon, Esau."

The two rode away with the nameless young hound trotting along at the side of Tommie's mule.

The Dodger hit the thicket just according to Esau's prediction, and far ahead of schedule. But when the six hounds Cap'n Zack loosed picked up his trail there was no resting. He ducked and dodged through the heavy underbrush, but fresh hounds were right behind him all the time. He ripped through a favorite haunt of low-hanging grapevines, honeysuckle and blackberry bushes and brought his pursuers to a temporary loss, giving him a chance to race for the open country. But, foreseeing this, The Judge loosed his portion of the pack—and again there was no resting. It was hammer-and-tongs for an hour and a half, and The Dodger was confused. "Head for the ledge in the hills," was his reasoning and he streaked in that direction.

Esau and Tommie and the young nameless hound heard him pass. "Turn 'im loose, Mister Tommie, an' le's see what he's made of," said Esau. The plunging young hound couldn't miss the hot trail, far ahead of the pack. And Tommie and Esau rode like hellions over that rough country, without thought of life or limb.

"Come 'is way, Mister Tommie!" yelled Esau. "We'll see it all when we git on top!" And they did.

The Dodger, circling higher all the time, headed home with the young hound right behind him. Fagged out and tail drooping, the big dog-fox gave one frantic leap for his lair in the shadow of a cliff— and made it. The young dog tried to follow, but he couldn't scramble like a fox. On the third try he toppled back, to fall with a rib-cracking thump on a sharp rock. Painfully gaining his feet, he laboriously worked his way to the top of the cliff, and looked down. The hot scent of the exhausted fox smashed against his nostrils and he leaped into space—to land within three feet of The Dodger, done in but snarling. A brief struggle and it was all over.

Tommie and Esau watched it all—and Esau's struggle with Tommie was greater than the combat below. "He's caught him, and he belongs to me. The Judge told me so and I gotta get him!" yelled Tommie.

But the wise old negro would have none of it. Once he had calmed the trembling boy, he lifted his hunting horn and blew the notes which signalled the end of the hunt. Then carefully picked his way down the cliff to retrieve the body of The Dodger and the exhausted young hound.

In front of Ellis Nelson's fireplace, the young dog lay dozing. Tommie ran a caressing hand over a brier-torn ear. The Judge sipped a hot toddy, fortification against a long ride home.

"Tommie," he said, "we tricked The Dodger tonight and, frankly, I'm none too proud of it. But you won a good young dog and he proved his worth. We've never given him a name. What are you going to call him?"

The youngster's back straightened, and again he looked The Judge squarely in the eye. "If you don't mind, sir," he replied, "I'll name him The Dodger."

Old Croc

By JASON LUCAS

Long, long years ago old croc was hatched. There was a shallow, weedy spot near the shore of Tamarack Lake, and to it came a huge northern pike laden with eggs and escorted by three or four much smaller males. She had spawned there, she had laid more than half a million eggs at one time! Three days later she had chanced to meet one of her mates. There had been a streaking dart through the water, a swirl that barely showed on the surface, and where there had been two fish there now was only one, a huge female who looked much bulkier than a moment before, and who sank slowly to the bottom, lazily opening and closing her great gills in contentment. Such was the heritage of Old Croc.

At first Croc was only a tiny barred needle which seemed to shoot through the water without the slightest movement of tail or fin. Now she would be motionless; now she would be streaking off like an

arrow from the bow. Straight as an arrow was her aim; many was the
tiny water creature which entered those diminutive but rapacious
jaws.

The needle grew. Larger insects were engulfed in those ever-
hungry jaws...bugs, larvae, everything that moved. Larger grew
the needle. There were thousands of other needles among the weeds,
but this one grew fastest of all. At last came the day when this large
needle swallowed one of the smallest needles—one of her brothers.
This was much more nourishing food than the bugs and spiders, so
her size increased in leaps and bounds while the other needles
vanished.

There were little minnows; there were tiny fry of other species;
but to this little cannibal nothing seemed so tasty and desirable as one
of her own kind. On this one thing the larger pike of earlier hatches
thoroughly and whole-heartedly agreed with her...they agreed
among themselves that young Croc would provide a most delightful
lunch if she could be caught. Of course, two pike had to be of practically the same size to agree on anything; if they were not, the larger
swallowed the smaller as the quickest way of settling all arguments.

Croc took very good care not to be swallowed. Not that she re-
sented the attitude of the larger pike; well she knew the one great
moral code of her tribe, "Swallow that which moves and is smaller
than thou." Had a bigger fish failed to try to live up to this rule, she
would have wondered...but her brain was far too tiny for such
abstruse things as wonder. In that little brain was room for nothing
but the overpowering desire to chase, to kill, to swallow.

It was not long until the time came when she was over a foot in
length, although she was still endowed with the shape of a huge
needle. Now she had her adult coloration, a sort of greenish-gray,
thickly speckled with yellowish-white spots. Toward the back she
grew darker, almost black, and her belly was silvery-white. Her tail
and fins were a beautiful transparent bright red with black blotches.
Already she had become a little terror to the smaller species of the
lake, so much so that she fancied herself mature and made her first
jaunt to the deep water. This over-confidence almost ended her history there and then.

Out from the shallow weeds near the shore she swam with wonderful grace. Her tail seemed stiff behind her; not a fin seemed to move;
still she glided along like some diminutive, noiseless submarine bent
on death and destruction. She was almost invisible from any side.

Seen from the bottom, the white of her belly blended with the sky and the shimmering surface of Tamarack Lake. From above, her dark back merged with the muddy bottom perfectly. From either side the gray-green ground color and dapplings of yellowish could hardly be seen.

Three feet of water—four—five—ten. Nothing had happened... nothing but little fish flying in panic to the weeds at her stealthy approach. She rose higher, and drifted like a slender shadow above the tops of the weeds. Now she had come to the edge of this particular stretch of weedy forest, but far ahead she could see another. Of course there was a long distance of open bottom between; but was she not a pike, whom all things feared?

She hesitated a moment, scanning the water with her fierce eyes. Nothing could look more peaceful. In fact, there was but one thing in sight, some great fluffy thing that floated quietly on the surface of the water halfway across, with two broad paddles very slowly waving in the water beneath it.

Croc started forward slowly, watching those slowly-moving paddles cautiously. Of course it was some creature of the other world, the world where there was no water, but it was well to keep an eye on it. Instinct made Croc sink deeper and deeper as she approached the air-creature above. Presently she was almost beneath it, and here she paused, her cold, evil eyes fixed on the paddles. They were moving, therefore they might be good to eat.

Then there was a slight splash beside the floating thing; a long, snake-like neck was thrust far under the surface; jetty, expressionless eyes swept the bottom. But Croc had hung motionless, so the loon had not seen her. The great bird raised his head, opened his bill, and sent a wild, laughing call to his mate at the other end of the lake. With head on one side he waited for the answer, and having heard it his neck went under again.

This time Croc was not so cautious; she was becoming accustomed to that air-thing floating innocently above. So it was that she permitted a slight waving motion of her tail. Immediately, where the loon had been, a silvery explosion of light broke the surface of the water, a great burst of light that dazzled Croc when she looked that way. Then the blinding light was traveling outward in ever-growing circles, and in the middle of it appeared a dusky shape that came downward like a bolt... the loon, strong wings and webbed feet sending him through the water at a terrific rate, sharp bill straight ahead to cleave a way.

Across the barren bottom shot Croc—never before had she looked so like a well-sped arrow as now—straight toward the nearest point of the weed-bed. She heard a snap like a closing steel-trap just behind her, and the tip of her tail seemed to burn. Instinctively she knew that it would be only an instant until the next snap came. The weeds were now only ten feet off, but she could not reach them.

Croc doubled her body and shot straight toward the surface. After her sped the loon, agile as herself. Next a wild letter S, and then a broken circle. Around and around in wild gyrations went the two— two indistinct, whirling blurs, so fast they doubled and maneuvered. Again and again Croc felt the quick tremor of the water as the strong beak of the loon snapped, barely missing its mark by a fraction of an inch.

There came a snap that was duller than the others. Croc felt her movements suddenly arrested, felt a great weight hanging to her tail— a dull pain in that tail. The loon had seized her!

Then against Croc's side came the scraping of strong weeds—bare inches to safety! The pike's body doubled like a snake's, seeking purchase among the weeds; her tail thrashed wildly. There was the vibration of something tearing dully, and the pike was flashing into the weed-bed, a tiny stream of red behind where skin and flesh had been torn loose close to her tail . . . lucky that the loon had not had a better hold! Into the weeds, too, shot the great bird, only to soon have its wings hopelessly entangled. For a few seconds it struggled to go forward, little black pupils expanded to see in the half-light and seeking the fish that had barely escaped. Then it rose slowly, angrily, to the surface, where it shook its bill and sent a wild, baffled call to its mate.

For perhaps an hour Croc lay there invisible in the weeds. Her tail hurt—slightly—nothing could hurt her dull nerves very much. At first she was very cautious, but this caution did not last long; soon it was drowned in her one great passion—to kill, to eat! She had almost forgotten the loon, but when next she would see one the memory would come back, dimly, just enough to make her careful.

She was hungry—rarely was she otherwise. She worked slowly out to the very edge of the weed-bed, sank close to the bottom, and waited, motionless as a water-logged stick. Presently she saw a brownish shape approaching; a young dogfish. That would be her meat! Dogfish, she had decided, was just as good to eat as another pike.

A blue-gill passed, a small bass. These she ignored—she ate such occasionally, but that ridge of terrible spines on their backs made the bass and his relatives undesirable as a rule.

Apparently without her willing it, she sank lower and lower into the level bed of weeds under her, until nothing showed but her eyes—cold, motionless eyes that saw everything but were themselves unseen. Now the unsuspecting dogfish was almost over her. Then, somehow, Croc was no longer in the weeds. She had not seemed to move, but now she hung in the water above and down her capacious throat was traveling a flopping tail. Slowly she sank back, gill-covers working lazily. That had been a good meal! Nor did she know that it had been also a good deed, for the scavenger dogfish is one of the greatest destroyers of the spawn of pike, bass, and other game fish. Perhaps if she had known it was a good deed she would not have eaten him, for her dull little brain held nothing but evil and voracity.

Evening came, and she stirred lazily. She was already hungry again—it was one of the days when fish, for some unknown reason, are always ravenous no matter what they have eaten. Again she worked close to the edge of the weed-bed, and again her cold eyes searched the water for prey.

Soon she saw it—some strange little fish that she did not recognize. It was long and thin and round, and kept curling and uncurling its pinkish body as though in pain. There was some slender thing running from it to the surface of the water where what appeared to be a great log floated harmlessly. Croc did not know what the little fish was, but it had life and therefore should be eaten.

She drifted toward it slowly, ready to make a dash if it tried to escape. She smelled it—it had the odor of earth. Slowly, she took it in her mouth.

Immediately something seemed to almost tear her head from her body. She whirled in consternation and headed back toward the weeds, but something brought her around in a half-circle. Again she tried to turn, but before she knew what was happening she felt herself shooting out of the water, to land flopping in the bottom of a boat.

There was a whoop of joy as two tattered, freckle-faced boys bent over her. She shook the hook from her lips, but that helped none at all, for the sides of the boat were high and she did not know that beyond them lay the open water. One of the boys—his skin was much lighter colored than the other's, although his nose was very red—reached quickly for a short club that lay under a seat.

"Let's kill him!" he yelled, and he sounded fearfully blood-thirsty for so small a boy.

But the other boy, no larger, kicked the club back out of the way. His freckled nose—what there was of a nose—wrinkled up superciliously.

"Huh!" he grunted, and his tone showed how very superior he knew himself to be; "My father says I should let all the little fish go without hurting them, and other kids should do the same ... and even grown men. My father always lets 'em go. He says then there'll be lots of big fish for all of us when we get to be men, but if we don't turn 'em loose, why, we won't have any big fish later on."

"We—we won't?" the other little boy had wrinkled up his face ... he had never heard of such a thing.

"No, we won't—that's what my dad says, an' he knows all about fish. Gosh!" his mouth opened. "Wouldn't it be turrible if there was no big fish to catch?" He was actually gasping at the thought of such an awful calamity.

"Well, yes—but— Well, this ain't such a very little fish; mebbe we'd better—"

"No, *sir!* My dad says anyone who kills a little fish ain't a sportsman, an' he says if a man ain't a sportsman he'll bear watchin' in everything because he's likely to be just no-'count every way. You just ain't been livin' near the lake as long as I have, an' you don't know things like I do." Evidently he was trying hard to make allowances for the other's terrible ignorance, but was having a hard time of it.

"Well—uh—all right, let him go. Gosh, I hope we ketch a big one—a great big whopper! 'Spose we will, Hank?"

"Sure! If we're good sportsmen we'll have good luck, but if we ain't—well, what could you expect?"

All of which conversation was not at all edifying to the pike who lay in the hot air with rapidly-drying gills. But presently the amateur lecture on sportsmanship was finished. Croc was seized by the gills, and gently placed back in the water. There she lay on her side apparently dead, the boys watching her anxiously. They had now firmly decided that the pike's death would ruin their chances of getting a "whopper" for that day at least. To complicate matters, it occurred to Harry Weaver—"Hank," his chums generally called him—that this pike by dying would automatically shut him, Hank, out of the ranks of true sportsmen.

It was a painful moment for all three. At length the second boy reached out a cautious hand to touch the apparently dead Croc. Immediately the water boiled, the boy got a sound slap from a strong tail, and the pike was gone. They could see it swim toward the weeds slowly, apparently dazed. But anyway it was alive, and they were sportsmen—which fact was a huge relief after all the suspense.

Years went by, years that would have been monotonous to anyone but Croc. Still she grew and grew. At last came the blissful time when she need fear no creature of the lake, not even the loon himself. Her bright colors had dimmed somewhat now, until she looked more than ever like the muddy, weedy bottom. Her head had grown to an immense thing more than a quarter the length of her body, and a terrible mouth split it its full length—a grisly mouth armed with hundreds of needle-sharp teeth slanting backward, so that what entered that awful cavern must go down, never back up.

Thousands were the fish that had entered there. Dogfish mostly, and other pike, but nothing was quite safe from her. Even the smaller water-birds swimming on the surface, even an occasional muskrat, had a way of suddenly disappearing in a swirl, never to rise again. Once she had swallowed a young loon and when its father dived and pursued her into her weed-bed she had felt more annoyance than fright, for what could he do more than break her skin slightly? She did not know it, but this was the same old male loon who had once almost proved her end.

More years passed and still she grew, though not so rapidly now, until she was truly a monster of her kind. Guides began to talk of her, and sportsmen. At one time she had as many as two spoon-hooks and one red-headed plug hanging from her wicked lips at the same time, but one after another they had dropped away or been caught on some snag and torn loose. Half a dozen hooks had been corroded and eaten away by the acids of her always-hungry stomach.

Only once had she been brought close to a boat... the guide, indeed, was reaching his sharp gaff toward her. She had been exposed, exhausted on the surface, but still back up. Only her wicked flat head and murderous devilish eyes were clearly to be seen by the three in the boat, and they were the head and eyes of the Congo crocodile, features which have been rare since the bloody Mesozoic age when huge reptiles held the earth. Those men had seen that awful head in the water, but no closer. One of the sportsmen in his eagerness had leaned too far over the side of the boat, so that Croc's last spasmodic swirl had upset the men into the water. That evening in camp they had all nodded solemn agreement when one recalled how like a crocodile she had looked. They swore to come back and get her again. They began by calling her the old crocodile, but that name was too long so they shortened it to Old Croc, and thus she became known for many miles around.

They did come back next year, and many years thereafter. They hooked her again, for she never learned to control her voracious appetite when something went wriggling and flashing past. But hooking her and landing her were two different things. She had learned to keep close to beds of strong and tangled weeds, and to dart into these weeds the instant she felt that she was on the end of a line.

Once or twice she failed to reach the weeds immediately but she had always succeeded in circling back to them to foul the line. The tale was told of how once in whirling back she had spun a canoe half around as though a cyclone had struck it. So her reputation grew, and sportsmen jokingly asked each other, "Well, going to catch Old Croc today?" But they said it in very much the spirit that the Bible asks, "Wouldst take leviathan with a hook?"

Resorts were built around the lake, and their logs weathered and grew old, for Tamarack Lake had become famous for many great fish, and especially famous for Old Croc, the monster with the evil face and the knack of breaking all tackle with which it connected. Many a sportsman had felt the great wrench of Old Croc's strike, and many a sportsman had been rowed to shore, swearing or groaning as the case might be, and ruefully looking at the remains of what had once been a beautiful split bamboo rod.

Even now she was still growing, though very slowly. She did not eat quite so often now, but when she did eat the meal was generally of gargantuan proportions. Hour after hour she would lie on top of the weeds, all hidden but her two evil eyes that never moved but saw everything that came near, waiting for prey.

Now she subsisted almost entirely on dogfish; they were big and fat and satisfying, and easier to catch than other pike. She would just lie there, murder in her eyes, until some big dogfish who was himself a scourge of the lake happened to swim over her on a scavenging expedition. She waited motionless until he reached a certain point, and then, effortlessly but not too fast, she just reached up and seized him. To an onlooker it would seem that her comparatively slow movements gave him time to get away, but he never did. Perhaps sheer terror of that fierce, reptilian face paralyzed him for the moment it took her to reach him. Now she swallowed very slowly, when her prey was large ... it might take a long time for the tip of the still weakly-flapping tail to disappear down her throat.

Now she rarely troubled to catch smaller fish; it would take almost a bushel of them to appease her appetite, and she had grown too lazy to bother to catch them. It was much easier to allow what would be called large fish to eat those smaller ones, and then she would eat the large ones. But even now she could rarely resist some little thing that went flashing and wiggling through the water, some little thing of silver, gold, or gaudy colors. And so the record of smashed tackle grew.

One day she was lying in her favorite place on the top of the weeds, when a boat came over, very, very slowly. For more than two hours it hung there, now moving forward, now back, now in slow, lazy circles. Over the edge of the boat hung two faces framed in slightly graying hair, one a pink, jolly face, the other lean, weather-lined and tanned a dark brown. The pink-faced man looked puzzled, and spent more time staring around than looking into the water, and sometimes he yawned. But the brown-faced man did not yawn; his eyes scanned the bottom as would a loon, his brow knitted as he tried to fix every solitary weed-stem in his memory.

The next day was windy, with the waves high, and so was the third. But the fourth was fairly calm, with bright sunshine. This day the boat returned again, and now it dropped an anchor not far from where Old Croc lay. She sank slowly into the weeds until even her eyes were covered.

Now a black, tubular thing came over the side of the boat. One end of it went slightly under the surface of the water, and on the other was the face of the bronzed man, his head covered by a coat that he could see the better. The pink-faced man yawned, grumbled, took a nap, woke up again, yawned again. At last the end of his patience seemed to be reached, and he growled:

"Excuse me for interrupting your fun, but I just want to ask if you died a couple of hours ago—it's that long since you moved. How about trying a few casts?"

The bronzed face came very slowly and cautiously out of the improvised water-telescope, and there was a tolerant grin on it:

"Doc, you're a great specialist now. *Of course* you just start and cut a customer up without taking time to study the case?"

"Well," sighed the specialist, "thank Heavens I'm not a great fishing authority like you. What a heck of a profession you chose! As I was saying—about casting—?"

He reached tentatively for his rod.

"Wait a minute, Doc; there seems to be—"

The rest of what he said was muffled as the face disappeared under the coat again. A moment later a dull bellow came out of it, and in another moment the face came out, with the mouth wide open.

"Oh, my gosh, Doc! Old Croc—! He's as big as they say he is —he just reached up and grabbed some fish passing over him. *Whew-w-w!*" The great fishing authority blinked and gasped.

"No doubt—no doubt!" The doctor was too weary from sitting still to become enthusiastic. "Hank, maybe it's that little fellow we turned loose here that time—you remember it was somewhere about this hole." His voice sounded sarcastic. Hank laughed tolerantly— of course he knew the Doctor was only joking.

Croc saw the boat row slowly away without a single cast having been made. But the next day it came back. It anchored quietly a very long way off—so far off that Old Croc did not even trouble to sink into the weeds, although she did keep motionless, even when a good-sized juicy fish swam overhead. There was no movement from the boat, not the slightest sound of a scraping foot to send little tremors through the water. So presently, she forgot it entirely.

It was fully an hour after the boat had anchored that Old Croc heard a slight splash in toward the shore—some little fish jumping. Then straight over her came a wiggling, darting thing of silver. It hung in the water, dived down, shot up again, fluttered, and performed the thousand evolutions a wobbling spoon can perform when handled by an expert. Straight over her it went, and toward the boat— the boat she had forgotten. Her tail twitched slightly, and her great gill-covers worked a little faster, but she let it pass. She was not feeding well that day.

Again the little silvery thing came over, and this time she rose halfway out of the weeds—only to sink back. A third time it came. Now it was traveling very slowly, with a new motion to it—a tantalizing, rocking, crippled movement. Not three feet above her eyes it passed. It was too great a temptation!

A wave of her tail, and she was following it, her nose not six inches from the single trailing hook. Once or twice she opened her mouth, but she did not quite take the bait. Still, she could not help following lazily.

Then, halfway to the boat, the little silvery thing seemed suddenly to see her. It darted forward like a streak, paused, shot sidewise, darted forward again. Her wicked, cold eyes glared suddenly, and seemed to bulge. Oh! It would try to get away from her, would it! With a rush she lunged forward and snapped—only to miss... it had darted straight down.

Fury swept over her, a fury that was almost madness. It could not get away! She *had* to catch it! Her terrible armed mouth opened to its widest and her great tail-muscles sent her ahead with a great lunge. It tried to dodge, but could not. There came a snap that broke many teeth and left deep scars on the metal of the spoon.

"Got 'er!" A whoop went up in the boat. Harry Caton Weaver, the great fishing authority, had decided that the taking of Old Croc was to be the crowning achievement of his career—that one glimpse he had got of her told him that she was easily a breaker of all records.

Old Croc turned back toward the weeds. Gone now was her voracity. She had a feeling of being swindled, tricked. It made her furious. She shook her head like a bulldog, and drove straight ahead. Not quite straight—somehow she found herself turned aside from the point of the weeds, although the pressure was not strong. Still she did not worry—she had broken too many lines in her long life to have real fear of them.

She doubled and twisted, not with the dash and fire of her youth, but with a terrible strength and slowness. The weeds—somehow she always just missed reaching them. Oh, well—she knew a better way! She allowed herself to be led easily almost to the boat, so close, indeed, that the florid-faced Doctor saw her, sat down suddenly, gasping, and mopped his face... he was beyond all words after seeing such a monster.

Then she doubled her body, whipped her tail, and was shooting back toward the weeds again. *That* would take them off their guard, break something! But it did not! Even in the midst of her whirl the pressure of the line did not seem to vary an ounce, and not once did it grow slack so that she could throw the hook by a shake of her great head.

She sulked on the bottom and refused to budge, but finally the taunting jerks stirred her up again. She would try swimming off somewhere else—surely nothing could stop her! Swim she did, but not straight—that slight, steady pull always brought her in a circle, and nearer and nearer the boat.

Then, suddenly an awful realization came to her. Where were the weeds? Somehow, she had gotten far from them, away out into deep, clear water where there was nothing to foul the line. How had she got there?

Now the pressure was even lighter than before; the great fishing expert was using all his skill. Her rushes grew more and more futile, though still sometimes punctuated by a mad drive toward the now far distant weeds. Panic came to her. What a little, thin line! ... the lightest she had ever seen—but she could not break it. She sawed her vicious teeth, but evil though they were they could not cut the slender strand of piano wire.

At last she was within six feet of the boat, her huge, wicked head partly out of the water, her eyes glaring as though she were indeed a crocodile. She opened her mouth, and the sun flashed on a multitude of reptilian teeth, on a shiny spoon far down, near her gills.

"Gaff 'er, Doc!"

"Gosh, I—I'm afraid of losing her. You do it."

Hank Weaver grinned, but without once taking his eyes from the monster floating closer and closer, he reached back and took the gaff the other handed him. Very quietly he thrust the hook under the water and led the great pike over it. His wrist muscles tensed for the stroke.

Then, almost in the same instant, he was standing there, consternation on his face, a smashed rod in his hand, and a foot or two of line dangling gently in the air. Hazily he remembered seeing a dark streak shoot under the boat. What had happened? Had the line backlashed from the jerk and a loop gone over the reel-handle? Or had it caught on a splinter on the bottom of the boat?

But one thing was certain. Old Croc had escaped again, broken another rod. The great fisherman sat down weakly ... he could hardly believe his senses. He could not believe that a fish could break his rod in open water. The Doctor sank his head in his hands and groaned. There was a silence, and the great fisherman looked up. He was not groaning; he looked almost pleased:

"The she-devil! But there's one consolation, Doc—if I'd caught her —well, I'd have her. Now, whenever I find time to come back here I'll have something to look forward to. What a brute—and still to be caught!"

Back in the weed-bed, Old Croc lay shaking her huge head savagely. There was something in the great cavern of her mouth—something that tickled—something that would neither go down nor up. Sometimes she would rest, and sometimes she would shake her head again. But it seemed hopeless to try to dislodge it.

It was almost dark when she saw a great dogfish approaching, and she sank out of sight. Tickle or no tickle, she was hungry and that dogfish looked fat. Toward her he came, unsuspectingly, until he was almost directly over her. Quietly she reached up and engulfed him. He was small enough to enter her capacious maw at one swallow, big though he was in actual size.

She sank back into the weeds contentedly, her stomach full. Something was trying to force itself into her tiny, fierce brain, some thought trying to crowd in where there was no room for thought. What was it? Oh, yes—something that had been tickling her mouth inside, but it was gone. Maybe the dogfish had swept it down her throat.

Oh, well, such things were too trifling to worry about. Chasing those little shiny things made her fierce spirit feel good. When would the next be along? But at that she felt tired—she must be getting old. And so, thinking her vague, dull thoughts, she sank farther and farther down into the weeds and fell asleep.

The Second Battle of Gettysburg

By COL. HAROLD P. SHELDON

AUNT 'TILDY'S LATEST DELECTATION, CONSISTING OF BATTER-dipped partridge—each one a lump of fragrant succulence fried to the same pale bronze of the sedge fields where they had been found and slain the day before—had been gone for two hours. Aided by a heaping platterful of crisp potatoes, slices of cracklin' bread, muscadine preserves and a great pot of coffee fresh from the kitchen hearth, a full dozen of the delicious birds were now encouraging a drowsy contentment among the sportsmen as they sprawled before the fire in the "big room" at Red Knoll. It still lacked an hour of bed-time, even for men abroad all day following as keen a quartet of setters as ever were braced and tossed down anywhere in the lower valley of the Old Mississippi. The dogs had been fed, and their pads searched for thorns, the guns cleaned and tackle repaired, and now the gunners sat in a blissful and wordless contemplation of the joys that were theirs.

The door creaked softly to admit Uncle Horace bringing fresh firewood. Black as a boot was Uncle Horace, with a benign fringe of white wool encircling his wrinkled poll, and bent with the gentle burdens of four score happy, useful years. No more for him the

duck blind when at dawn the chill fog sweeps across the rice-fields
and the mallards are on the wing, no more for him the long days
astride his mule, following his white folks and his dogs. But behind
the old rascal's eyes, bright as a wren's, was stowed a treasury of
wisdom, of recollection and philosophy so unique that its like was
not to be found elsewhere in the w ʊˈ

His advent, gentle though it ha 1 ˌ ˈ ˌ roused them—perhaps
this had been the old man's purpose to do. Having mended the fire,
he withdrew, to reappear presently with a tray filled with illicit
paraphernalia. With this he wrought deftly, measuring brown sugar
and wringing lemon peel, and afterward presenting in a courtly
flourish the results of his intricate labors.

Meanwhile, not a word had been spoken, but now, sipping the
amber liquid, Mister Nash said:

"Uncle Horace, better fill another tumbler for yourself, pull up
a chair, and tell us straightly the truth about that great dove shoot
at Turkey Bend, to the best of your knowledge and belief."

"Thankee kindly, Mistah Nash, an' dat I will," replied the old
negro. Listening, it occurred to the Captain that Nash and Uncle
Horace, guided by rare sympathy and understanding, had been
subtly arranging events since supper-time to provide this moment
and, moreover, to prepare the rest of them for it. There had been
some casual remarks at the table about dove-shooting—insignificant
bits of flotsam dropped here and there into the broad stream of the
conversation—apparently without any more purpose than can be
ascribed to the detached and seemingly unimportant stuff that floats
by on the brown current of "Ole Miss'." But the Captain realized
now that these bits, bobbing and eddying here and there, were somehow controlled by a deeper scheme; that there was, after all, a kinship
among them like that of the flotsam of the river, a definite attraction
drawing them all together to form at last an incident worthy of
profound consideration.

During supper, Horace, serving Aunt 'Tildy's partridge, had
joined in the discussion of the subject, spacing his comments respectfully between ladlings of gravy. The relative value of wheat, hemp
or millet plantings as attractions for the birds, the best size of shot,
and general lay of the field, and whether the gentlemen's breakfast
should precede or immediately follow the morning shoot—Horace
thought it should be served first—all these details received some
judicious attention. It was obvious that neither Mister Nash nor
Uncle Horace held much with modern practice—their memories

turned fondly back to the traditional dove shoots of the deep South, when gentlemen came a-riding across misty fords before daybreak, each accompanied to the rendezvous by a servant mounted on a mule, carrying a Manton or a Purdey or a Greener or a Scott in its mahogany case slung across the saddle. The Turkey Bend shoot had been mentioned again with a customary absence of detail. For the Captain had heard of it before—a legendary affair occurring apparently about 1880, at which some extraordinary shooting had transpired. But all inquiries as to particular circumstances had always led nowhere; either they were lost in the mists of tradition, or else the inquirer had been led deftly away, like a whippet by a stuffed rabbit. The Captain had come finally to the conclusion that whatever the tale, it was not one to be unfolded for the ear of every passing stranger, and so with proper delicacy refrained from further inquiries. But Horace, it seemed, had witnessed the affair, and at last having satisfied apparently some initiatory requirements, the guests were now to be permitted to hear the story of the mysterious episode.

Uncle Horace sipped and sighed. The light from the hearth played across the old man's faded cotton shirt and raised dark, saintly gleams from his face.

"Um *hum!*" he began judgmatically, referring to the beady amber-colored mixture in his glass, "a mite more er lemon wouldn' weaken hit none. An' yit hit don' do t' monkey wid dese 'scriptions atta dey been 'stablished. Dat wuz de kin' o' monkey-business whut caused de whol' o' de Turkey Ben' trouble—a smart fat yaller N' Yawleans nigger defyin' de Scripture and foolin' wid de ingredients o' milk punch. 'Poly Jackson wuz dat boy's name, an' poly did he do." A chuckle shook the old man's frame. "Marse Dave Fayston fotch him up de ribber t' Red Knoll 'count o' he kin cook right good. I'se 'bleeged to admit, suh, dat 'Poly boy, while he don' know nuthin' 'bout sho' nuff good liquah, wuz right cunnin' wid er skillet. In p'tickler ef yo' gin him a han'ful o' aigs, a couple o' t'maters an' some onions an' bacon an' all kin' o' no 'count odds an' ends, I boun' he'd shake out somethin' whut'd fotch a scairt 'possum right outen a gum tree an' down amongst de dawgs. De smell o' dat dish cookin' des' kind o' paralyzed a man—an' when yo' come to th'ow yo'self upon hit wid a ladle in one han' an' a slab er hoecake in d' uther—well, suh, dar you' wuz! In all my days I ain't nevah met up wid no person, black er white, male er female, dat kin transmogrify hen aigs de way dat boy kin do. Ner dey ain't nuthin' I evah comed across yit dat smell quite so appetizin' ez onions an' aigs an' bacon an' N' Yawleans coffee early in de mawnin' er a shootin' day."

Uncle Horace paused. It was obvious that to him who had sniffed these fragrances and fed on these viands, 'Poly's skill in Creole cookery was of a sort deserving the tribute of a minute of respectful silence, like that by which the Armistice and other great events of national importance are honored.

"Dove shoots wuz big doin's in de ol' days," he resumed, "an' all de folks 'could rally roun' one fiel' er 'nuther whar dey had invites, long befo' daybreak on de fus' day. Some yeahs de fus' shoot would be h'yar, sometimes us would meet at Marse Pristly's at Bellevue, sometimes at de Breckenridge plantation, but wharevah hit wuz, us boys would be ridin' h'yar an' d'ah fo' days carryin' 'pissles an' makin' 'rrangements fo' de big jubilee. Dove shootin', you' see, suh, sigmafied de comin' o' de season o' guns an' horses an' dawgs. Pa'tridge shootin' and turkey shootin' an' deer an' fox huntin'—not t' mention squir'l an' 'possum hunts—an' de holidays, wid feasten' an' dancin', sho' to be comin' 'fo' long!"

The old fellow indulged in another moment of meditation.

"Dat yeah," he resumed, "Marse Dave wuz holdin' de fus' shoot right h'yar at Red Knoll. De ten-acre fiel' yant de bayou wuz standin' thick wid late wheat, an' de full haids wuz jes' er bustin' down de stalks, an' de doves wuz a usin' so thick look like you coulden' fi' inter 'em wid a one-ball gun widout killin' a basketful.

"So Marse Dave, he tol' me t' git on a mule an' kerry invites to Marse Priestly at Bellevue, an' t' Colonel Steve Breckenridge, likewise t' Colonel Bill Sumner, an' t' young Bob Quinn—Marse Bob wuz er debbil fo' mischief—an' likewise t' Major Jones an' ez many mo'. In de meantime, he had dis 'Poly nigger and d'uther boys buildin' a fireplace in de live oaks next t' de fiel' an' fixin' benches an' tables fo' de bobbycue.

"Den come up de question o' whut an' whar de eatin' an' liquidatin' wuz to occur.

"'Poly,' Marse Dave sez, 'I b'lieve de bes' scheme is t' give de gent'men hot coffee an' milk punch so soon as dey 'rives, waitin' de reg'lar brekfus' 'til de buhds stop flyin' good, long erbout eight o'clock er dar' 'bouts.'

"'Poly say, 'Yaas, suh!'

"'An', 'Poly, git up a cask o' dat 1812 brandy—one o' dem kaigs whut wuz buried in de bayou bank endurin' de wah,' sezzee, 'when de confounded Yankees'—'scuse me suh—'when de confounded

No'the'ners wuz a rampin' th'u dese parts a-seekin' whut dey kin devour, an' have it at de fiel',' sezzee. 'Let it be de prop an' mainstay uv de punch,' sezzee. 'Fo' de brekfus' dish, le's have dem aigs Creole, puhpa'ed wid onions, peppers, t'maters an' bacon—jes' dat an' nothin' mo'—un'nerstan'—but co'nbread an' hot coffee served in 'bundance an' pipin' hot. I aims to show de gent'mens a trick er two 'bout punch an' dove shootin' an' aigs.'

"Well, suh, long fo' daybreak we wuz at de 'pointed place. 'Poly he had de fiah goin' brisk, an' ez fas' as de gent'men come ridin' in, dey would light down an' come to de blaze—fo' de air wuz middlin' sharp 'long de bottoms—an' we'd ladle 'em out de punch an' de coffee. Atta' while Marse Dave cut his eye to'des de East an' 'low hit time to take stan's. So de shootin' mens dey went on off th'u de woods to de aidge o' de fiel' whar dey places an' pickups wuz.

" 'Poly he watched 'em all go, standin' dar wid a drippin' punch ladle in his han', an' he say to me, sezzee, 'Ho'ace, dat pale lookin' liquah sholy mussa' done los' hits stren'th wid age. De folks done drunk up two buckets o' milk punch a'ready," sezzee.

" 'Mebbe yo' right,' I tol' him, not payin' no p'tickler mind, 'but she allus done had plenty animosity up t' now. Boy, yo' better mix up 'nuther bucket, 'case when de gent'mens gits t' shootin' good dey gwine start hollerin' fo' reinfo'cements.'

" 'Dat I will,' say 'Poly."

A less knowing one might have thought Horace's sigh was for the tragedy of the spoilt brandy. But Nash, having more intuition, instructed the old sinner to replenish his glass. Having accomplished this, and having tested the fluid for reassurance as to the perfection of its proportions, the narrator resumed his tale.

"Well, suh, dat wuz de bigges' dove shoot evah in dis county. If'n de gent'mens hadn't got deyse'fs sidetracked, I b'lieve we'd ha' busted all de records fo' dove shootin' anywhar. I wuz pickin' up buhds fo' Marse Dave, an' I couldn' in no way keep up wid him. D' uthers wuz doin' 'bout ez well, an' fo' an hour de firin' wuz fas' an' straight, 'Poly kept plyin' the fiel' wid de punch bucket an' de ladle, an' 'twixt de shoutin' fo' 'Poly an' de shoutin' fo' boys to fotch shells an' de bangin' o' de guns de 'casion wuz ez merry ez er camp meetin'.

"De fus' I notice anythin' wrong wuz when Marse Dave miss two single buhds, one right afta d'uther. 'Bam—Bam!' an' 'bam!—bam!' agin, soon ez he could load—nice easy shots, too, dey wuz—an' Marse Dave ain't miss a dove befo' in ten year!

" 'Whut de debbil, Ho'race,' sezzee, rubbin' his haid. "I had dem buhds straight down de rib,' sezzee, 'de hull flock of 'em,' sezzee, 'bofe times.'

"I say, 'Yas, suh,' kinda wonderin' lak.

"De sun wuz up by dis time an' wa'm. De buhds jes' erbout ez thick ez bees, but dey ain't so many fallin', spite er de fact de shootin' des ez loud an' fas' ez befo'.

" 'Bout dat time I heah ole Colonel Sumner 'ddressin' som' stray'nyus remarks t' Colonel Breckenridge. Dem two ain't quite so 'greeable ez mout be, 'count o' some diff'unce in 'pinion ez to who wuz h'yar an' who wuz dar at de Gettysburg fightin'. Ol' Colonel Sumner argify dat ef'n Colonel Breckenridge had suppohted him wid his big brass cannons on dat 'casion, he'd tukken de hull damn Yankee —'scuse me, suh—he'd tukken de hull damn No'the'n Army. Colonel Breckenridge nachully contend dat dis ain' so. Dey bin 'sputin' de point fo' twenty yeahs widout 'rrivin' nowhar.

"Well, Colonel Sumner he holler at Colonel Breckenridge, an' say, 'Hav' a care, suh, ef yo' please, whar at yo' is discha'gin' yo' piece,' he say. 'Yo' done put a load widin two paces o' my stan', suh!'

" 'Suh,' 'sponds Colonel Sumner, 'ef'n yo' stay behine yo' tree, ez yo' did at de Gettysburg trouble, suh, yo' will be in no danger f'om my weapons,' sezzee.

"Marse Dave pacify 'em, fo' dey wuz bofe red an' bristlin' like a couple o' gobblers. An' we fin'ally gets 'em back to dey stan's widout neither challenges ner bloodshed. But bofe o' dem wuz pretty mad yit.

" 'Ho'ace,' Marse Dave say to me, 'dem two ol' gladiators ac' like dey is tight as bees; I b'lieves us'll do well t' watch 'em er us'll have de whole war over agin right h'yar in dis fiel',' say. 'Hit sho' look like dey is full ez ticks, but I don' see how come such—dey ain't took nuthin' but er few sips o' dat milk punch, an' hit *cain't* be dat a few ladles o' punch kin disturb gent'men ez dram-proof ez whut dem two is,' sezzee.

"So he kin' o' keep an eye on 'em fo' a spell.

"Presently he say, 'Ho'race, looka h'yar, who is d'uther gent'man behine dat tree wid Colonel Breckenridge?'

" 'Nobudy, suh,' I say, 'nobudy but de Colonel.'

" 'Look agin, 'Ho'ace.'

" 'Not nobuddy, suh,' I tol' him again.

"Marse Dave say, sorter 'sprised, 'Zat so? Den, Ho'ace, I 'bleeged t' confess dey is sumpin' pow'ful odd 'bout dis h'yar business. Us bettah blow de brekfus' call an' cl'ar de fiel' fo' sumpin' happens,' he say.

"But jes' ez he say dat, ol' Colonel Sumner give a whoop an' slap his coattails like a bee stung 'im, an' th'owed down on Colonel Breckenridge's tree.—'Ker bam!' say, 'take dat, you onprincipled ol' scounnel! Firin' into yo' own troops! or my name ain' Sumner!'

"Colonel Breckenridge mek haste an' retu'n de compliment wid his lef' barrel, an' in no time at all dey wuz yellin' an' cussin' an' shootin' at one 'nother, p'int blank. Den somebody—I 'spect dat Quinn boy did it fo' pure debblement—put a load o' dove shot inter Marse Watson's tree, an' befo' yo' could spit dey's all at it. Bless Gawd de stan's is a good sebenty paces apaht, an' numbah eights ain't gwine t' do much damage at dat range—less'n o' co'se yo' gits one in de eye—but dey sho' do sting like de debbil, an' de mo' dey sting, de hotter de gent'mens gits.

"So fur, Marse Dave ain't engaged, an' he observe de proceedin's wid amazement, an' yit hit make him laugh, too, fo' it wuz sho' ridic'lous t' see dem white folks leapin' an' prancin' an' cussin' an' shootin' wid de doves circlin' overhaid like dey wuz 'stonished at sech conduct. Hit am a fac' dat dey ain't no dignity 'bout a charge o' buhd-shot. Gent'men who kin be proud an' stately when pistol balls is flyin' des' boun' t' dodge an' squirm when folks gits t' slingin' dem little hot stingin' fellers.

"Marse Dave say, 'Us got t' stop dis, somehow,' sezzee. 'Those damned idjits gwine ruin dis shoot. Dar go Cap'n Bulwer openin' on young Quinn! How in de worl' did all dis git goin'? Look dar,' he say, p'inting, 'look at ol' man Priestly wid his ol' fo'teen-gauge muzzle loader! He ain't shootin' so often ez de yuthers, but I d'clar he fetches a whoop an' a cuss ev'y time he do let go.'

"Soon he gits a new worriment. 'Ho'ace,' he say, over de roar o' de skirmish, 'some idjit gwine ter lose his haid in a minute an' start cuttin' ca'tridges like us do fo' deer shootin', an' den us gwine t' have a sho' nuff battle!'

"'Marse Dave,' I say, 'listen t' me, suh, please. I knows whut'll stop dis massacree—brekfus'—dat fool 'Poly's Creole aigs, suh! De gent'mens is hongry, but dey so 'vigorated right at de present time dat dey don't know dey is hongry. Ef'n we kin get 'em a whiff o' dem aigs an' onions, dey'll come outer dey trance ez meek ez a 'coon kotched in er chicken roost.'

"De Cap'n say, 'By Judas, Ho'ace, I b'lieve yo' right! Do yo' reckon yo' kin make hit to de cookin' place wid'out drawin' fire?

So fur,' he say, 'de 'sponsibilities of courtesy has 'strained dese gent'-
men from shootin' at dey host, but in dey present fix I dunno whether
I kin confidently rely on my sacred neutrality er not,' he say. 'Ol'
Man Priestly ain't puticulully kin'ly tow'ds me since Bluebell won
over Sweet Dreams at de Steeplechase las' season, any how, an' I
don' like to risk tempin' him wid a fair running target in de open.
Howevah, dey kin be 'pended 'pon not t' shoot a boy—'thout some
provocation,' he say, 'so you slip out er h'yah an' git to dat damn
fool 'Poly an' tell him, fo' me, t' git his aigs an' onions an' fixin's
t'gedder an' de bigges' skillet he kin fin'. Tell 'im t' fotch de coffee
pot an' de charcoal burner an' assemble his fo'ces on de windward
side o' de fiel'—yander live oak is 'bout right," he say, feelin' fo de
breeze—'an' den to git at dem aigs Creole wid de utmos' dispatch er
I gwine tek de seat off'n his pants!'

"So I done ez Marse Dave direct an' coon it over to whar 'Poly
wuz at, an' gib him de 'structions.

" 'Poly say, 'Whut de debbil got inter dem gent'mens? Dey went
outer h'yar walkin' strict an' friendly ez er flock o' turkeys!'

" 'Well, de hull caboodle o' 'em got dey hackles riz now an' hit
ain' no time fo' niggers t' relax,' I say. 'Yo' git dem aigs out dar an'
de onions an' bacon an' coffee an' begin yo' fumigations.'

"Well, suh, we got de fixtures out to de fiel', and' dar under de
live oaks 'Poly went to shakin' de big skillet an' soon de immortal
fragrumce o' de Creole aigs wuz driftin' across de fiel' an' blendin'
wid de smoke o' de gunpowder. De firin' had slacked, mostly 'case
de gent'mens wuz runnin' sho't er ammunition an' dassent run out
to git no mo'.

"When I wuz sure dat de fragrumce had got clear 'n down to
Marse Priestly in stand Numbah Ten, we sounded 'Cease firin',' an'
den blow de ol' Confed'rit brekfus' call.

"One by one de gent'mens come out, an' some ob 'em wuz limpin'
a mite an' d'uthers wuz rubbin' deyse'fs, an all ob 'em wuz lookin'
mighty puzzled an' sheepish."

At this point, Uncle Horace paused to sup additional vigor. Flames
purred about the logs, and outside in the frosty moonlight lonely
"squinch" owls whimpered.

Reluctantly Uncle Horace put down his glass and resumed.

"Marse Dave say, 'Serve de aigs, 'Poly,' an' hit wuz done. Likewise de co'nbread an' de coffee. In all my bo'n days I never did see
mo' vengeance done t' vittles, an' de mo' o' dem Creole aigs dey

flung 'emselves eroun', de ca'mer dem gent'mens gits, an' de ca'mer dey gits de mo' sheepish dey 'comes.

"Finally Colonel Sumner riz himself up an' say: 'I am completely at a loss,' he say, 't' 'count fo' my ext'odinahy conduc' this mawnin', an' I desiah heah an' now to offer my humble apologies to our host, and likewise t' any gent'men who were present an' who may have sustained injuries, either f'om my langwidge er my fiah,' he say. 'Colonel Breckenridge, I 'pologize to yo', suh, in p'tickler fo' my unwarranted heat an' violence, an' I furthuh desiah t' say dat on de Gettysburg 'casion yo' conduc' wuz exemplary, suh. De position an' strength o' de confounded Yankees'—'scuse me, suh—'o' de confounded No'the'ners wuz such dat all de fo'ces o' Hell couldn't a' budged 'em.'

"Colonel Breckenridge done ekally han'some an' 'lowed he couldn't in nowise 'count fo' his unseemly conduc', an' d' uthers jined in, 'splainin' an' 'pologizin' an' takin' mo' helpin's o' aigs an' coffee.

"Marse Dave inquire ef'en anybody got hurt in de ruckus, an' hit develop dat all de gent'men got some shot inter 'em som'whar, an' dey helps one 'nother dig 'em out an' put raw brandy on de places. Colonel Breckenridge done stan' aloof while dis goin' on, an' Colonel Sumner inquiah, 'Colonel, has yo' got any dove shot in yo', suh? If so, kin I assist yo' to remove 'em?'

"Colonel Breckenridge say, 'I am 'bleeged to yo', suh, fo' yo' consideration, an' I do b'lieve I got de best paht o' three loads under my hide, but dey is in a po'tion o' my anatomy where de attention o' lovin' an' sympathetic friends would be highly embarrassin',' he say. 'I belive de character o' my wounds requiahs de ca'm, impussonal services of a physician.'

"An' wid dat dey all start whoopin' an' laughin' fit ter split.

"Us boys done all bin pretty nervous up t' now an' walkin' soft an' brief an' sober, 'case hit ain't advisable t' fo'm positive opinions when white folks ain't know dey own minds, but now us jines in de laughin'.

"Marse Dave say, 'Us best keep close concernin' dese ondignified proceedin's, fo' we'll be de ridicule er de county ef'n dis mawnin's wuk evah gits out. But how in de worl',' he say, 'did it happen? Well, thank de Lawd, it's ovah an' no great damage done. 'Poly! Draw off some o' dat brandy an' serve de gent'men!'

" 'Poly say, 'Marse Dave, ef yo' please suh, yo' bes' had de Bourbon.—Yo' is boun' t' be disapp'inted in de brandy,' sezzee.

" ' 'What yo' mean, boy!'

" 'Well, suh, seems dat ol' liquah done got antiquated wid age. Hit ain't got no mo' coluh, er smell, er taste, er powah to it dan whut col' tea done got. When I open de kaig fo' t' fix de punch dis mawnin' I reelize dat brandy done los' hits animosity, suh.'

" 'Hum,' sez Marse Dave, moughty int'rested, 'an' whut did yo' do 'bout hit?'

" 'Well, suh, on 'count of de enfeebled nature o' de liquah, I done double de cha'ge in de punch,' say 'Poly, 'an' when dat don't seem to git nobody nowhar I gib her a little suppoht wid a jemmy john o' dat Bourbon.'

"Marse Dave say, 'Great Scott! nigger! So wonder dis all come t' pass,' sezzee, puttin' fo'th his han' an' shakin' de brandy kaig. 'Gent'men, by de Lawd Harry, we've invertently consumed, by rough estimate, near two gallons o' de bes' brandy dis side er N'Yawleans! Hit ain't su'prisin' dat we has expe'ienced some 'zileration dis mamnin' 'Poly, yo' black idjit, f'om now on yo' is to confine yo' activities to cookin', an' yo' is fo'tunate to git outen dis mess wid yo' hide on-striped. Yo' don' onderstan' fluids ez yo' do aigs.'

"Den he call me up an' say, 'Ho'ace, yo' is de s'preme custodian o' de wicked flagon f'om now on,' he say, 'de ruler o' de kaig, an' de trusted governor er de bin an' bottle.—Give ovah de keys, 'Poly! An' Ho'ace—'

" 'Yassuh.'

" 'Yo' may begin yo' duties by solicitin' de wishes o' de gent'men!'

"An' so," concluded the ancient black one, rising to discharge these responsibilities, "hit has been up'n to dis good day."

The Stream

By BILL WOLF

HAVE YOU EVER HAD THE EMBARRASSING EXPERIENCE OF PER-
suading some doubting friend to try your favorite bit of water and
then see your stream turn sullen and refuse to yield him a single fish?
You put him in the best spots, let him work the best pools first, tell
him where to cast across the fast water so the lure drifts into
the still stretches. You hover around him like a mother hen and catch
nothing yourself because you are too interested in seeing he has a
good day. Nevertheless, he catches nothing, gets a few half-hearted
strikes in water that you *know* holds fish.

It happens nearly every time—not because you are a congenital
liar or because your friend can't fish. The reason is plain: Since it
is your favorite water, you know it as well as you know your home.
You know every current and eddy, every pocket and rock. You
know where the fish feed and live.

Your intimacy with it has been gained through many visits to the same water and I believe that, once the fundamentals of fishing are learned, the beginner can do nothing more important than gain just such close acquaintance with some creek or lake. Yes, it's fun to fish new waters; but even here your thorough knowledge of one stream will make you look in new country for conditions duplicating those found in your "home" creek and you will catch more fish as a result.

I have such a favorite creek which, since it is near a large city, I will designate simply as The Stream to conceal in anonymity a place I like very much with a selfish liking. It runs for many miles, but I claim only about three miles of its water as my personal property. No, I didn't buy it; but I feel it is my own since I'm the only one who would notice if a fist-sized rock were removed from some of the spots I fish.

My stretch of The Stream starts in a wooded and brushy region. From there The Stream flows into an open meadow like those seen in England and then returns to woods again until the stretch ends at a highway bridge. Anyone who wishes can have that section below the bridge because too many persons visit it; and I seldom go above my stretch unless I want to try for the few trout its headwaters hold. You see, mine is a small-mouth bass stream.

This is the first water I fish near the end of winter for chubs and suckers. Here I go late in the fall and until frigid weather and the hunting season arrive. In winter I often go back to it to see how it is getting along, or, perhaps, to turn over rocks and see what insect life it holds.

Let us examine this stretch and see what is meant by knowing a section thoroughly. Starting at the bridge and working upstream, as I invariably do when fishing, the first hundred yards or so contain pretty dull water. I know because I fished it carefully when I first met The Stream and for several years afterward and became convinced it held few fish. In those first years I fished The Stream as any newcomer would, trying every bit of water, passing up nothing. Now, however, I know this shallow stretch hold chubs and that only an occasional bass will enter it.

Huge old maple trees (somehow a few fine trees were left along The Stream when the country was timbered off) shade the first good pool. Really, there are two pools here, both formed by rocks which were run across the creek to form a sort of dam. Below the rocks the water runs swiftly and is about three or four feet deep over a rocky bottom that just suits sunfish. At the far end of this run it smooths out into the lower pool and here there are bluegills.

The upstream pool, however, holds smallmouth bass and here I do my first serious fishing. It doesn't look like much and a stranger probably would pass it up if he were the haphazard sort. The water runs swiftly into the head of the pool, glances against the opposite bank which is being eaten away by erosion and then it flattens out above the rock dam. One or two bass can be hooked on a small streamer every fishing trip exactly where the fast water smooths out into a glide. They are always on the far side from where you must fish, at the base of the high eroded bank.

I know almost exactly when they will hit, so well do I know this favorite pool. The streamer alights in the fast water, directly opposite me; I turn the rod tip upstream and the lure swings in an arc, rising to the top of the current right where the bank is undercut beneath the surface and where the bass must lurk. They strike viciously as smallmouths do and they fight until I land them. I always put them back. Why not? Next year I can come back and take the same gleaming bronze fighter from the same spot, except he will be grown a little larger.

A few yards below this spot is a deeper hole where chubs hover like a cloud on the bottom—but just below it the angler can see cutouts in the clay bottom that exists there and a wet fly or streamer played carefully above the edge of such undercuts usually will bring a strike from a bass. Still farther down a tree overhangs the quiet water and, just where its roots wet their feet in the pool, more bass hang out. In the whole length of this pool, these several are the only places where bass are caught. How could a stranger know that?

The next pool upstream presents a difficult problem in fishing, which makes it a correspondingly interesting stretch to fish. It is a long, quiet pool and a difficult one to approach because there's little room on the banks and tree limbs hang over it like an archway, making casting almost impossible. At one spot a stump protrudes from the water and below it is the half-sunken trunk of the tree. It's been there for many years, through storm and flood. It is the one place where fishing is not too impossible and, also, the one place where the bass live.

I can step (very softly, because the bass scare easily in this quiet water) to the stump and from it to part of the log which projects above water. This gets me away from the jungle along the bank and gives me room for a fairly long side-arm cast. I drop the streamer on the opposite side, sink it carefully and let it drift with the current until it nears the end of the sunken log. Then I start retrieving it just along the edge of the log. There are bass, and big ones, hiding there. Sometimes they come out and follow the lure cautiously without striking. Sometimes there is a whirl in the water, a splash of spray and I have one on.

The Stream enters this pool with a rush. The swift water looks fishy; but it isn't. I have fished it many times and taken chubs from it or sunfish from the edges of the fast water, but nothing else. The bass live only near my log.

At this point I leave The Stream for a little while and travel by a path which crosses a small brook, leads through a tangle of saplings and across some jumbled rocks before returning to The Stream. Here I usually surprise a woodchuck and stop to watch his silver-gray body waddle out of sight. Here, for some unknown reason, pheasants often are found.

It is impossible to fish the stretch I skirt by path. The banks are all brush and the water is so quiet that wading is out of the question in so small a creek. I have tried plugs and succeeded in catching some large overhanging trees but I couldn't land them. Above it, however, is the Rock Pool and some of the best fishing in The Stream.

The Rock Pool gets its name from the stream bottom, rather than from the several great boulders on the one bank. Towering above the pool is a giant oak tree and here the gray squirrels flatten out on limbs to watch the crazy human being below who walks up to the head of the pool, fishes the riffles there, works down into the smoothly gliding water and then to the deep pool at the base of the tree.

The deeper the water, the larger the bass here; the little ones where the water ripples musically over a gravel bottom. Where the channel narrows and gets deeper, the bass are correspondingly larger and at the end of the pool, where big rocks line the banks and bottom, there are some respectable fish. I like them all, from the midget fighters scarcely longer than the streamers they hit to the ones that bend the light fly rod from butt to tip.

Above the Rock Pool there is no bass fishing except for one peculiar spot where there always is at least one nice fish. At the base of a small tree is a tiny pool, no more than one or two feet deep and four feet square. Under the water is a sunken limb about six inches thick, not more than that. If a streamer is placed right, a bass will flash up from beside that limb, or dart out from the undercut bank and seize it. I wonder how often I have caught the same bass there. Perhaps I should tag the fish.

The next two likely-looking places are quite disappointing. One is a nice pool into which fast water pours, but which contains suckers only around the roots of a tree. The next spot seems perfect for fish. A big rock stands about eight feet above the center of the stream and at its base is a pool which looks ideal for bass, but only a few chubs live there. I always make some casts there because it seems impossible that fish would not favor it as a home; but they are fruitless.

Therefore, I move on quickly to the Swimming Hole pool where the presence of boys diving and splashing in the water doesn't disturb my fishing at all because the smallmouths do not live in the deep part, but upstream where an island separates the creek. At the downstream tip of this island large bass can be taken and careful casts to a stump protruding from the water almost invariably catch fish. Sometimes I cross to the island and fish the channel on one side where the current is strong and here an occasional smallmouth is picked up.

From the Swimming Pool to the next good fishing stretch is a long way, perhaps a quarter of a mile. There are bass in this long stretch, but they await a better fisherman than I am. I can't catch them. The Stream enters the meadow section here. It is part of an estate and the grass is kept like a lawn. The banks are straight up and down and it is impossible to approach the water without frightening every fish in it. I have tried wading and it doesn't work because the ripples spread on the smooth water and put down the fish.

So I leave The Stream and walk up the road to the White Bridge. Above it is the Big Rock pool where The Stream has cut through a ledge of rock and the high, gaunt stone stands guard over the water. I often sit on this rock and watch the pool below. More than once I have seen a big bass swim out of the deep recesses of the pool into the quiet water beneath the ledge and forage there for food. More than once, I have climbed down from the high rock and cast to a bass which I had spotted, and caught him. Above this pool is a rocky run of water where small bass playfully hit the lures and look so foolish when they are hooked and brought in. Have you ever noticed that foolish, surprised expression fish can achieve?

All this water is in the region we call The Meadows, part of the huge estate which owns the land, and upstream from the Big Rock pool is some of the loveliest country on this earth in a formal sort of way. One side of The Stream is wooded and the trees rise to the crest of a hill. On the other side is the meadow, neatly-trimmed and always bright green. Here there is peace and quiet at all times unless a few crows make things noisy.

Here, too, is an exasperating pool which holds big bass and, yet, few are taken from it. I recall only one good day there. Late in the afternoon a hatch of big brown drakes appeared over this pool and bass started to roil the water. One after another, they slashed at dry flies in a crazy feeding mood. Then it all died down and the pool returned to its usual calm. The bass all rest in deep water here beneath an intricate network of roots from several trees which overhang the water and it is hard normally to lure them out of this safe retreat.

Beyond the neat formality of The Meadows is a region of thick underbrush, weeds and briers, tangled trees, wood ticks and cobwebs.

An old bridge abutment is at the beginning of this wild stretch and sometimes I toss grasshoppers from it into the pool below to watch the bass slash at them. Just try to catch those same bass, however, on a dry fly or bass bug. It can be done, but most of the time the lure floats over them as though there weren't a bass in The Stream.

Fortunately, the fishing isn't quite as good in this overgrown stretch of The Stream as it is in the more open sections (or is that just an alibi?) and I visit it less frequently.

Such are the physical characteristics of my creek. I know every foot of its water and immediately notice the slightest change that occurs between visits to it. When winter comes to end all fishing, I occasionally walk the length of my stretch just to check up on it. During one extremely cold spell I walked most of the way on The Stream itself because it was frozen solid. Sometimes I fish it in the autumn when its waters carry a gaudy fleet of red, gold and brown leaves sailing bravely to an unknown destination. My brightest streamers are eclipsed by the colorful leaves which they catch more frequently than they do fish. I know it in February when I fish for suckers, in March when I try to catch the first chubs, in spring when the pastel colors brighten The Stream, in summer's heat.

So, too, do I know the wildlife beside it. No one hunts the raccoons which travel along The Stream and some of them are huge old ones, judging from the size of the nearly-human footprints found in the mud. The wild upper reaches hold many muskrats and I often have approached so quietly that they would go on with their feeding without noticing me. Even mink cruise along the banks although I have seen only their tracks. The inevitable kingfishers hurl their billingsgate at me as they fly away when disturbed, a somber heron is often encountered or sometimes I see an ungainly bittern which is known in my country as a shitepoke. One summer a pair of ospreys fished The Stream with me and each spring and fall migratory ducks drop into it for a visit. Usually, they are mallards and blacks, but once I was quite pleased with The Stream when eight canvasbacks got up ahead of me, gained altitude, circled and came back over me with a powerful rush. In winter cardinals, redheaded and downy woodpeckers and juncos add color or animation to The Stream.

I even know its different voices. In spring, The Stream actually sounds excited and busy. When the summer sun is on it, The Stream becomes placid and languid. In autumn it seems preoccupied and thoughtful about the coming cold. When winter is at hand, The Stream seems to become sullen and hurries along as though anxious to get wherever it is going and have done with it.

Perhaps this will give some idea of what I meant by knowing a stream well. Each fisherman eventually acquires one which he comes to consider as his own. It's fun to go elsewhere and try other water; but it's reassuring to know that your stream is there, waiting for you to come back. It will welcome you like a friend and, because it is an old friend, you will know its every feature.

Great Day in the Morning

By NASH BUCKINGHAM

WHEN OUR AUTOMOBILE SLOWED TO ENTER THE ROAD TURNING
westward toward Beaver Dam Lake, I told Johnny to stop and let
me look around a bit. It was coming dusk.

Across dimming cotton fields I could see lights springing up in tenant cabins and winking through vague sails of low-hanging wood-smoke from fall burnings. Eastward, I could just make out the black rampart of the vast Owen cypress brake—thousands of forest monarchs towering just as God grew 'em. Beyond and without blemish of ax or saw lay the Dooley and Savage woods with Walnut Lake winding through them. Ample stocks of deer, wild turkey and bear harbored there, and I figured on contacting some of them, too, before winter wore out. South of us lay clearings crosscut by a wide bayou winding luxuriantly through second-growth. Westward, stars brimmed above sundown's afterglow. A jagged sky-line of timber stood clear-cut against a belt of dull, smouldering amber.

Just then the rattly "Limb Dodger," evening accommodation train from Memphis pulled out of the hamlet of Evansville and whistled sharply for Beaver Dam's lonesome, uncovered stop-sign amid the tall and uncut. Hal, I told myself, would be getting off it, with old Horace on hand to assist him in unloading the bird dogs, pointers Ticket and Flash, from the baggage car. I could even spot the gigantic pecan tree lording it over the moss-shingled club-house. Many's the rough night I had been able to locate the boat dock by glimpsing that old patriarch's bulk through an opening in the willows.

Then I told Johnny to pull on down the lane and over the ramp to the home-close. And, sure enough, there were Hal and Horace and Aunt Molly and the dogs.

As usual, any number of delightful pre-supper chores confronted us. The pointers were allowed to ramble before feeding time. This included a visit to the boat dock to observe the water stage and listen to roosting geese raise sand in the saw-grass sloughs of the far South End. For early December the water was still pretty low and the moss heavy. Those honking geese were music to our ears, for we planned a long hunt at the goose camp over on the river. Our tent there was on an Indian mound just off Ship Island sand-bar, and we itched to get in behind the denizens of that game-pocket.

Then we retraced our steps to the club-house for those puttings-away and settings-about that are, to all intents and purposes, ritual with any long-organized and convivial wildfowling outfit. Ticket and Flash made themselves strictly at home. When Hal and I go shooting, those bullies never step out of character as home folks. This includes bunking on our beds if they so elect. As Hal used to say, "What are a few fleas among pals?"

The club ledger revealed that only two members had hunted at

Beaver Dam during the week previous. This was rather surprising in view of Horace's report that there was a "worl' o' ducks."

Came supper, and what a meal! Nothing but smothered mallard, rice and giblet gravy, grilled tomatoes, and savory bacon for snack garnishment with the hot biscuits. Hal and I are notorious "one-dish" men.

Aunt Molly, expecting us, had quite thrown herself away in getting those ducks to just the right stage of juicy succulence that no other cook or chef in my lifetime has ever even tied. And I've done trencherman's fatigue behind some of the allegedly top-flight sauce-pan and spider artists of terra firma's kitchens. From cajun con-coctions to *salle à mangers* where the help wear fancy pants and bumblebee weskits, and the carpets are so thick that you need snow-shoes to stay on top. Let me give you Aunt Molly's recipe for smothered mallard just as she told it to me that evening in her own kitchen.

"Whin I heahs you an' Mist' Hal is comin', I teks 'bout fo' mallets whut's bin hangin' out in de col' fo' two-three days, an' dresses dem ve'y keerful. I don' nevah put no watah on my ducks. No, suh! I jes' wipes 'em dry wid er rag an' lets 'em set awhile. Den I gits me er stew pot an' puts in some red pippers, vinegar an' fine yarbs outa de gyarden, an' den I adds er li'l watah an' lays in de mallets.

"I brings all dis to er slow bile fo' 'bout tin minutes. Den I teks out de mallets an' dries 'em off an' sets 'em out in de col' air fo' 'bout er hour. But I saves de watah dey done bin biled in. Nex', I gits my ol' deep skillet hotter 'n de hinges o' hades an' swinges off de mallets quick on bofe sides. O' cose, dey done bin split wide open up dey backs.

"Atta dat, I sets de skillet onto de back side o' de stove an' po's in some melted butter an' some o' de bile watah. I puts de ducks back into de skillet wid dey breastes down'ud an' covers 'em wid er flat top an' lays er smoothin' iron on top o' dat. Ev'y now an' den I adds er sluicin' o' elderberry cordial an' er li'l mo' bile watah. Den I draps in er few bay leaves an' er mite o' Tabasco. O' cose, I keeps de baste po'hd ovah de mallets all de meanstwhile.

"When I heahs de Limb Dodger blow fo' de platform, I sets dem mallets in de oven to jes' sorter brown 'em er li'l bit mo'. I meks my gravy an' stirs de hot bile watah an' some mo' elderberry wine into hit. Den, whin I sees you-all is really heah, I finish wid de tomatoes, rice an' biscuit. Dat's de way I cooks dem mallets, suh!"

Ah, me! Aunt Molly of marvelous culinary attainments! Cooks have gone to Heaven for far less than those "mallets."

After supper we sat around in the snug club-room with its prints and antlers looking down on us from walls and rafters that began accumulating grime in the late 70's. Then began preparation for the morrow.

An English friend had just presented me with a trim, handsomely engraved 16-gauge autoloading shotgun with two sets of tubes: improved cylinder for upland birds, and a full-choked one for wild-fowling. I decided, however, to use it only on quail next day, for I was headed for some tall-timber gunning and never believed in sending a boy on a man's errand. I can hear some reader sniff and allow as how he can kill as many high ducks with his 16-bore as I can with my 10-gauge and hand-loads of five drams of powder and an ounce and a half of hard 4's. I've been trying, unsuccessfully, for a great many years to see the color of such money.

I put the shorter tube on the 16-gauge autoloader, however, and false-swung it a bit to get the hang and feel. The stock specifications were just about right. Then I readied my tin shell box with ammunition, water bottle, camera, emergency kit and strong cord. That is about all I ever pack except when I'm out for all day. Iron rations are then included.

Hal and I never shake the dice-box or draw for stands and paddlers when no other members are at Beaver Dam. Horace just naturally takes charge of my boat, and burly Jesse Taylor looks after Hal's interests. Hal likes to jump-shoot ducks in the North End trails, for big Jesse is particularly adept at squirming the sneak-boat noiselessly through button willows and elbow brush. But, of course, we have an understanding that, if the shooting turns out poor for either of us, the other fellow comes at once when the sport sounds good.

When bedtime came, Hal took the walnut couch in the northwest corner by his locker, and I always favored the feather-bed in my southwest niche. Horace left the club-house door wide open; and when frost cooled the stove, the dogs each crawled aboard a bed. Breakfast was, as usual, informal; we never bothered going to Aunt Molly's dining-room unless a crowd was down.

Stirrings-about in Horace's quarters and wood-chopping generally awakened us. Then Horace entered, got the stove going and lit the center lamp. Returning with the white-china coffee dripper, he tinkled on a cup with a spoon. That meant the end of extra snoozing and to come alive. And by the time that eye-opener and ablutions were over, Horace was back with eggs and batter-cakes.

That particular morning, the 5:30 Y & M V express had just rumbled northward when we parted at the dock. The last thing Hal said to me was: "If I'm not in by nine o'clock, don't wait for me. Take the dogs and kill a mess of quail—Irma and Marion want them for their dinner party."

Then he and Jesse disappeared in the swallow-up of misty pre-dawn.

Horace yanked our little duck boat's nose southward and paused to take bearings off a big white star. I knew that by holding it true aft we would hit the trail opening into the South End right on the nose. But before hitting that mark, we had to pole across a quarter mile of willow stumpage.

Masses of mallard, gadwall and widgeon thundered into flight, and we could hear them resettling nearer the woods. The geese we had heard the evening before had moved westward during the night; I could hear them cackling and grunting over in the Teal Pond. Horace and I decided to wade and sled the boat rather than push through the top moss. We entered an aisle through the forest and, though walking as noiselessly as possible, raised clouds of birds ahead.

It was breaking day when we rounded the bole of a huge stunted cypress, with our destination—the Clover Leaf Hole—in front of us. Hundreds of mallards roared out of it. Their strident alarm set the whole marsh a-spout with ducks. Through lacelike boughs the heavens were a-twinkle with milling *Anatidæ*.

Suddenly a bunch of perhaps fifty widgeon lowered delicately into the pool just across the buck-brush from us. Quietly they settled to feed and preen. They were perfectly safe, too, for what Horace and I had in mind was a shot at those geese in the Teal Pond. He knew without my telling him that his next job was to wade a circle around those honkers and, if possible, send them over the woods my way. Leaving me seated on the end of the duck boat, he picked up his gun and faded from sight up the trail.

Distant goose agitation soon told a story of suspicion. Rasping cackles and guttural conversation became more and more confused. Then a muffled beating of wings told me that the flotilla of *Branta canadensis* was getting under way. In stalking game, Horace had the past master's super sixth sense. I heard him shouting, and knew that he was on the outside of the gaggle and trying to shoo them against the bank timber and more nearly over me. By then I saw them too, gaining altitude over the willows and headed my way in a swinging loop. I sat perfectly still; that was no time to flush the unsuspecting widgeon and have them flaring skyward in alarm.

Then the geese were over me. I turned the heavy 10-bore ahead of their veering mass formation and scored a double kill with its first tube. At the report the widgeon leaped and almost obscured my second blast, which downed another bird. I heard Horace's yell of congratulation. There were ducks every way I looked. Now was my time to start scoring.

By the time Horace rejoined me, he had quite some retrieving to do. But I delayed this and stationed him across from me about fifty yards. The ducks were crossing heavily, and our combined calls lowered them just above the treetops. The 10-gauge cracked regularly and successfully. It was one of those mornings when a fellow doesn't let many get away. So heavy was the flight that I shot only greenheads. It was just eight o'clock when Horace, sloshing through the woods, called out: "Dat's de las' un, Cap'n. You got de limit."

Laying aside my gun, I helped him pick up, and we waded up the now sunlit trail. Out across Stumpy Opening and into paddling water, and the lake became a picture. Its deep, unmolested coves, rimmed with yellow saw-grass, were packed with ducks. Its broad bosom flashed with color off the white and black of concentrated scaups. Great patches of greenish moss seed swung with the wind drift, and I thought of summer and fall days when a bass fly tossed to the edges of such scum fetched heavy strikes and battles royal.

At the club I cleaned up a bit, changed to field boots, unleashed Flash and Ticket and shoved the 16-gauge autoloader into my gun scabbard. By then Horace had the mules saddled. We heard Hal's gun working in the North End; so I knew it was all right for me to begin accumulating those bob-whites for the girls.

Hardly had we crossed the railroad and skirted new-ground east of the club before Flash found, and rugged Ticket honored the point. When the bevy flushed, I repressed the inclination to empty the piece, and downed two birds with three shots. The gift gun handled superbly.

Horace marked the escaping singles beyond some mutton cane and briers separating the new-ground from a cornfield. Emerging there,

I dismounted hurriedly, for, almost side by side, Ticket and Flash were pointing stanchly in opposite directions. Off to the right a bit two negroes pulling corn stood watching the scene.

I walked in ahead of Ticket, and a cock bird buzzed to my left. The two dogs stood shot like statues. I clucked softly, and Ticket pussy-footed to the fetch. Dilating with intensity, Flash's gaze was still "eyes right." I swung into firing balance just as a jack-snipe floated from the muck. Flash's optics popped, but he held his ground. Over went *Scolopax*, and the big pointer retrieved at command.

Then, happening to look down, I noticed that my gun was empty and open. I had failed to reload after firing at the bevy rise; so now the weapon needed refueling. I dropped a shell into the carrier and pushed the release pin. Down went the action with a sharp clang. Horace cried out in amazement, for up from a wet corner of the mutton cane and brier patch flapped a mallard drake. What that lone duck was doing in that out-of-the-way spot will forever remain a mystery. Almost by instinct I bowled over the fellow, and Ticket fetched at a lope, head high with pride at this unusual package.

I made a present of the mallard to one of the corn-pullers.

"Cap'n," he said, in thanking me, "whut kinda funny li'l ol' long-billed bird wuz dat you jes' kilt?"

I told him it was a snipe.

"Shucks, Cap'n," he replied, "ef you laks to shoot dem things, dey's er whole passel of 'em uses not fur from heah. Whin you an' Ho'ace come roun' de lane pas' Aun' Molly's cabin, why jes' look in dat wet place out in her cotton fiel'—hit's plumb packed wid dem fellers."

I thanked him kindly for the information, but with the mental reservation that he had merely noticed a lot of killdeer.

For two hours or more Horace and I rode through cornfields, sedgy new-ground tangles and weedy bays. The work of Flash and Ticket was superb. Conditions couldn't have been better, and by eleven-thirty Horace's pouch was puffy. We turned homeward across the corn and, by sheer accident, found ourselves passing Aunt Molly's domicile.

Remembering what our colored friend had said, we dismounted, put Flash and Ticket at heel and went over to have a look at that wet place in the cotton patch. A hundred yards from the house we struck it, just a jelly-textured depression among the bare brown stalks. But out of it whizzed clouds of snipe. I sent Horace scurrying to its far end to keep the birds from pitching there, and hunkered down in the scant cover.

Ticket and Flash, flat on their bellies, looked on in amazement. Snipe hung over the area like a locust swarm in Egypt—a sight I shall always remember.

I fired away as fast as I could cram quail loads into the new fowling-piece. Had that gun jammed, I would have gone stark mad; but it functioned perfectly. Hal said later he never heard such a bombardment. And before very long Horace and I and the dogs gathered up twenty-five snipe that further heavied the sack.

Hal hadn't been in very long with a limit of ducks and three geese to show for his forenoon. He hadn't taken a stand and put out decoys; had just eased along, shooting at leaping or overhead birds. Horace strung up the entire bag for a snap-shot just as Aunt Molly came out on the porch to ring her dinner-bell. I can see her standing there right now and hear her admiring cry of "Great day in de mawnin'!" There were seventy ducks, six geese, twenty-five quail and twenty-five snipe.

But hold! Hold! Don't bawl Hal and me out for a pair of law violators or unmitigated bristle-backs. Don't wire Federal and state enforcement agents to hop on our trails and track us down. I began this article by telling Johnny to stop the car and let me look around a bit. Well, so I did, not long ago. But the old club's record book and my private shooting diary of decades' standing remind me that our bag of seventy ducks, six geese, twenty-five snipe and the same number of bobwhites was made one rare morning in early December of 1909, just thirty-two years ago, come next gunning season.

I can even tell you exactly where all that wild game went, too. Three honkers went to the Old Men's Home, and the others went into cold storage for the Christmas quail hunt at Hal's home in Aberdeen. Most of the ducks went to the Church Home and St. Agnes Hospital. And Hal and I worked on the quail and snipe aplenty when Marion and Irma gave their big dinner party. It came just before the debutantes' ball at the old Chickasaw Guards' Club, and I can shut my eyes and see those two lovely girls who later became our "missuses" standing on the grand staircase with their arms full of long-stemmed American Beauty roses and the stags in windrows at their feet. Ah, me!

In 1909 there was no Migratory Bird Law, and in the state where

Beaver Dam lay there were only county game laws, and those wholly uninterested in waterfowl. In fact, most of the duck clubs of that region were shooting daily limits of from forty to fifty birds. But at Beaver Dam there was a self-imposed one of thirty-five ducks.

There was no limit, for instance, on wild turkey. But those fellows were none too plentiful by 1909; nothing like the late 80's and early 90's, when I first began hunting the big gobbler. We had a rule against more than twenty-five quail, snipe or woodcock per day per gun.

Our hotels and restaurants served wild game openly and legally. And be it remembered that when the Migratory Bird Law did set a Government limit of twenty-five ducks and eight geese per day (a very generous one, if you're asking me) it was, to all intents and purposes, eighteen years before obvious impairment of basic stocks necessitated the lowering of those figures.

So when I had Johnny stop our automobile for me to look around, I figured, in surveying the landscape, that where we sat was just about in the middle of that patch of snipe bog in Aunt Molly's cotton field. But there was no distant Owen cypress in sight, and I guess the bear and deer and wild turkey that we used to hound and dog through the big woods are about things of the past. Maybe there are a few here and there on over into the Tallahatchie country, Beaver Dam Lake took its name from beaver colonies that kept the forests wet before the railroad went through that country. And that clear, deep bayou overhung with cypress and full of game fish is now a silted and muddy drainage ditch.

Today, everything is pretty much cotton, and the countryside, from the farming angle, is almost manicured. Rarely do you sight a real specimen of the old-time log cabin like Aunt Molly's sturdy structure. But there are any number of elegant, electrically equipped residences, with radios wide open. Laundry, bakery, grocery and soft-drink trucks supply their every want. All of which, no doubt, is as it should be.

Mighty little smoke drifts off new-ground burnings, and the homey smells and sounds of a pioneering backwoods country are missing. But, strange to relate, there are fallow fields and woods pastures where some pretty fair quail shooting can still be had if the cornfields and pea patches help out. The farmers collect for not planting some grounds, and such lands lie out or are planted to lespedeza and non-shatter beans. But most plantations are now posted, and their owners co-operate with the State Game and Fish Commission to restore and maintain well-fooded habitats for wildlife.

The younger generation of plantation owners is just as hospitable as their forbears, but they are a sight wiser as to the value of game crops. These, they realize, have become an integral and valuable part of the farm's yield and the county weal. Quail, duck and fish bootleggers are beginning to fear fines and jail sentences. Town and country sportsmen are frowning upon and turning up the chiselers. Not alone as good citizenry, but because, as a basis of sound sportsmanship and justice to others, it is the right thing to do.

Beaver Dam Lake still has a goodly sky line of timber. Even some of its saw-grass rim is intact. But drainage and varying water levels have hurt its once magnificent fishing, and at times endangered duck shooting because of drought. Gone are the coon-tail moss, duckmeat, yonquapins and other aquatic naturals which once fed the migrations. For many years the old club baited the lake, but a Federal edict stopped that and hurt the gunning to some extent. The members shot over live decoys, too; something we of the older times didn't have to worry with particularly.

Somehow they still have pretty good shooting at old Beaver Dam, and occasionally, on a right water stage, the bream, crappie and bass fishing picks up. But there is no huge pecan tree sheltering a moss-shingled clubhouse. A cyclone bowled over the patriarch and crushed the building. All I salvaged were some English sporting prints, deer antlers, pictures of the club's founders, and the historic logbook.

In 1909 there were probably not more than half a million pioneers and less than ten million acres going out of circulation in the duck factories of the waterfowl-producing Canadian provinces. In much of that area the beaver was still the chief hydraulic engineer in charge of water levels. Chances are, the plains country we used to gun outproduced more northern breeding grounds. There was plenty of water, and only casual drought. Offhand, I'd guess the supply of 1909's waterfowl as two and a half times that of today. And to think what has happened to wildfowl habitat in our own and the Canadian country is to heave a long sigh.

How do I approximate such matters? Purely from memory. I shot ducks on the Canadian prairies and the plains of our own Northwest just after entering my teens. The other evening I came across a hunting license issued in South Dakota (1902) to Young Buckingham. I wasn't out of college, but a veteran at wildfowl, chickens and big game. We had grand sport at prairie chickens, but I had an idea that the ring-necked pheasant has rather displaced the glamor boy of the old wheatlands as the major target for South Dakota's sportsmen.

In fact, barring a few states in the Union, I have gunned waterfowl pretty much wherever they use. Black ducks in eastern Canada and coastal flights from New England's goose stands to the rice paddies of South Carolina. I've tumbled velour-headed canvasbacks from Currituck batteries and taken like toll at shore blinds along Potomac broadwaters and Virginia's rushy ponds.

The "bluffs" and duck ponds of Saskatchewan, Manitoba and Alberta were friends these many years agone. In September, 1938, judging the Saskatchewan Field Trials, I rode a week over the southern plains country—recently made a shambles for wildfowl by eight well-nigh rainless years. Shades of Nebraska's sand-hills and bird dogs statuesque on chickens of the wheaty Dakotas! Colorado's plateaus! My tawny Chesapeake crouching in the rushes! Ribbons of weaving, flashing teal!

From Minnesota to the Gulf of Mexico are moored memories of house-boat days and nights along "Ol' Miss." I'm remembering stately cypress, dismal stumpage of the delta's sunk-lands, the "limberjacks" of Reelfoot, and flooded pin-oak bottoms in the heart of ricelands once grand, lush prairie. Across those prairies we drove in approaching springtime, when snipe hosts swung their long-billed migration homeward via the vast Mississippi Valley and we shot our guns hot when *Scolopax* fled the slashes. Too, Louisiana's tidal rims of sere grass and, in far-gone times, acres of redheads rafting off the Texas coast. Lullabies from drifting flights of blue geese and deeper-throated honkers lower to winter-graze off the bays of Lafitte. Add fifteen years' prowling with gun, camera and binoculars—and my waterfowling saga is brought rapidly to date.

All in all, old Beaver Dam is typical of those duck-shooting properties that have weathered the storms of encroaching civilization because of sporting idealism that cares for and protects them. Down the years, its membership refused to quit for hell and high—or low—water. That is what tradition and the will to hunt will do for a bunch of gentlemen.

There are probably two thousand "Beaver Dam Clubs" in this country today, exclusive of the fine guides who operate on public waters and the strictly commercial gunning places. Mighty few, however, have been steadily shot over for more than sixty years and survived to offer sport. Some of the largest have been sold to the

Government for wildfowl refuges; others couldn't stand the pressure of drought and restrictions, and folded up.

One thing is definite. If, during the droughts from 1929 through 1934, the majority of the worth-while duck shooting clubs of this country hadn't stuck to their guns and, at great expense, co-operated by hoarding water and feeding highly concentrated migrations, we would have had closed seasons quite a while ago. And last but not least, the most wretched move that ever impeached the integrity of Conservation was that propaganda which branded all duck-club members as wealthy game hogs and, in setting class against class, dismembered our union of sportsmanship and set back the clock of wildlife restoration at least two decades.

There is good, sound restoration work going forward. But one major waterfowl problem remains, and that is the adjustment of commercial shooting's status.

It's a far cry back from my telling Johnny to stop and let me look around after we turned off the concrete highway. We could stand out there nights in the long ago and hear the swish and gentle whir of duck wings overhead. But now the only swish is that of car tires whizzing endlessly north and south. Why, that strip of concrete runs from the very breeding grounds of the North into wintering grounds of Louisiana and Mexico.

It's still farther back to that lovely forenoon of December, 1909, when Hal and I had our pleasant yesterday and our great-day-in-the-morning at old Beaver Dam. Writing this, there is a true prayer in my heart that the old club's members of today and their sons, too, will in some measure relive Hal's and my good times there. What wouldn't I give to see those gorgeous mallards floating over the lacy cypress tops and hear Aunt Molly ringing her dinner-bell and calling: "Great day in de mawnin'! Come an' git it!"

Leader of the Flock

By W. J. SCHOONMAKER

A STUBBY TAIL TWITCHED NERVOUSLY; FIERCE YELLOW EYES bored through the tangle; then a short spurt, a mighty leap and the wildcat was bearing down upon the great Canada goose. Honker, leader of the flock, fled when the rush began, ran with flapping wings and outstretched neck, sprang into the air, climbed frantically into an azure sky, and the cat's flashing claws missed their mark.

Hundreds of wing beats filled the air as the entire flock joined their leader, circled once the danger zone, and headed into the spring breeze that blew from the land of the North Pole.

High they flew, winging their way in a great wedge-shaped formation, over village and city, valley and mountain, river and lake;

honking, babbling, excited, wild and happy. Ice still covered some of the ponds, and the wood frogs had not yet begun to croak, but this flying wedge, pressing toward the Arctic, was a promise of spring.

The earth people thrilled to the clangor and many gladdened hearts responded in ways that were not understandable. Strong men yearned to wander—destinies unknown; the city-bound cried for freedom, and youth pined for love, because there is something in the call of the wild goose that is mysterious and stirring, saddening and gladdening, alluring and thrilling; a something that men hear and stir to, yet cannot explain.

Onward, the feathered visitors to the great northern wilderness flew until Saratoga Lake, cold and blue, yawned below. Rafts of ducks rested on the water, and, as the great wild geese slanted down, their smaller cousins welcomed the voyagers with excited babbling and quacking. Mallards, black ducks, golden-eyes, buffle-heads and the saw-billed fish ducks, as well as grebes and loons, awaited the migrants. All mingled, friendly and contented, and a bald eagle soared above.

Soon after dawn the next morning, the flock resumed its journey, driving swiftly ahead to a land where the great birds would swing away in pairs to find a place that would be theirs alone—until the eggs hatched.

Honker, the gander, with Gray Mate, swung over the low spruces of the northland and dropped into the beaver pond that had been their summer home for three seasons. For the geese it was the love moon, and with necks entwined they rubbed cheeks and rejoiced.

Soon the nest, a mass of twigs and weeds, was completed. It was fully exposed, and on the very top of the beaver lodge, but there was nothing to fear, for the pond was far from the trails of men and the nest, surrounded by water, was difficult to approach.

Late in May the eggs were laid, six yellowish-white, precious eggs that were to be the pride and treasure of the white-cheeked pair, but only after a full month of constant attention and vigil. Gray Mate was patient and seldom left the nest, and the great black-necked gander, alert and watchful, never neglected his duty of guarding mate and home. When the goslings came forth the parent birds were happy. Their long flight and tireless efforts were well rewarded.

The pond people looked on when the flotilla of geese passed—the mother, proud and tender, with graceful arched neck, in the lead; six fluffy, downy, goslings strung out behind; the defiant gander guarding the rear. From the shore the mink thought of the possibility of a tender dinner but dared not attack; the young fox, well concealed, hoped that a youngster would stray near. The beaver, however, broad tailed and well furred, swam alongside and was regarded as harmless—if it was not a friend, neither was it a foe.

The world was one of sunshine and happiness and rapid growth for the goslings, and the insects, worms, roots and other foods that they sought were in abundance. Their cares were few, for their parents, stout-hearted, alert and keen-eyed, guarded them well. But even the mightiest may err or be caught off-guard, and one day, as the family fed far from the edge of the pond, an enemy stalked toward them with an ease and stealth unequaled in the vast northland. With ears laid back, the great Canada lynx approached on large padded paws to within two bounds of an unsuspecting gosling. The set was perfect, the kill was sure and the big cat bounded forward.

Honker saw the first leap, raised high and struck a powerful blow with his great wing. It landed solidly, with a force that might have broken the arm of a man, across the eyes and face of the lynx. Hurt, amazed and temporarily blinded, the foe was halted while mother and young raced for the pond. Honker, the father, was not now leader of the flock seeking to escape. His sole purpose was to protect his family, and fearlessly the valiant bird faced the enemy and struck several hard blows. The lynx was young; this was its first year of hunting and the determination of the great bird was too much. With a snarl of rage, the baffled cat slunk off and the goslings were safe.

Seven weeks after they were hatched, the young geese made their first short flight and rejoiced in a new found pleasure. Each day thereafter the entire family, headed by Honker, took flights that ever increased in distance, and by mid-August the young birds were strong fliers and ready to begin their first journey toward the warm southland. Honker and Gray Mate were proud, and their black eyes shone with satisfaction as they looked upon their six sturdy offspring.

Soon came cold frosty nights, the maple leaves grew brighter, and skim ice fringed the pond. Honker and Gray Mate became uneasy. The journey of peril and sorrow was at hand, and early one morning the family of geese flew south to the big lake where hundreds of other great, black-necked birds had already congregated. The autumn migration of the Canada goose, one of the finest and wisest of waterfowl, had begun.

Slowly at first the huge flock moved south, from lake to lake and river to river, stopping often to rest and feed, for intense cold was not yet forcing their flight.

The journey was pleasant and peaceful; the flock was well fed and vigorous. The young birds, joyful and amazed, followed cheerfully the will of Honker, leader of the flock. But peace for the wild folk is not for long; not near the haunts of man.

One night they slept contented, unworried; the next, at dawn, began a lasting terror—the terror of the hunting season.

At the first shot the great flock took off as one bird. High toward the heavens they climbed and peered down with keen, black eyes upon two of their kindred that would never again obey the commands of the majestic Honker. And they saw more than that. Carefully concealed in the wild rice and flags the circling band observed dozens of hunters emptying their guns on small flocks of bewildered ducks and mud hens, snipe and yellowlegs. They saw many birds stop in their swift flight, crumple in the air and fall with a tiny splash on the blue water. They heard the sharp reports of hundreds of shots. The geese of the year—youngsters of the flock—twisted their lovely necks and with terror-filled eyes beheld the murder scene below, as man the mighty greeted his feathered and distant brethren.

Brave hearts beat rapidly as the huge flock formed a wedge and headed again toward the land of warm breezes. But this was not the determined, anxious rush of the Canada goose in the springtime, heading toward a summer home and a life of love. This flight was forced by winter, which closes the waters and seals in ice the foods of the waterfowl. And this flight was filled with constant watchfulness and restlessness, for at every point and feeding ground danger and death lurked. The first danger was now far behind and the birds were speeding on. The lines of the wedge often wavered and broke, for many of the flock were young birds that had never before followed the long southward course. Neither had they arrived at their full strength, and too often the flock was forced to face dangers so that the tired ones might rest.

For weeks the journey continued over a hostile land, and the numbers of the flock were tragically reduced. The greatest loss, however, was suffered in the sunny state of South Carolina.

The flock was tired. Honker knew that, for he too felt the strain of the long forced flight, added to which was worry and terror. So, when a small flock of his kind called from the rush-fringed waters, the great leader circled once, then set his wings and the whole flock spiraled down. Over the rush tops they swept and their excited kindred "honked" a welcome. The bushes moved, ever so slightly, and Honker's watchful eye saw the gleam of steel gun-barrels. His warning was not terrifying. Yet it was urgent, commanding and the flock climbed. Four rapid shots roared behind them and two of his followers dropped. On sped the others and the scene faded while the decoys—victims of man's craftiness—honked and pleaded and fanned the air with clipped wings. But the slender chain that anchored them fast did not yield and, try as they might, they could not follow their disappearing kind.

Honker looked back. The wedge had formed; the flight was strong. He turned to the left and on his flank was Gray Mate—but something was wrong. Even as he looked, death came and his valiant mate plunged to the open water below. The old gander dropped and the flock followed. Around his mate he swam, talking, pleading, low and sorrowful, but to no avail. Night settled and the wise birds waited while Honker, their leader, mourned his greatest loss.

Morning stirred them and the old gander looked about. He did not, however, look upon his mate, for during the night her cold body had drifted shoreward and was now tucked among the reeds.

The flock babbled and Honker felt their restlessness. They must go on, and with a stout though sorrowed heart he gave the command.

Their course was dangerous and trying. Foes seemed to be everywhere and hundreds of charges of shot tore through their ranks. Many fell and some struggled on, sorely wounded. Then, as though a truce were declared, another hunting season was past.

The geese mingled with others of their kind, as well as with great flocks of ducks and other birds that had escaped the hunters' death. Together, on peaceful southern waters, they waited for the call of the northland.

The call came. None heard it but all felt it, and the Canada geese crowded close to their leader. Quiet and still, like a statue, he stood—listening, watching, hoping. Then, as though he could bear it no longer, Honker, lord of the flock, called once—clear, loud and trumpet-like. His flock thrilled and stood tense; then they rose and slanted steadily toward the north. Eager and strong and joyful they were—all but one, their gander leader.

The great northland was reached and pairs swung off alone. Honker dropped into the beaver pond that had been his summer home for some years past. With a lonely heart he swam silently about. For days he pined, and often he stood for hours on the old beaver house, motionless, silent, sad and alone.

The Canada Goose mates only once, but mates for life. Should one pass on, the survivor is doomed—like Honker—to a life of loneliness. His very staunchness is his greatest burden, and with a brave but lonely heart the old gander waits to lead the flock—his children and theirs—back over the safest route he knows.

Hail the Humber

By LEE WULFF

THE AFTERNOON WAS BEAUTIFUL IN CORNER BROOK. THE SKY WAS cloudless and from the studio window I could see the evergreen-blanketed hills of western Newfoundland bathed in brilliant sunlight. The week had been hectic and now that the uncertainty of planning was over, I could breathe easier. There was still plenty to do but nothing that couldn't wait until tomorrow. I had finished my weekly broadcast and I had seven days in which to prepare the next script. My salmon tackle was downstairs in my room, dusty from a month of idleness. There was nothing to hold me back.

Cliff, the station manager, and Ella, one of the stars of its firmament, didn't seem to be working very hard and I tried to enlist them in a few hours' fishing on the Lower Humber. Cliff couldn't be budged from work which he claimed was important but Ella decided to join me. She didn't feel like tackling the Humber's heavy water for the big fish of its run until she'd had more practice where both the fish and fishing were less tricky, but thought she'd come along and watch. The Humber is a tough river and I could only hope that there'd be something besides casting to watch. It still was a little early for the salmon to be coming in to the Lower Humber shoals.

We passed the mouth of the river where the tide lapped high at the base of the limestone gorge through which the Humber pours its brown, peat-stained waters into the Bay of Islands. The road ran close beside the bank and we saw that the river was in good flow but the tide was too high to give good fishing conditions at the first pool above tidewater, Shellbird Island Shoal, where the tide still backs up the flow.

The old eagerness to wade into the river and sink into the rhythm of casting was strong inside me. I decided to fish the Quarry Pool a little farther upstream. We looked down upon the river from the high ground, saw the sunlight glinting on its lazy flow and the reflection of the gray crags bright on the dark, cool waters. Then we were walking down the narrow path through the alders to the river.

The day was too beautiful to have found the pool deserted. Sam Wells and Joe Kenney were fishing the lower section below the drop-off where the water swirls in, deep and black, against over-hanging alders. It felt good to have the water brushing coolly around my knees as I waded the ledgy river bed above them. The delicate seven-foot fly rod made casting a pure pleasure and, in spite of occasional gusts of wind from the west, line and leader swept out cleanly to drop the fly into the chop and swirl of the deep water. Each time the fly swung inward I knew it should pass over the heads of some magnificent salmon, the first of the run to come in, bright and fresh from the sea.

The Lower Humber is the name of the sleepy flow of water that drifts easily out of Deer Lake and courses between bluff limestone mountains for a distance of twelve miles to salt water. Thousands of salmon travel upstream through it on their way to the headwaters in late June and early July but few of these early fish pause even momentarily in the lower river. They're headed upstream far beyond Deer Lake and beyond that staggering barrier at the big falls where they depend upon the heavy run-off of the late spring to make good jumping conditions for them. Later, in August and September when the sun is warm and the river's flow has eased, the special salmon of the Lower Humber come back to their native waters on the spawning journey, big, deep-bellied fish that wait out the remaining weeks to spawning time on the shoals in the lower river's heavy flow and rarely rise to a fly.

I fished through fifty feet of water just above the ledgy drop-off, using a low-water Silver Gray on a No. 6 hook. There was no sign of a fish's movement behind my fly, no swirl or boil in the heavy water which would indicate that a salmon had moved up briefly from his resting place to have a look at the swinging fly.

A second time I worked down through the heavy water, this time using a No. 6 low-water type Dark Cahill. That pattern is common enough for trout but is rarely used for salmon. Still, it had been effective for me before and especially in circumstances like these when the fish had seen a good many of the standard pattern salmon flies pass over their heads before mine were put to them. Halfway down the second time, my line tightened. I saw the swirl as the fish caught the fly and then felt the heavy drag as he moved upstream against the sweeping water. The movement was steady but swift. Then the fish stopped and hung motionless near the bottom for a moment. How big would he be? He leaped. I saw then that he would be big enough.

The Humber is about 150 yards wide at the Quarry Pool and the flow is a steady sweep that continues right on downstream except for a small eddy at the tail of the pool on the southern bank, the side from which I was fishing. Those salmon that the fishermen are lucky enough to save come in on the quiet waters of that eddy. Knowing that if my fish was to be saved he'd be brought in at the eddy, I moved rapidly in that direction. This put me well below the fish where I could exert the greatest pressure on him. When I passed the spot where the black waters swirled in hard against the alders as the drop-off touches the shore, I swung the Leica camera from my neck and passed it to Ella who stood wide-eyed, watching the salmon leap.

The fish was bright and he threw a silvery light when he curved into the air. He worked upstream, then he fought his way out into the central flow and finally moved down with the current until he was below me. I relaxed the pressure from the light rod and the fish struggled back through the flow to a point opposite me. A little pressure and persuasion brought him into the eddy, but the sting of the fly in his jaw nagged him and he came into the air again and moved well out into the current.

We played a little game then, the fish seesawing back and forth in and out of the eddy, punctuating the play with leaps. The hook was of the fine wire type and its hold couldn't be tried too much; the leader would stand up to about three pounds on the fine end of the taper, no more. More than once the fish fell away with the current to a point below me. This was bad since the way downstream for me was blocked by a small island that would be inshore of the fish if he went on downstream, yet which was in water too deep for me to reach by wading. The game went on until he'd made his ninth clean leap and returned to the eddy in a wide loop that brought him close to me. Snubbed hard, he bored toward the sandy bottom and found strength enough to move out with the circling water of the eddy. I detached the tailer from its snap on my left shoulder and set it up. The fish came in again, and in one of his spasmodic twists, the tailer went over his tail and I drew it tight to set the noose and bring him ashore.

"He" turned out to be a female fish and I stretched her out on the wet sands thirty-five minutes after the rise. Scales taken from her side showed her to have spent probably three years in freshwater as a parr before migrating to the sea. Here she grew fat for a little more than two years after which she'd returned to the Humber and spawned, probably weighing about twenty-three pounds at the time. She'd lost weight in her period of fresh water starvation at spawning and had gone back to the sea the next spring to regain that poundage and more. She had come back again on a second spawning journey a few days ago at her final weight of twenty-eight pounds.

Sam Wells came over and said, "I've hooked four here in the last three days but I didn't bring any of them in. One of them was bigger than this fish, too."

I knew how he felt. I'd been lucky and my salmon hadn't been too hard to handle. It was a tough place to land a fish without a canoe and a poor spot to use one.

All day Saturday I worked and watched the rain stream down my windows. Long after midnight I could still hear the big drops beating against the panes as I lay in bed waiting for sleep and picturing the rising river. I gave it an eight- or nine-inch rise if the rain stopped by morning. How lucky I'd been to have gone out the day before. Still, a rise of water would bring in new fish and help the fishing conditions, especially in a day or two when the flow steadied off at its new level.

Sunday morning's skies were bright and blue again, with a soft, warm wind from the west. I spread my fly-tying things on the table and proceeded to make up a few flies that I felt might turn the trick with the river at its new high level. They were unorthodox for the Humber, being No. 1 hooks, much larger than those in common use. The body was of golden-yellow wool with oval tinsel spiralling down its length. The hackle was of guinea hen neck feather and the wings of black squirreltail with a golden pheasant crest feather topping it off. It had no tail and was tied slim and small of bulk. With higher water a larger fly might be in order to compete for the salmon's attention with all the debris a rising river picks up and carries upon it. With the current swifter than usual, I wanted a heavy hook that would tend to hold the fly under water instead of letting it lift up to the top and skim along, cutting the surface, as a light fly often does when the water is fast and the line lies near the top.

Monday's midday sun was bright as I walked along West Street. My mind, of course, was strictly on business and the Humber River was completely out of my thoughts. With a rattling of fenders and squeaking of springs Ray Doucette pulled in beside me at the curb and his head poked out of the window. "How about it?" he asked grinning. "Let's go up to the river this afternoon."

At two o'clock I was waiting for him in the lobby of the Inn, my waders and other gear piled beside me. Captain Bill Davies of the Canadian Army Public Relations came over to ask me what I thought of his chances for getting some fishing pictures, still pictures in color.

Having spent months waiting for perfect Kodachrome conditions of bright sunlight in combination with hooked and leaping salmon, I couldn't be too hopeful, but since the sun was shining and the river was handy I suggested that he come up to the Quarry Pool in about half an hour on the bare possibility that one of us would hook a fish. At least he'd be able to snap his shutter on some fishermen casting on the broad river.

Ray came along then and we headed up-river to the Quarry Pool. The water was high and the waves curled over the rocks near the head of the shoal with a swishing sound. Ray fished below the drop-off while I worked through the stretch just above with the water rougher and the wading more difficult under the new conditions. I tied on one of the black and gold flies I'd made up and sent it out into the crisp white waves.

One cast was like another as I moved down with the flow. Each time the fly settled on the water it was swept quickly toward the shore in a downstream arc. Sometimes I could catch the glint of the sun on the fly as it swam an inch or so beneath the water and more times it was lost from sight in the general darkness of the twisting current. Then there was a heavy swirl where the fly had been a moment before but no pressure on the line followed the fish's rise. He'd been interested but not quite enough. He'd risen short. I stood stock still, marking the length of line I had out and remembering exactly the direction of my cast.

For ten minutes I cast repeatedly, the same distance from the same spot and in the same direction. There was no sign of life from the brown water. Sometimes these Lower Humber salmon will make a dozen false rises... and end up still refusing to take the fly. This one seemed to have exhausted his interest with one good look at the feathers and steel.

I'd just started through that short stretch of water a second time, using the same fly, when Bill Davies showed up on the bank behind me. He had scouted the possibilities and taken a couple of Kodachromes of the pool and its fishermen when I reached the spot from which I had risen the fish before. This time I felt the line tighten before I saw the swirl of the rise. Bill was in exactly the right spot with a cloudless sky above and a bright sun burning behind him, the conditions color photographers pray for.

The salmon went through his bag of tricks with more than the usual abandon, piling one jump upon another. He wore himself out quickly and I slid the tailer over his waving caudal fin in the eddy after a concentrated period of non-stop excitement. When I slid his sleek, silvery twenty-pound body up on the sandy beach I heard Bill's shutter make a final click and turned to see him smiling broadly. I couldn't help thinking of the empty hours I'd spent waiting for just such a chance in comparison with the ease with which this opportunity had come along for him.

Ray and I fished for half an hour without another rise. Two other anglers who reached the pool just after we had went without action, too. Then, with Bill joining us, we drove a mile farther up-river to Steady Brook Pool. There the river pushes its flow over a series of shallow bars that end in deep drop-offs and build up slowly to a shallows again. The salmon lie on the shoals in an easy flow and we waded out to cast our flies as far off-shore as we could, letting them make a long swing through the easy, rippled water. The same fly was still tied to the end of my fifteen-foot leader, even though the water here was shallower and the need for a large fly should not be as great. The nylon line rode high in the water and, once or twice, in spite of the heavy hook, the fly skimmed along the surface instead of traveling beneath it.

Then, when the line was thoroughly wet once more the fly rode beautifully and up from below came a sleek, swift salmon to take it in his jaws. Ray left off fishing to get the boat and bring Bill out close to the spot where I was playing the fish. It was insurance, too, should I need the boat to take me downstream if the fish headed that way into water too deep for me to wade. The salmon took me down across two of the deep shoal-ends where the bottom dropped off abruptly. In crossing them the water came up to my armpits, lapping at the very tops of my waders and the force of the deep water swept me across those deep spots with a speed equal to its own.

This fish, like the first, spent himself quickly with a splurge of activity that piled leap upon leap and run upon run. Strangely enough, he made no very long runs and never took out more than a hundred yards of line. With three fish out of four that size I'd have needed the boat to take me downstream to slower water to land him. But, to my advantage, he stayed close most of the time and did his leaping right around me. Again Bill was presented with a fighting, fresh-run fish in bright sunlight. His shutter clicked repeatedly on a gleaming twenty-pounder that came ashore in twelve minutes, exactly the same time his cousin of identical weight had required less than an hour before. The rod was the same seven-foot, 2½-ounce fly rod balanced with a specially tapered D nylon fly line.

I was grateful then, and I'm grateful now as I write, for the pleasure that went with the capture of those three salmon on my first two afternoons of the season on the Lower Humber. Each time I fish those heavy waters, I go with the thought that I'll enjoy the fishing and absorb the beauty of the moving water and steep, bare mountains that hem it in...and if I'm lucky have a fish rise to my fly. As I write now I wonder if I've at last solved the riddle of where to fish the Lower Humber's pools and which flies to present under varying conditions and just how to present them. It seems more likely to me that I was just attuned to the river and that in another year, granted the grace to fish it, I'll have fewer salmon for my casting hours. But I can be certain that the pleasure of fishing those brown waters will be the same and the look of the river from the high road will always make my heart beat faster.

Life among the Wood Ticks

By GORDON MACQUARRIE

ONCE I WAS SO YOUNG I THOUGHT THERE WERE GOOD TROUT streams devoid of wood ticks. Later, however, I came to know that only the happiest dogs harbored fleas. I quit looking for tickless trout streams.

I have come to terms with wood ticks. If they will let me take a couple of trout I will leave them alone unless they crawl on my neck. My shirt collar is the deadline. Above that they are out of bounds.

The arrangement has worked well. I tramp the brushy trails of the trout streams and the wood ticks fall down inside my shirt. Under the terms of our treaty I do not even scratch. I concentrate upon fishing.

Wood ticks like me. I taste good. I consider myself one of the leading de luxe, itinerant wood tick cafeterias in Wisconsin. I send few wood ticks away hungry. One day I fed 55 wood ticks at one sitting.

On that day a fellow named Helge, a sterling fisherman, took me to his favorite stretch of trout water—the Flagg river of North Wisconsin. (You go in through Carlson's sheep ranch, bribe him with a fresh box of snoose, then turn down the old Battleaxe railroad right-of-way, and there you are.)

We fished hard and profited by our labors. It was hot in the deep valley of the Flagg and the wood ticks were sitting on their front porches in their Rockford socks reading the Sunday papers.

When I would pass a wood tick's dwelling I could see the Old Man make a dive for his hat and shoes, vault the porch railing and parachute down my bosom, yelling over his shoulder, "Hurry with the kids, Ma! He's a fat one!"

That night, before the lights of the car, Helge and I stripped and went to work. He had a paltry 40 wood ticks and I had the grand total of 55.

That was a night to be remembered. I have forgotten the limits of hard-bodied trout we took, I have almost forgotten the two bottles of beer we stole from the cooling river bed where other hands had placed them, forgetting that their bright caps were above the water and caught the glint of the sun.

But I have not forgotten the wood ticks. Fifty-five. . . .

Two over a full deck including the joker.

Unquestionably I am a shining mark for wood ticks. I once gave a wood tick a 700-mile ride from Lake of the Woods, Ontario, to Milwaukee, with a stop-off at Duluth. And I have never suffered any ill effects. Our north woods wood ticks are not the fever ticks of the West, although they are capable of becoming so. Any veteran lumberjack will bear me out in saying they are nothing but wild bed bugs.

The worst things about wood ticks have been said by women. A woman alleges she detests wood ticks as much as she does mice. I don't know. I am waiting for complete proof that a woman, seeing a mouse, will jump up on a table when there is no man around.

However, I do resent the general lack of character found in the wood tick. But as long as he is around good trout holes I will get along with him. A wood tick has his own private life to lead and I am not one to pry into it too far.

I have seen old patriarch wood ticks out there in their front yards swinging in their hammocks and listening to the baseball broadcast while I toiled in the hot sun with 75 pounds of camp duffel on my sweaty back. That, to be sure, is galling.

How those same wood ticks can get down inside my shirt so quickly is beyond me. One minute they are rooting for the Dodgers and the next thing you know they are walking across my chest carrying their shoes, so as not to make a noise.

Once aboard, the first item on the agenda is a tour of inspection. A wood tick knows more about what people wear than an underwear salesman. Consider the exultation of a wood tick as he slides down inside a millionaire's collar. One whiff of the talcum brand on the fellow's neck and the tick knows he's in clover.

A bit farther down the wood tick stops, adjusts his spectacles and says, "Ah, silk!" On a job like that a wood tick wastes no more time exploring. He just sharpens his face with a file, braces his feet and gets at it.

Picture the wood tick returning home in the cool of the evening, stopping at Louie's place to talk over business conditions with the boys—

"Dined with a general today," says one.

"That's nothing," says another, setting down his dinner bucket. "I hooked a ride on a Sunday school teacher. You should have heard her!"

"Faw," says a third, "I let a dozen go by before I got what I wanted—a Chicago ward boss. Did you fellows ever hear of a champagne supper?"

On lesser fry a wood tick may have to sink several dry holes before he strikes a gusher. But you can count on one thing. When a wood tick is down there with his wife going over the premises he is not letting on. He is going around on tiptoes saying, "S-s-sh! Drat it, Margie, I wish you'd wear rubber heels."

After a wood tick has had his fill he grows careless and belches. Or he may make other warning sounds, like pushing his chair away from the table with a scraping noise. Then you reach down and extract him and he rolls over in your hand with his belly up and leers at you as much as to say, "What've you got for dessert?"

Taking wood ticks out of the folds of one's trousers and looking around for two-by-fours to bat them with is as unprofitable as beating back the ocean tide with a broom. In any given five-acre patch of superfine trout country in the north from May through June a man ought to be able to gather a bushel if he works at it.

Down in the southern states the ticks get so thick that land owners set forest fires to "get shet of them."

The wood tick will fasten itself to creatures other than man. Deer, bear, partridges, and especially dogs, are among the better known wood tick restaurants. The more rugged Winchester farmers of our northern states develop a certain resistance, they claim, by virtue of their leathery skin.

Just the other night I had a bear over to my house for supper, one Tuffy, weight seven pounds, a fellow of undeniable poise and charm. He crawled into my lap and left behind two wood ticks, neither of which, from the size of their stomachs, had eaten for weeks. Now there is something for wood tick experts to ponder. Tuffy had not been in wood tick country for two weeks, yet he had brought those ticks along and neither had dined.

To be sure, it might be explained that it is only the female wood tick that goes out for dinner, just as it is the female mosquito which does the gadding for her family. I did not establish the sex of the two ticks Tuffy left behind, but traveling in pairs like that a man might suppose they were mates. A well-fed wood tick looks like a small wad of bubble gum. These were thin as rails. They may have been worrying about something.

It is strictly a caution the way a wood tick will eat, swelling up as big as the end of your little finger. Their supreme contentment at such times may be judged by the way they wiggle their toes.

Ridding oneself of wood ticks is no great trick. A brisk rubdown with kerosene will cause them to withdraw their heads and yell, "Holy Mackerel! Who threw that!" Standing in the dense smoke of burning cedar boughs is also recommended. Wood ticks will turn backward somersaults getting out of there. I was so smoked up one June day that when I got home the neighbor's cats must have thought I was a herring, the way they followed me.

In the case of just a few wood ticks a pipe smoker can make them let go in a hurry by dropping a little pipe juice on them. A gurgly pipe burning damp tobacco is best for this work. A wood tick will scream bloody murder at such treatment. One quid of chewing tobacco accomplishes the same end.

Of course the rookie in a North Wisconsin logging camp soon learns how to get rid of them. He is instructed by sourdoughs to strip and cover himself with salt. This generates a ranging thirst in the wood ticks. Then he is told to stand by a door, beyond which, outside, is a pail of water. All he has to do is open the door, let the wood ticks see the pail of water and after they jump off, shut the door on them.

The confirmed man of the trout should resolve to get along with wood ticks. Any other procedure will fail because the wood tick is determined to get along with trout fishermen. Wood ticks are associated with some of my better fishing moments.

There was that night last summer on the Namakagon river—

Squishing back upstream in the dark I could hardly wait to get to the car for a long look at a three-pound brown I'd taken. On the stream in the gathering darkness there is never time to admire such a fish. He is slid into the creel for more leisurely gloating later on. It is a familiar ceremony to all trout fishermen.

I squirmed out of waders and turned on the head lights. It was a fine moment. The brown was a glorious fellow, dark and heavy through the center. Admiring him, I became aware of a companion helping me celebrate my hour of victory. He was a wood tick, of course. He crept down from my wrist and out onto the back of my hand. I think he tipped his hat to me when he saw the size of that brown trout.

In that hour of jubilation did I scourge him with kerosene, or purge him with droplets from my gurgling dudeen?

No, sir! I let him enjoy the spectacle, then I tucked him back up my sleeve.

Business is so good among the wood ticks in the north woods that they are able to knock off work early in July. A few stick around to keep tab on the clothing fishermen are wearing, so they may devise means of getting into them next year. Inasmuch as the wood tick does not start work until about May 1 in the north, it can be seen he actually labors gainfully only a little more than two months out of twelve each year.

Right there, possibly, is the reason we hate him so.

As for me, I decline to envy his lot for I have used him to good purpose many a time. Returning from a fishing trip I am often asked, "How many'd ye git?" Right there the wood tick earns his way with me for I can truthfully answer:

"The limit—and how!"

With Woodcock

By COL. HAROLD P. SHELDON

AT THE POINT WHERE THE BELDEN BROOK LEAVES THE HILLS above the Old Beaver Meadow its character undergoes a change. Its youthful turbulence subsides when it reaches the valley. It assumes the reflective demeanor of maturity as its amber flood slips quietly along the old channels twisting about through the wide thickets of birch, pine and black alder. After miles of apparently purposeless wandering it joins a larger tributary and eventually reaches the sea.

The Captain, with three years of camps, battlefields and hospitals behind him and a new bird gun tucked away in his baggage, was returning home from the wars. Despite his eagerness to reach the old white house among the maples, he paused for a moment on the wooden bridge to survey the familiar landscape. Nothing had changed here. The farmers' "young cattle" had probably forged new paths through the thickets; the stands of young poplar, golden in the October sunlight, were undoubtedly a bit taller than when he saw them last, but all else appeared as he remembered it.

This was his favorite shooting ground. It had been favorite for Sody Baker and Old Man Juckett, too. They used to gun for the market and had taken many a bag of woodcock and grouse from these covers, but that had been before the Captain's time. The grouse remained but the woodcock had vanished, probably never to return.

The Captain sighed for the lost birds and drove on to his welcome.

His room under the eaves was just as he had left it. Loving hands had attended to that. There was the ragged bullet hole in the wall left unrepaired to remind an over-confident youngster that guns are dangerous tools. How it had scared him that day when that old green pistol cartridge turned out to be no dud after all! His old Indian blanket lay folded across the foot of the bed and on shelf and walls were the accumulated trophies and treasures of boyhood, harmless things that reminded him of happy, peaceful years before the grim times came.

And, bless her heart! If she hadn't dug out his old shooting kit, the stained corduroy jacket and breeches, the battered wreck of a hat, and the scarred boots.

The Captain put out his hand to touch the stuff.

"You haven't changed one single bit!" She was watching him from the doorway with shining eyes. "When you used to come home from school you never could wait until you got into those awful looking things and found a gun or a fish pole."

The Captain's eyes twinkled as he corrected her gently.

"It's a fishing rod, not a pole, Mother. I've told you that times enough."

"Well, I'm sure I can't see why." She smiled, delighted that he had remembered their old joke. Then she resumed: "Everyone in town will be coming to see you tomorrow. You always got away when company came. I suppose, as usual, I'll have to explain that you've gone off shooting."

"Yes, ma'm I guess so," he admitted meekly. Then, with a motion too swift for her to avoid he swung her up in his arms. "That is if I can find anyone around here who'll fix up a little lunch for me. Maybe I'll bring her a partridge feather and a handful of wintergreens."

There was a white frost that night to make the ancient timbers of the house creak and sigh. It put a border of thin crystals along the edges of the brook and on the puddles of the cow path that the Captain followed. He carried his new gun, a slim, polished twenty-bore that had cost him a month's pay in a famous gun shop in the City. Occasionally he paused momentarily to pitch the weapon to his shoulder at an imaginary target, trying to recover the bird shooter's knack, so long unpracticed.

His boot crushed a mushroom of ice crystals. The small sound set off an explosion in a thicket of birch and a grouse roared up, its marking of gray and brown and black clear and distinct in the light. The gun caught the old drummer at the top of his leap and tumbled him back in a cloud of shattered leaves and floating feathers.

There were two more at the edge of a well-remembered cluster of thorn-apple bushes. One vanished instantly among the thick growth, but the second bird rose like a pigeon in a high sweeping course that carried it back over the gunner's head and squarely into a lethal charge of No. 7's that the new gun sent aloft to intercept the arrowy flight.

"I wish old Stub could have seen that one," thought the Captain, but his friend and comrade of other days slept now in a far foreign field and would never again go gunning in the covers of Tranquility Township.

With two plump birds in his pockets, the Captain was in no mood to hasten. It was enough to wander again through the autumnal landscape, sniffing the pungent odors that betrayed the dissolution of the lush growths of summer and listening to the peaceful sounds that told of the shy, busy harvesters, furred and feathered, at work all about him. It was enough to see the misty blue walls of the Adirondacks beyond the shimmering waters of the Lake and the darker masses and peaks of his own Green Mountains, standing firm and constant above the lesser hills. If he thought of the friends now gathering to greet him he forgave himself any discourtesy, for those hills and valleys also were his friends welcoming him home again with a carnival of color fit for an emperor.

The sun was slanting toward the crest of the western mountains when the solitary hunter turned his steps toward the brook. He wanted a drink of cold water and he knew there was a good prospect, at this time of the day, of finding grouse feeding in the wild grape-vines that grew along the stream side. The thickets were less dense here and interspersed with small grassy glades and the tangled strong-holds of blackberry bushes.

The Captain was crossing one of these faint clearings when it happened. A woodcock sprang from underfoot and with a brief provocative whistle and a light whirr of cupped wings darted down the glade before the eyes of the astonished gunner. It hung suspended for an instant against the sky, then it vanished like a wraith. But there was no mistaking the royal orange and black of the bird's plumage nor the long bill seen for a moment as the tinkling bird turned sharply to fly down some invisible passageway of air.

"By the Lord Harry! That's the first—"

The exclamation was left unfinished, for another bird was in the air. This time the gun was ready and the woodcock collapsed into the birches, leaving a small puff of soft feathers floating in the air to mark the spot where its last flight had ended.

The Captain gathered his game tenderly, observing as he did so that the ground 'round about was marked with the white splashes that are the woodcock's sign.

"Just two birds couldn't have done all this," he reflected. "There must be more around here somewhere."

He began a careful exploration, giving special attention to the edges of the thickets and the bare damp earth of the cattle paths.

Almost immediately he flushed another bird which offered a ridiculously easy shot as it went straight away across the clearing.

"Well," muttered the Captain as he snapped out the smoking cases and reloaded. "Old Man Juckett used to say that the easy-looking 'cocks were the hardest to hit—and he must have known."

The next bird was neatly dropped, although half the charge struck the trunk of an elm that the Captain hadn't even seen until the bark flew.

And then from the path ahead two woodcock rose together and went drifting and darting away through the tops of the birches against the sunset sky.

The first fell at the shot, but the other seemed to be hopelessly out of range, no bigger than a butterfly, when the Captain finally had him over the rib and pulled the trigger.

He reloaded and found the first woodcock.

Then he went toward the spot where the other had vanished, checking his course by the white shot scars on the twigs. While doing so he found his bird, not on the ground, but hanging lifeless among the twigs of a sapling.

"That's enough," said the Captain aloud, "and even if it wasn't, a man would be a fool to risk spoiling the flavor of that double with another miss."

He found a log in a clearing, laid his birds in a neat row on the cool grass and lighted a cigarette.

He had always held a notion that at the close of a day in the field, on along a stream, a man ought to thank Someone for these gifts, and the Indian way was as good as any—an offering of the incense of tobacco and a few minutes of quiet contemplation. The sun had gone and over the Adirondacks the glory of the sky glowed and faded with the ebbing pulse of the dying day. The Captain watched, and as he watched, pondered long on the mystery of the woodcock's return.

With Quail

By NASH BUCKINGHAM

Dear Noelly:*

My red-letter day on quail? The one incident high-lighting more than fifty years staring down shotgun ribs at exploding bevies? The one such day I'd prefer reliving? Lad, you almost sent me scurrying to kodak-books and diaries out-dating the turn of the century. But I've figured it all out now, and I'm really obliged to you for

---

*Noel Sheldon is Hal (Col. H. P.) Sheldon's son. In Nash Buckingham's Derrydale book "Ole Miss," a collection of unpublished stories, is one titled "Surrender to Youth." The Christmas before Mr. Buckingham had given young Noel his old rucksack, skinning knife, and several other "possibles" including a mess kit that had gone through two hot corners in World War I. "Surrender to Youth" tells the story of the rucksack, and Mr. Buckingham's reasons for giving it to young Noel Sheldon.

"Noelly" is now full grown—six feet two, 195 pounds, and served in the Army Air Corps.—Ed.

putting the thought on me. It's been like sitting in the attic some rainy afternoon before gunning season, pawing over wornout plunder you've been, let's say, "instructed" to discard.

Somehow though, wadding up a smelly, tattered coat and patched pants, incidents crop up about them too arresting to warrant separation. Not right now, anyhow, you tell yourself. So, moths and orders to the contrary, you lie like a gentleman to the Missus, stall the business through with a fake bundle, and gain temporary respite for staunch friends. They get as close to one as a feeble and beloved old dog worth a million times its keep just for association with those golden partnership days some folks accuse locusts of eating. Let 'em think what they please; in most cases (and in mine surely) they've been damn good eating, win, lose or draw.

I've gunned quail with Gladstone, Peep o' Day and many another field trial champion in front of us. Too, many a brilliant, faithful and lovable "potlicker bird dawg" shares my hearth in memory. I've shot from Texas coastals and the Panhandle, around through Oklahoma and Ozarkian woods rims at bevies flushing like blackbirds from wintered reed beds. If there's a state in Dixie or the midlands I haven't dogged *Colinus*, let it speak now or forever hold its peace.

Fortunately, my earliest hunting contacts were with gentlemen who thought ahead in terms of sporting decencies and their obligations to outdoor posterity. Thus "mine eyes have seen the glories of the coming" of national conservation. Many a stern lecture, abstract and concrete, was read me or applied to same by my peers afield. My eye's been wiped so often that Humility long since became handmaiden to my questionings. But to counter-attack the mutton! Which of all my days after quail would I prefer reliving?

Was it that frost-crisped one I downed my first bobwhite a-wing? Daddy and Mister Arthur hunted the Lemaster farm, now well within our city's suburbs but miraculously preserved in almost wilderness aspect by that fine old family. Our long, star-spangled teaming before daylight. The warm welcome and shining hospitality awaiting us. My delight at riding mule-back behind giant black Elmo. And how we two maintained strict tally on the steadily fattening game pouch.

We shot over Mister Arthur's sterling pointers first, and Daddy's Gordons, Buck and Ball, later. What ground-devouring, keen-nosed, perfectly-mannered braces! The hunt moved like clockwork, with lunch in a cheerful, red-berried holly grove beside a deep, clear bayou and Elmo's coffee-boiling fire. I was permitted to shoot at five bevy rises and managed three birds with father's light, twelve bore hammer-gun. Elmo boasted vociferously of my skill and produced alibis for the misses with the ease of a New Deal magician's pulling rabbits from F.D.R.'s fabulous stovepipe hat.

What a day of breeze-drifted wood and powder smoke, blending scents of wild grapes, persimmons, sassafras, nut-mast and sun-ripened berry mats of the jungled new-ground. Yep, youngster, what with a wonderful country supper and a nap under the buffalo robe driving home to Mother. That was the kind of red-letter day so many, many hunters carry in their souls long after their hearts are stilled. One symbolizing all that is best to rudder by and live up to in honoring, or at least trying to honor, a now embattled but do-or-die heritage.

Or could it be that last day of quail season barely a decade agone? When Hal and Lucius and I swung through Houston Bottoms, touched at the Big Spring for sandwiches and tea, and shot Newton's section that afternoon? The sun staged a hard battle for admission that bleakish morning, but won out. Bill and Britt found a world of birds and we were holding it on 'em, too. Dawss brought along noble Trueboy and Flirt for the postprandial session. But bagging limits was so easy it became secondary to picture making.

Lucius and I lazied beside Paninted Pond while dear old Hal followed the dogs into a blackjack copse after some singles. We talked hopefully of his only too apparent slowing down in recent months and agreed that because he was so cheerful and brave we musn't let him notice our waiting on him to catch up, or the extra saddling boosts. He was getting just a bit suspicious, too, that his turn over scattered points was coming around overly fast. And sitting there watching the jays and peckerwoods and listening to the distant shrillings of a hawk, I thought Lucius looked tougher than a pine-knot.

Crossing onto Waldrip from Newton a woods road waists steep knolls and winds through silent, brook-worn hollows deep in tawny sedge. At nightfall, riding past that black blob of cedared crow-roost this side of the family cemetery, we talked enthusiastically of our big-running derby-dog prospects. Over our toddies we toasted a glorious season ending, and an even better one ahead.

It never seems possible nor right that shooting pals of a lifetime will ever check out. I still see Lucius and Hal sitting there warming their shins by the open fireplace in the Waldrip guest-chamber—little suspecting they'd fired their last shots over Bill's and Britt's and Trueboy's and Flirt's points. Much less over those up-and-coming derby-dogs. How I'd love to hear those old southern boys sing out "How" at their beading toddy glasses. Even nowadays after a day's fine sport I rarely say it myself without somehow listening for their vague echo. . . .

That's right, youngster, I met next gunning season alone. God, it puts a crimp in a fellow! Just remembering to relive that last day with a pair of such gallants, sets it apart. I'm dog-grateful and proud to rise and make the nomination. But Old Hal would probably quietly move that it be tabled, and offer a new motion that I'll yield and second, too.

When Hal and I were gay blades, he used to entertain a group of boys and girls with a Christmas-week house-party and bird-shoot at his father's ancestral plantations. That holiday season we were Bayard and Bright and Hal and I, with Wee Anne, the two Marys and Irma. Some mornings the girls took hunter's breakfast with us and shared a full day. On others, after a dance, they slept late, met us with picnic lunch and rode out the afternoons. Each fellow brought three brace of dogs and I doubt if we ever touched the same territory twice, so vast and birdy were those protected and fooded holdings. Picture a composite, inside and out, of all the loveliest southern manors you've seen in the movies, and you're still only fairly close to Allourn, Hal's ante-bellum home.

Away back yonder the state limit on quail was, as I recall, twenty-five a day. Regrettably, but rightly so, it is now less than half that figure. We shot a daily five dollars each per high-gun, a similar team-race, and high-over-all-for-the-week, on like basis. All ties were split. It meant getting down on your stock, ethical eyewiping, no quarter asked or given, and no holds barred except laying off trying to handle the other fellow's dogs. That last day, New Year's eve, was a quail hunter's dream.

Hal and Mary and Irma and I rode to the Gillespie plantation with lunches saddle-bagged and dogs on our saddles. We used Hal's pointers, Flash and Ticket, as first bracemates and they did a really great job. My overwhelming complex was to keep my eyes on Irma. We lunched at Slave Quarters by the free-flowing well atop Piney Ridge, where Anderson met us with my white setter Jim, and his consort, Lucy. Memory of that enthrallingly exquisite afternoon, replete with engrossing and outstanding dog work, is as fresh in mind as though 'twere yesterday.

Stealthy shadows infiltrated slopes and ravines as we cross-countried to meet the buckboard with its cargo of pickaninny jockeys to bring home our mounts. I needed four bobwhites to fill my limit—and never worse. They meant at least an even break on the day's individual race, maybe a team win, and, according to latest figures released at breakfast, a shot at the grand prize. I'd also been worrying considerable about asking a certain damsel a highly important question. In some way my stylish little setter Lucy and I (God rest her brave bones) got separated from Hal and the girls and Jim-dog.

Just as dusk surrendered to full moon, the bitch whipped past me along the fence-row of an abandoned burying-ground. Suddenly she whirled, flash-pointed, broke, cleared sagging rails with the slinking grace of a panther, roaded boldly a few paces and froze. That high-tailed, lofty-headed statue, silvered in moonglow, will fill my eyes forever. Fortunately there was skyline off an open hillside through the pines, for the blighted straw tops were cloaked in gloom. With gun half-hitched to shoulder readiness, I knelt and knee-wormed to behind Lucy.

My gorgeously postured setter held those roosting birds right under her delicate nose. Away roared a black, spouting mass I heard rather than saw. There was but time for a snap-shot, and I scuffled erect, panting. Sitting on a stump I gave Lucy the green light to fetch-dead. Four times that blessed little creature insisted upon searching. And each trip she delivered me a bobwhite. Do you wonder I gave her a smothering hug and promised a ride home in my lap, with extra grub?

Yep, I won the day's purse, team wager with Hal, and hit the week's jackpot, thanks again to Lucy. But you ain't heard nothing yet, Noelly. On account of seeing to it that Lucy and Jim-dog got their promised extra bait of victuals, I was last to tub and dress for dinner. Just as I emerged from bachelor quarters and crossed Allourn's vast upper hall, the door to the girls' apartment opened and out stepped the Vision to whom for so long I had devoted so much tender thought.

We met at the head of the winding staircase and the loveliness of her melted me down like a candle. I took her hand, but somehow neither of us spoke. On the landing not a soul was looking except a towering, benevolent grandfather clock. Maybe such sights were old stuff to him, but anyway the gruff old basso-profundo had the kindliness and good taste (with surely a great sense of humor) to keep his head shut and give a poor, rattled fellow a break. And there the age-old question was asked, answered and sealed with a kiss no whit sweeter, thanks be to HIM, than its counterpart of this morning.

So there's your answer, and the same to you someday Noelly, with all my heart—and hers.

Faithfully,

Nash Buckingham

With Grouse

By BURTON L. SPILLER

Living, as I have, a varied career, I have at times tackled things that were well nigh impossible of accomplishment, and curiously enough I have gained but little knowledge thereby. Like Don Quixote, I'm still ready to joust with a windmill, and if I'm not mistaken, *Outdoors'* request for an account of my best-remembered day with ruffed grouse falls in that category.

In looking over almost forty years of grouse hunting, I find that I have been singularly blessed. Born of hunting stock, reared on wild moose milk and educated in the school of woodcraft, I learned early in life that in my case money was but a medium of exchange for freedom to roam the out-of-doors, and until the present world melee broke out I have never let work interfere too seriously with my hunting and fishing.

To choose from a thousand days afield one more memorable than all the others seems like another of those impossible tasks, for as I pause a moment in retrospect, glorious day upon glorious day comes trooping back to thrill me anew, yet always when I turn my train of thought backward to review the fullness of my years I invariably think first of one particular time.

Exactly twenty years have elapsed since the tale appears on this printed page, yet I can still remember the crisp tang of the autumn air, the complaining murmur of the stony vexed brook, and the thunderous tumult of rising grouse as plainly as though it were but yesterday that it happened. It must be that this is my best remembered day.

Grouse have been plentiful for several years, but they were just beginning to drop off on their periodic decline. There were still enough left for fair shooting, but I remember that we crossed off several of the best covers from our list when we deemed we had reduced their number to that which would only safely assure another year's crop. It was disturbing to know that they were growing scarce, for while we had no desire to kill more than we then were, we longed for the easy conscience that comes with knowing that the seasonal take is but a small part of an abundant surplus. Then a native told us about the mountain valley.

Usually I discount such stories by several hundred per cent and then find that I have been too liberal, but there was an earnestness in the fellow's voice and a truthful look in his eye that sold me. We memorized his directions, went home for a night's rest and an extra supply of ammunition and returned the following morning.

There is a pleasurable thrill in looking upon a new hunting country for the first time, but now it was intensified, for I instinctively knew that in this remote mountain valley lay covers that were practically virgin. Straight northward it ran, rising from the narrow entrance in which we stood, in a series of level steppes, and widening until it touched the base of the mountain wall that curved like a giant horseshoe before us. Barberries and thornplums were everywhere. The alder runs, through which myriad rivulets trickled to merge with the brawling brook, were fringed with thrifty pine, while in the background the steep mountainside was cloaked with a million gnarled black birches. Here was seasonal food for a thousand grouse and adequate winter protection for them. We surveyed it for a moment or two, the dog whining to be off, then we loaded our guns and went in.

That first corner will be one of the last things I shall ever forget. There were alders and iron bushes in it and a few scattered maples— and a snow-white setter stretching out and out in a glorious, intensified point. I went in behind him and a woodcock went vaulting upward on its last flight. My shoulder had scarcely absorbed the recoil when a reverberating roar beat upon my eardrums as a flock of startled grouse burst into the air before me. I remember how I dumped one back to earth with the left barrel, then broke the gun, flipped out the right empty case, slid a fresh one in its place and caught the last bird just as it was clearing the top of a maple forty yards away.

Gene, good old deadshot Gene, was still learning to hunt grouse in those days, and I remember now the look on his face as the dog brought in the birds one after another. There was no envy in his eyes (there never was in the old days and there is never any need for it now) but there was a puzzled wonderment in them and a hint of awe and admiration.

We stowed the birds away and sent the dog ahead to pick up the singles, which to my mind is the sportiest of all upland shooting. Less than a hundred yards away he pointed again, and there in a corner of that little two-acre patch we flushed a second flock of birds.

The brook, we found, wound in and out across the valley floor, and always along its banks we found grouse. They went up in singles, in twos and threes and dozens until the dog, a sturdy old campaigner, became bewildered in the confusion of scent that assailed him from all sides.

I had dreamed in my youth of a day like this when I should be literally surrounded by grouse, but although I had enjoyed many peak seasons where there were birds enough to satisfy anybody, I had never seen anything that remotely approached this. There was something joyously mad and primitive about it all, and I felt a thrill of awe as I realized that I was seeing a bit of nature but little changed from the time when the world was young. We had long since taken our limit of birds, but with guns unloaded we went on up the steadily ascending valley while grouse hammered out and away to the right and left, or reared upward in straight-away flight before us.

At the upper end of the valley, where the almost unscalable sweep of the mountains crowded in upon it, we found the grand-daddy of all grouse flocks. Undoubtedly some had been driven before us into the last narrow alder run, but they must have found another goodly covey there when they arrived for they went fanning out before the dog in small units to seek sanctuary among the birches on the steep mountainside. I had worked well ahead of the dog along the edge of the run, and a dozen birds passed me within easy gunshot. What easy targets they appeared to be as I swung on them one after another, and how much will power it took to refrain from shooting, but I let them go unharmed upon their way.

There, in the highest point of the valley, we turned and looked back over the entrancing land. I knew then as I know now that I had experienced something which only a few fortunates are privileged to see. I had been transported back a hundred years and had seen, for a day at least, grouse shooting such as our ancestors must have known.

The aftermath of the story is not so pleasant. Loggers came the following year and stripped off all the pine and much of the hardwood. They robbed my valley of its beauty and they robbed it of its grouse, for winter cover is as necessary to them as is their daily food. Although the beauty of the place is gone, I go back there once each year hoping that I may find birds again in something like their old numbers. That I have always been disappointed does not deter me. Already the young pines stand head high, and the birches are large enough to provide ample winter feed. The years have been lean of late, but ruffed grouse will surely come back. They always have, and when they do I shall meet them again—I hope—in my own private little corner of paradise.

Bob Hines.

With Pheasants

By BEN EAST

When you've hunted pheasants close to twenty years and loved every hour you've been afield, it's not easy to pick the best day of them all.

You start thinking about it, running back over the years in your mind, and memories come crowding. You recall birds you killed and birds you missed, frosty mornings and hot afternoons, cold autumn rains and blazing sunsets, thrills and laughs and good companions, the dogs you worked and the guns you used—and it's hard to say which day was the best. But if I were to name one and only one, I'd choose a day we hunted over a certain young springer. It was her first fall and we didn't expect too much of her.

We stood in the gray October dawn that morning, Mac and I, and listened to young roosters crowing in a distant farmyard and half dreaded the first plunge into the wet weeds. We had watched the big, round, hunter's moon the night before and smelled the smoke of leaf fires at the curb, and hoped for a clear cool morning. But it had turned cloudy in the night and just before daybreak a drizzle of cold rain had fallen. We'd be drenched to the belts in ten minutes and we knew it. But it was the first morning of the season and a little water on the grass and goldenrod can't stop you at a time like that.

We waited while shooting light brightened across the level fields and finally a gun blared away off to the west, dull and heavy in the morning stillness. A half minute later the same gun spoke again, twice in quick succession. Mac opened the door of the car and let the springer down and we swung into the lane, toward a weedy cornfield at the back of the farm.

We were halfway to the corn, with the dog romping ahead of us, when she ran into something that checked her like a tight leash. Beyond the lane fence, thirty yards to the left, a dry swale no bigger than your living room rug made a patch of cover in an open field. The light, uneven morning wind flowed like a broken ribbon from the swale to the lane and midway of that ribbon a thread of bird scent suddenly had filled the springer's nose.

She swung around and stood sniffing while you could have counted three. Then her tail commenced to make pheasant talk and she went through the fence like an eel, streaking straight for the tall grass.

Mac and I hit the fence together. He was over and I was still on it when three pheasants clattered up. The last to leave the weeds was a big cock, cackling his alarm. Mac opened on him while he was still in a steep climb and he fell between two bean rows with a heavy thud. The dog brought back the first ringneck she had ever retrieved, and I knew we were going to have a whale of a pheasant season!

We decided to save the corn till later. We went on across the beanfield into a stubble where the cover seemed too short for ringnecks but where experience told us a bird was likely to lumber up any second. The hunch was good. Midway of the field the dog made game, scurried around in a frenzy of excitement for a half minute, and busted two hens out literally from under our feet. But she didn't seem satisfied with that achievement. She went on working and fifty yards ahead she found and flushed a third.

"There'll be a cock in here somewhere," Mac warned, and even as he said it Sir John took off, no more than a tail length in front of the frantic springer. He swung my way and I laid the gun on him as he leveled off and made a clean kill.

Mac looked at his watch. We'd been out twenty minutes. We

went on across the stubble to a willow-grown ditch bank and the dog put her nose to the wet ground and went suddenly in to overdrive.

That was close to a sight chase. The bird was hightailing down the ditch bank, through the short grass and open willows. His tracks were smoking in the springer's nose and both of 'em meant business. Mac and I lumbered along behind 'em, one on each side of the ditch, but we never had a chance. At the end of the strip of cover the pheasant flushed a good hundred yards ahead of us. He sailed derisively off for the next township and we called the dog in and started for the cornfield.

So far we had stayed almost dry, but that was too good to last. The ragweed in the corn rows was waist high and dripping with cold water. Before we had gone fifty feet we were as wet as the dog. And then we came into one of those lulls that happen every so often in pheasant country after a brisk beginning.

We combed the corn and found it empty of birds. We tried an alfalfa field beyond it, and after that a couple of brushy fencerows and a big swale where the goldenrod was as tall as our heads. We got wetter and wetter but we put up no more pheasants.

"They've holed up," Mac decided finally, "and I can't say I blame 'em much." He looked at his watch. "I've got to be back by 9," he remarked. "Whatever we do we'll have to do in the next half hour."

We turned back toward the house, drenched and chilled and not too happy. At the end of the cornfield the dog made game along the fence with sudden violence. There was a clump of wild grapevine there, festooned on the wire for twenty feet, and a little strip of tall grass among the tangled vines. It was a thumbnail patch of cover, the kind of hideout an old cock ringneck loves when the gunning is heavy or the weather bad.

I called a word of warning to Mac and braced myself. The springer dived headlong into the vines at one end and at the other end there was a clatter of wings and an angry, alarmed squawk, and two pheasants with white collars went thundering up. One swung over the open pasture on my side of the fence and I scored. I heard the sharp crash of Mac's gun as he took the other and I turned in time to see the bird spin down into the corn. But from the way it fell we knew we had a cripple on our hands.

We went through the cornfield with a fine-tooth comb, the dog and the two of us, but it wasn't any use. We lost the springer in the weeds finally and kept on crisscrossing ourselves, searching the field row by row. I have some pretty strong feelings on losing a wounded bird and Mac shares 'em. We hunted long after we knew it wasn't any use. When we came out of the corn finally we were just a little downhearted. Mac stopped to lay a match to his pipe.

"Guess I'm one short for today," he said thoughtfully. "Serves me right for not doing a clean job. I thought the springer would find him sure but maybe it was too much to expect in that cover."

He turned to call the dog—and then we saw her coming between two weedy corn rows. Her head was high and she had the pheasant in a grip so soft and sure it wouldn't have cracked a robin's egg. His long tail was brushing the wet ragweeds at one side. She didn't look like a springer registered in the files of the AKC. She was full of burrs from ears to tail and she looked like a little, wet, black and white rag. But she brought the bird up to Mac prouder than any queen and her brown eyes were fairly shining when she gave it over.

It wasn't the shooting we did that morning. It wasn't the fact we were home at 9:30 with our legal limit of four pheasants. It wasn't because the weather was good or bad and it wasn't the way our dry clothes felt when we finally got into 'em.

It wasn't anything but the great work of a young dog, making her beginning in the business she was born for, meeting Johnny Ringneck on his own terms, outsmarting him, knowing her job and doing it a little better than the boss expected. That was what made that day the best I have had in almost twenty years of pheasant hunting.

The Wilderness

By SIGURD OLSON

A FLEET OF ROCKY, PINE-CRESTED ISLANDS FLOATS BETWEEN US and the western horizon. It is dusk in the wilderness, a time of quiet and sunset-colored waters. The white tents are pale against the dark forest. Canoes are overturned on the shore, beds made, all equipment under cover, everything snug for the night. In the calm air the smoke from our dying supper fire rises straight into the sky. A loon calls and is answered from a lake over the hills. For a moment the timbered ridges echo and re-echo with their wild notes.

A week ago we had left the steel. One of my party was the head of a great corporation in Chicago, another a well-known surgeon from New York, and the third a judge from Washington, D. C. They had come north to get the feeling of wilderness, to renew companionships and associations almost forgotten during the mad rush of the war years. Like many others I have guided on wilderness expeditions, these were men in their prime, highly successful in their professions, suave and cultured; but they were fatigued and worn by responsibilities in the great cities. Now they wanted to have fun. They wanted to forget for a while the enmeshing tentacles of civilization and industry, and for a few weeks to feel that old freedom they used to know. In camp each night they sat near the water's edge and talked until dark.

"Queer," said the judge, "to think that a thousand miles south of us, people are rushing around just as busily as the day we left. Somehow up here it doesn't make sense."

"Yes," said the corporation head, "I can see the Chicago Loop this very moment with people pouring madly out of their burrows and heading for some place else just as we'll be doing again in a week or two. From here, Chicago and New York and Washington and the other cities seem like gigantic anthills. But every person in them has a purpose in life, or thinks he has; yet, to me, as we sit here amid this beauty, their endless rushing, or at least the speed with which they move, appears foolish."

"What gets me," replied the surgeon, "is the peace and quiet up here. In the big hospitals a man is apt to forget that there is anything but tension in the world. You come back here, and the tension is gone. The world is quiet and peaceful again, and there is no pressure."

"You're right," agreed the judge. "It's good just to know that a place like this exists. When I get all tied up in a knot over some legal problem, I'll shut my eyes and remember."

"And when I sit in at my next board of directors meeting," said the man of affairs, "and try to explain what's happened to a block of stock or a contract that hasn't been going too well, I'll recall how we sat on this rock, and I'll remember how little difference it all makes in the long run."

"Two weeks from now when the operating rooms have been working overtime," mused the doctor, "and I've been flying from Chicago to New York, and my brain is whirling with speed, I'm going to think of those loons. They'll still be calling, no matter where I am. Yes, just the memory of them will be good medicine for me."

I watched these men for a week. Now freed of mental strain, taking vigorous, pleasurable exercise, and breathing pure air twenty-four hours a day, they became normal human beings with much of the spirit of the carefree boy about them. These, my companions on a wilderness cruise, had again discovered how a man can find release; where he can recapture his perspective and the calm of untroubled years; where he can shed responsibilities and know the meaning of freedom and the joys of simple living. They, like others I have known on wilderness expeditions of the past, have found it here. The untouched rivers and forests and lakes were the answer. Now they could return to the cities with peace in their hearts.

With the coming of twilight, hermit thrushes were singing in the hills behind us. From a near-by cove came the disturbed quacking of a mallard hen, then a splash, and a pair of mallards whistled overhead. A moose was the cause of their disturbance. We saw him wade into the shallows to feed on water lily plants there.

Soon the evening star came out and hung like a lantern in the sky. The hermits were silent now, but a few white-throats sounded their clear notes back in the hills. The turbulent world of civilization was far away. Noisy, dirty, bustling cities, like nightmares, seemed no part of reality.

According to Webster, wilderness is a trackless waste uninhabited by man. To the people of America, as typified by the men who were with me on this particular trip, it is far more than that. It is something so closely tied up with their traditions, so tightly woven into their cultural backgrounds, their emotions and philosophies of life, that it cannot be ignored or neglected.

Wilderness to the people of America is a spiritual necessity, an antidote to the high pressure of modern life, a means of regaining serenity and equilibrium.

I have found that people go to the wilderness for many things, but the most important of these is perspective. They may think they go for the fishing or the scenery or companionship, but in reality it is something far deeper. They go to the wilderness for the good of their souls. I sometimes feel as though they had actually gone to another planet from which they can watch with cool detachment the fierce and sometimes meaningless scurryings of their kind. Then when the old philosophy of earth-oneness begins to return to them, they slowly realize that once again they are in tune with sun and stars and all natural things, and with that knowledge comes happiness and contentment.

I believe this need of wilderness is inherent in most of us, even those seemingly farthest removed from it by civilized living. The cities may cover it up, make us forget temporarily; but deep underneath is an inherent urge for naturalness and simplicity and a way of life different from the one we know.

Henry Thoreau sensed this need of mankind when he said, "We

can never have enough of nature. We must be refreshed by the sight of vast and titanic features—the wilderness with its living and decaying trees. We need to witness our own limits transgressed and some life pasturing freely where we never wander."

There is a school of thought that considers wilderness solely as an opportunity for nature study and scientific research and sees no spiritual value in the effect of wild country on those who come in contact with it. These people lack vision, for if they understood the primary purpose of the accumulation of knowledge generally, they would know that unless such effort results in furthering man's sense of companionship and understanding of the earth, and thereby contributes to his spiritual contentment and happiness, it has not achieved its purpose.

There is another group made up of practical minded individuals who see no sense in setting aside an area for esthetic or recreational purposes. This group considers wilderness devotees as irresponsible wildlifers who have gone off the deep end in their enthusiasm for the out-of-doors. They look at the last remaining bits of primitive America as a final opportunity to "get rich quick" in the best pioneer tradition. They are the ones who would dam Yellowstone Lake, cut the last sequoias, and convert the canoe country of the Quetico-Superior into a huge storage reservoir. To them the wilderness has no other value than the practical and they think it criminal for resources to stand commercially unused. They also need the wilderness, but their need is blinded by greed.

There is a third group larger than all the rest. That is the great mass of recreation-minded Americans who see in the wilderness not an opportunity for exploitation or for the furtherance of knowledge, but rather as an opportunity to satisfy a vital spiritual deficiency within themselves. They are the ones who head into the wilderness regions because they must. Wilderness to them is a tonic, a panacea for nervousness and monotony. They go to it once a month or once a year as a sick man might go to his physician. These people know that wilderness to them is a necessity if they are to keep their balance.

To place a value on wilderness is as difficult as to speak of the value of a landmark or an heirloom in terms of money. There are certain things that cannot be evaluated because of their emotional appeal. Wilderness is in this category. While a certain area might have worth as a museum piece, or because of certain economic factors, its real worth will always depend upon how people feel about it and what it does for them. If it contributes to spiritual welfare, if it gives them perspective and a sense of oneness with mountains, forests, or waters, or in any way at all enriches their lives, then the area is beyond price. It is as hard to place a true value on wilderness as it is to decide what type of wild country is the best. What one man needs and finds satisfying, might not be at all what another requires. In the final analysis each man knows within himself what it is he wants, and in each case his choice is tempered by his own past, his dreams and memories, his hopes for the future and his ability to enjoy.

Some can find their wildernesses in tiny hidden corners where, through accident rather than design, man has saved just a breath of the primeval America. I know of a glen in the heart of a great city park system, a tiny roaring canyon where many seeking solitude and beauty can find release. It is dark in there, and damp, and in the heat of the summer it is cool. Ferns and lichens and liverworts cling to the rocks, and there grow flowers that thrive only in the shadows where the air is charged with mist. The water swirls through this canyon as it has for thousands of years, and the sounds are the sounds of a land far removed from civilization. A highway runs within a hundred yards and cars pass almost overhead, but the rocks and trees screen it from view and the only evidence of traffic is a vague hum that blends with the whisper of the wind and the music of rushing water. There, if a man wishes, he can regain in a swift moment the feeling of the wild, and steal, for a brief instant, respite from the noise and confusion of a big city. There, if he has perspective, he may recharge his soul.

There are men, however, who crave action and distance and far horizons beyond the steel. No little sanctuaries for them along the fringes of civilization. They must know wild country and all that goes with it, must feel the bite of a tumpline on the portages, the desperate battling against waves on stormy lakes. They must know hunger and thirst and privation and the companionship men know only on the out trails of the world. When, after days of paddling and packing, they find themselves on some bare glaciated point a hundred miles from town and stand there gazing down a great wilderness waterway, listening to the loons and seeing the wild rocky islands floating in the sunset, they, too, know the meaning of communion with nature.

Another finds his wilderness in the mountains of the West. There, camped in some high alpine meadow, with the horses grazing quietly along an ice-fed glacial stream, jagged peaks towering above him into the snow-capped summits of some mighty range, and all about him the beauty and grandeur of the high country, he finds his particular ultimate. To him such a setting is the primitive on a noble scale—there a timelessness that can never be approached elsewhere. The very bigness of the landscape gives him a sense of personal contact with immensity and space. He comes down from his mountains, as all men have since the beginning of time, refreshed spiritually and ready again for the complexities of life among his kind.

There are those who say that only in the great swamps and flowages of the deep South, in the flooded cypress stands and mangroves, or along the deltas and savannas of the rivers, can one understand what wilderness really is. And in a sense they are right, for it was in such places that life supposedly evolved. Some men may sense instinctively that there conditions more closely approximate the primeval phases of the earth's history than anywhere else. If it is purely the atmosphere of the wild that counts, then surely there a man might get a closer feeling with the past and the future than in any other wilderness.

Stephen Leacock, when asked why he persisted in living in Toronto instead of returning to his beloved England, replied that he liked living in Toronto because it was so close to the wilderness of Hudson Bay, that the very thought of the thousands of miles of barren country to the north, gave him a sense of spaciousness and adventure that did him good. In that statement he voiced the feeling of thousands of people who, like him, though they may never penetrate the back country, nevertheless enjoy the feeling of living close to it. For these the wilderness is just as much an inspiration as for those who travel through it by horse, canoe, dogteam or other primitive means. The very awareness of it gives to them that feeling of the frontier characteristic of all jumping-off places. In such regions the air itself seems rarefied and charged with something different that Thoreau might have called, "the early morning fragrance of the wild."

Whatever their type and wherever they are found, be these wilderness places large or small, mountains, lakes, deserts, swamps or forests, they do fill a vital need. Gradually wilderness has become a cultural necessity to us, the people of America, and while it does play an important recreational role, its real function will always be as a spiritual backlog in the high speed mechanical world in which we live. We have discovered that the presence of wilderness in itself is a balance wheel and an aid to equilibrium.

City life is artificial. Because artificiality leads to a sense of unreality and frustration, unhappiness often results. That is the price a people pays for high technological success, and that is the reason an intelligent, thinking people knows that unless it can break away and renew its contact with a slow-moving natural philosophy, it will lose its perspective and forget simplicity and wholesomeness.

Most Americans are not far removed from their pioneer ancestry, are still close enough to the covered wagon days and the era of backwoods settlements and farms, so that they remember, more than sense, what they have lost. And being so close, it is not at all surprising that when production lines and speed and synthetic living seem more than they can bear, they instinctively head back to the wilderness where they know everything will be all right. Once returned to the old ways of living, their serenity comes back and they find that their capacity for enjoyment has not changed. That is what the wilderness means to America.

In recognition of this now almost general need of our people, the National Park Service, the U. S. Forest Service, and the various states have wisely set aside many areas that may be classed as wilderness—areas dedicated to the spiritual welfare of all. They vary in size from the three million acre Salmon River Wilderness Area of Idaho, a region large enough for a man to travel for days without crossing his own tracks, to areas only a few square miles in extent—museum bits of the once vast primeval wilderness of North America.

Far-sighted conservationists have fought hasty developmental programs that had as their goal the exploitation of the few remaining sections of wilderness. Sometimes they have won, but more often they have lost, due to the fact that, as a people, Americans still do not realize the importance of wilderness preservation as an investment in future happiness.

The idea that America is a land of freedom and limitless opportunity is perhaps responsible for our lethargy in saving more of the wild than we have. A few short decades ago wilderness was something that had to be fought and overcome, the one great hindrance to the opening and development of the continent. We remember the pioneer days when the great plantations of pine were stripped and burned, when huge reclamation projects drained swamps and lowered the water tables to the danger point, when power projects were thought the only legitimate uses of streams. The old destructive "cut out and get out" philosophy of those days is still very much alive in our thinking, so that it is not surprising to find many who even now view the few wilderness regions we have set aside as a challenge to move in and make a fortune in spite of the outraged sentiment of those who do see their value.

We see these interests constantly at work backed by powerful lobbies, interests which call for the cutting of the last stands of virgin timber, the exploitation of the last untouched reserves of the continent. They make the preservation of any section of wild country a constant battle, and place the comparatively small reservations we have set aside, in constant jeopardy. The existence of this element in our population makes necessary the utmost vigilance on the part of governmental agencies in charge of the administration of our parks and forests, as well as on the part of those organizations scattered throughout the land that understand what is at stake. The reservations already created are woefully inadequate to meet the need and give to the people of all parts of the United States the opportunity of wilderness recreation. This is especially true in the large centers of population; yet it is here that the need is greatest and opposition strongest.

One highly encouraging aspect of the wilderness problem is the realization that as a nation we are approaching cultural maturity. No young nation ever worries overmuch about the intangible assets of wilderness as long as its great battle is to subdue wilderness and carve out cities and roads and farms from the wild. Now, for the first time, we are able to look back and see where our mistakes and short-sighted policies have brought us; and at long last we are slowly emerging from the old pioneer concept that governed our thinking for the past three centuries. We can see that we have squandered a national heritage of beauty and wealth and have only a few places left to remind us of the continent's past primeval glory.

We know now just how valuable these fragments of the old America have become to us as a people. We see them now in a new light and realize that in addition to being museum pieces of the past, they are vital to our happiness and investments in national character. We also know that if we are to retain our contentment and balance, then we must never lose our contact with the earth, never forget the pioneer traditions of independence and resourcefulness under primitive conditions, never for a moment exchange the philosophy of the backwoods settler and Indian fighter for the comparative ease of the modern city. To give the people of this country an opportunity to renew their old associations as a race, to find themselves and their real qualities, to rejuvenate their spirits through simple living in the out-of-doors, is the real purpose of the preservation of wilderness.

To Fish with Ghosts

By LIEUT. CLARENCE A. SCHOENFIELD

HAVE YOU EVER FISHED WITH A GHOST? SOME STREAMS ARE haunted as surely as a cemetery. Their water tells a hallowed story, as it quavers over sun-dappled rocks, or flows in deep green mystery beneath a shelving bank. The trees remember. When the wind blows, their leaves rustle as the echoes of never-quite-forgotten shouts.

It is so with the streams of the Quadrangle (so named from a Geological Survey map). The Quadrangle is 1700 square miles of Blue Ridge country straddling the Mason-Dixon line, bounded roughly on the southwest by Harpers Ferry, West Virginia, and on the northeast by Abbottstown, Pennsylvania. Four score years ago the Quadrangle was one big battleground. Here are the bloody fields of Antietam and Gettysburg, and Chambersburg town, sacked by Rebel cavalry. Now these Old Line farms are a prime maneuvering area for the bass fisherman. Yet something of the past lingers on, in a rusty CSA buckle picked up here, or a Minie ball buried in some old burr oak. One almost expects to meet a platoon of Pleasanton's horsemen watering at your favorite stretch of fly-water. To fish the Quadrangle is to fish with ghosts.

Just how many ghosts haunt these Maryland hills is shocking, even to senses calloused by casualty reports of the last four years. In just one afternoon of pitched fighting at Antietam, a few miles out of Sharpsburg, nearly 25,000 boys were killed or wounded.

In the second year of the Civil War, following his smashing victory at Second Manassas, General Robert E. Lee had decided to invade Maryland, aiming at Hagerstown. On September 17, 1862, General McClellan struck him near Sharpsburg. Four successive Union assaults, as fierce as any in the war, forced the Gray lines back to the Potomac but did not carry the day. Lee left his campfires burning that night and slipped away across the river.

The battlefield gets its name from Antietam Creek, which flows under Burnsides' Bridge, where a Northern general by that name made an historic attack, and on to the Potomac. After you have looked at all the monuments and plaques along Bloody Lane, you can try your hand at fishing the Creek. A lot of small-mouth bass live there, and from the fight they put up it is obvious they haven't heard about the Civil War being over for 79 years.

One of the best places to hit the Creek is through Sam Griffith's farmyard. You turn off the Hagerstown road, go past one of those granite memorials to a New England infantry regiment, bounce down a pasture lane, and there you are, in a welter of sheep, dogs, and tow-headed youngsters. For a consideration—a package of gum for the family and cigar for Farmer Griffith—one of the little overalled boys will bail out an old boat and even fetch a pole from the woodshed. Load up, shove off, rig your lines, and you are fishing the storied Antietam.

Doc and Larny and I were all in a single battered scow one afternoon in mid-September. The savory breath of fall hinted strongly of grouse and waterfowl. But this day we were intent on a final maneuver against the Antietam smallmouths. We—I mean I—poled a seesaw course out into mid-stream. We—I mean Larny—dropped the anchor. We—I mean Larny and I—arranged the bait buckets. Doc, meanwhile, issued directions from his command post in the stern, as befitting his age and assumed rank. We were to deploy first at the big bend, he said, and cast upstream, letting the current carry our stonecats down and around. It was the CO who went into action first, waving the long cane rod which he affects with a grace born of much practice—and muscle. It was the CO who made the first kill and they gloated over the fact that even the bass recognized the prerogatives of rank.

He had tossed his minnow far out, first whirling his leader around like a sling and then letting it go to carry along the slack line. Almost as soon as the wriggling stonecat hit the water a bass struck. Doc's line ripped like a torn sheet as the smallmouth charged downstream.

A stonecat is hooked through the lips. A bass grabs him by the tail, carries him away, stops, breaks his dorsals, turns him around, and swallows him head-on. To set the hook while your bass is making his run is to yank the bait right out of his mouth. You've got to wait for that pause. This requires the coolness of a machinegunner and the patience of a sniper.

Doc let his game run with the knowing air of an old campaigner. When the bass made his characteristic pause in the lee of a limestone rock, he set the hook with a vigorous whip of the bamboo. Like an exploding grenade the smallmouth broke water, shaking his wounded head. Then he raced downstream again, taking advantage of the swift current along the far shore. The reel spool was showing between the coils of fast-disappearing line before he turned and made straight for the boat. By a bit of frantic reeling Doc managed to keep a tight rein. Again the bass leaped, this time so close we could see the red of his flaring gills. He would go four pounds, the CO declared. (A healthy exaggeration is also the prerogative of rank.)

On order Larny and I pulled in our lines. On order we unlimbered the net. Skillfully Doc brought the fish in. The fight was over. This was the mopping-up phase. While the CO shouted directions and threats of court-martial should I miss, I slipped the net under the bass and brought him aboard. As adjutant, Larny weighed him. He went two and a half pounds—a nice fish in these waters, which have been known to sportsmen since well before the battle that made them famous.

After an appropriate ten-minute break spent congratulating the CO, the Antietam campaign continued. By sundown we—I mean Doc—had taken two more, both of them neat smallmouths with bronze backs that seemed to match the yellowing autumn foliage. Larny and I went fishless. The bass, it seemed, would surrender only to a brass hat.

As the shadows lengthened, our mess sergeant-wives arrived with the chow. We bivouacked in Farmer Griffith's orchard and ate, while the CO recounted exploits of veterans like himself before the ranks of fishermen were filled with such recruits as Larny and I. Farmer Griffith came out again while we were loading the convoy for home to pass the time of day and offer us a drink at his special well.

"You know," he said, "Ferrero's brigade spent the night right in this meadow after the battle. That was just 81 years ago. When you fish my Creek," Sam philosophized in his homely way, "you've got company. A lot of boys in Blue and Gray are still around these valleys."

Because its streams are history, the Quadrangle is a fascinating fishing ground. You are at once a part of the past and the present. Doc and Larny and I like to trace the course of those old battles while we cast. One of our favorite Quadrangle creeks is the Conococheague, which rises up above Caledonia State Park in Pennsylvania and flows down along the Mason-Dixon line to join the Potomac at Williamsport, Maryland. It is not only good bass water and as easy to wade as your bathtub, but it marks the route of Robert E. Lee's columns as he moved on Gettysburg via Hagerstown in late June of 1863. Whenever we fish the "Jig," we like to imagine that the General himself planned a Jeb Stuart raid down its valley. Indeed, like all angling combines, we are a miniature combat team ourselves and we run every Jig excursion like a minor military operation.

First time the prior preparations. This phase includes accumulating a stock-pile of gas, picking the day and hour after much consultation of almanacs (and wives), naming the assault spot (this an almost exclusive function of the CO), talking our mess-sergeants into fixing chow, cleaning equipment, checking on the ammunition.

On H-hour minus 18 the CO calls a conference. We troop into the living room and pay attention to orders. First, information of the enemy and friendly forces. Two, the general mission. Three, specific duties. Four, administrative details. Finally, communications.

"The smallmouths have been hitting rather well on the Jig lately," says Doc. "They're taking plugs. Spike got a nice string last weekend. We're going to take off tomorrow afternoon at 1600 and fish till dusk. We'll try the Ford first and then work from the Bridge on down to the Caves. Larny, you and Clay pick me up on the dot. Wear old clothes because we're going to wade. Clay, make sure Janie will be out about 1900 with that cold chicken. If it's raining, give me a call. I'll be in the office. Any questions?"

"Yes," says Larny. "What about boots? Will we need 'em?"

"No. You'd better wade wet, like me; water's still plenty warm. Anything else? Okay. The time is now 2145. Move out."

All was quiet on the Ford front this particular autumn day. We had started a mile above the old stone crusher and worked down to Carbaugh's shack. Not a bass could we raise. The water felt cool, soaking into our tennis shoes and lapping in places around our hips. The painted tortoises dropped from the willow stumps as we passed. The pickerel-weed sent up its blue and a vireo sang incessantly.

Doc was getting perturbed. These old COs demand action. When we got to the bridge, on the Branch road, he prescribed a change of lures.

"It must be our plugs," he declared. "I just know they're in here."

His "I-told-you-so's" were loud and long five minutes later when I took a small bass from behind a snag just below the bridge.

"I'll bet if you'd thrown away that crawdad sooner we'd have a nice string by now," Doc gloated.

I didn't have the heart—or the rank—to tell him I'd only pretended to change plugs. I've got a lot of faith in that crab wiggler.

It produced again in the next half hour—a nice two-pounder that came charging halfway across the stream to hit my plug as it dipped and weaved up the channel.

Like many baits the crawdad is most effective when retrieved in fits and starts. After all, a natural crab sort of bumps along the river bottom. So if you reel a bit, twitch your rod tip, reel again, pause, then reel again, your plug is going to look a lot better to a pugnacious smallmouth than if you simply toss it out and pull it in. Mine looked so good to this particular bass that he tried to swallow it whole and succeeded only in snagging himself on both sets of treblehooks. But that didn't bother him much. He lunged into the air a couple of times and tried to outflank me twice before I beached him right in front of the CO.

"Nice smallmouth," he grudgingly admitted. I was two up on him now.

Larny was far upstream by this time, heading for the Caves. There the river narrows considerably where limestone cliffs rise straight up for 200 feet on the right bank. The water is deep, as deep as anywhere on the Jig. It hides a thousand boulders, and the bass like to lie there of a hot afternoon.

Larny was around a bend out of sight when we heard him holler. I splashed ashore and raced down to see the action. He was armpit deep in the Jig, his doubled rod held above his head. What seemed like 50 yards downstream his line disappeared in the water as if fast to a snag.

"He's either hung me up or he's sulking!" Larny shouted. "I'll fix him."

He pulled out his pocket knife and rapped sharply on the reel seat. That was all the challenge Sgt. Smallmouth needed. He came charging upstream with all the abandon of a Commando, shaking, boring, churning. A bass is a good soldier. He always carries the fight to the enemy. But Larny's tactics were tough, too. As he regained his lost line he backed toward shore and, by using his rod as a lever, soon had the bass belly-up in the shallows: another two-pounder with a back as bronze as a medal.

Our CO was still upstream. Larny and I goldbricked, smoking in the shade. We shot the bull for an hour, about bass, about this war, about that other war when the Jig was on the battle maps. The mess detail had pulled in before Doc came around the bend.

"What are you doing bringing up the rear, Captain?" my wife asked. (She has a woman's scorn of rank.) "My boys've got three nice fish down here. They'll be getting promoted before long."

Doc smiled. "Your boys have been skirmishing with small fry. As commander of this company I deal only with the generals." He held up a smallmouth as long as his forearm. Doc is still the CO.

The Conococheague offers good bass fishing all the way from Williamsport up into Pennsylvania. Not far from its headwaters is the battlefield of Gettysburg, the best marked in the world and one of the most famous. Here for three days, July 1 to July 3, 1863, the North and the South were locked in bitter struggle. On the ridges known as Cemetery and Seminary they clashed until the Gray troops withdrew in the face of superior Union cannon. It was truly the highwater mark of the Confederacy—the turning point of the war.

The Quadrangle fisherman cannot fail to be interested when he takes time out to look down from the Round Top tower along the Union lines curving northward like a huge fishhook, where General Meade withstood a crucial Southern assault up Culp's Hill on the first evening; or stands along Confederate Avenue at the exact spot from which General Longstreet watched Pickett charge across the Wheatfield.

There are no bass streams in the battlefield proper, but just as Lee guided on a river valley when he approached Gettysburg, so Meade moved up the Monocacy and its branches. The Monocacy cuts Maryland in two along the Frederick axis. Between Meade's assembly points at Emmitsburg and Taneytown, Tom's Creek flows into the Monocacy. Our company has never operated on the Monocacy itself but has a number of rendezvous along Tom's Creek. Near Motter's Crossroads an outcropping of rock makes a natural dam. In its half-mile long flowage are plenty of smallmouths, none of them large, but all full of the scrap that puts a river bass in a class by himself.

Here of a summer afternoon you can see the CO deploying our company for the attack, with his rod waving in the lead like a guidon. And when the fight is over you can find us 'round a fire roasting "borrowed" corn. In the evening dews a column of thin blue smoke curls up through the honey locusts. There is ghost smoke mingled with it—ghost smoke from a hundred circling camps.

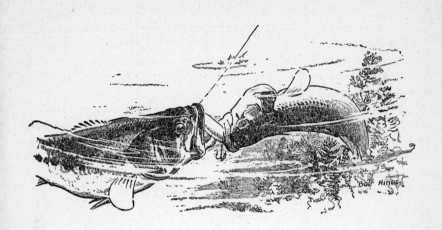

The Expert Learns a Lesson

By MABRY I. ANDERSON

"GRASSY LAKE," I REMARKED TO MY FRIEND PARKER WILLIAMS, "is a lake for experts only. To catch fish there, you've gotta grow up with 'em. Takes years and years of study to learn how to do it."

"Nevertheless my friend," he replied, "I've heard you rave about 'dear old Grassy' for seven long years and this time, you're taking me to it. See?"

"Okay, okay," I snorted. "I'm taking you to it but don't say I didn't warn you."

The roadway that led to Grassy was much better than usual, its former corduroy topography having given away to a surface of reasonable smoothness. In the pitch darkness of a September morning, the woodland that bordered the road was merely an area of more intense blackness and already we could sense that the day would be a late season scorcher. For weeks no rain had fallen and as we turned down the sloping side of the levee that led to the boat landing our headlights revealed that the shoreline grass was withered and sere.

Stopping the car beneath a spreading pin oak, we made our way to the water's edge, just as the first streaks of dawn faintly lighted the eastern skyline. In the hazy light the water before us seemed dead and lifeless and the shoreline, due to the drought, had receded far beyond its normal boundary. With apprehension I viewed the two lonely boats that lay stranded on the mud flats before us and picking my way carefully to the smaller one, I inspected it thoroughly with the aid of my flashlight. After determining that no sluggish cottonmouth lay coiled on its weathered bottom, I called on Williams for assistance and, together, we sweated the little craft from the clinging fastness of the mud. Hastily we loaded equipment and after more shoving and cussin', muddy water flowed beneath our keel. Laboriously we worked the boat through yonkapins and saw grass and as the light from the east grew stronger, we turned the bow toward rank, green timber.

All around us lay the flooded forest. Down to the west we could see where the open trail ended and beyond it lay a vast area of flooded woodland, choked and matted with elbow bushes, yonkapins, saw grass, and every conceivable type of aquatic growth, native to the Southland. For miles it ran unbroken, save for an occasional bayou run; a virgin forest of hardwood, lying covered with water and, in the past, its impenetrable tangles had proved to be a heaven for fish and wildfowl.

Within this timbered sanctuary, meagerly defined trails wandered hither and yon and the inexperienced woodsman might well lose himself with uncomfortable, if not serious consequences. For years, however, I had angled and hunted within this forest and it was with sure strokes that we hastened the boat across the open water and in to the woodland proper.

As we slithered into the glade of tupelo and cypress, I realized that something was wrong. Instead of biting cleanly into clear, pure water, the paddle dragged heavily and upon raising it from the water I found what I was expecting. Clinging to the blade in snaky tendrils was moss—rank, green moss, that nightmare of all Southern lakes. Stopping the boat, we surveyed the waters ahead and as the sun burst forth with brilliance its rays revealed a disheartening picture. All around us lay the stuff; acres and acres of it, literally blanketing the surface of the water. In isolated spots, open pools could be seen but on making our way to the nearest of these openings we found that only a few inches of water existed above the stuff. To fish it was clearly impossible and with a sense of resignation we resumed our paddling, hoping against hope that we would find at least an acre or two of open water before the summer sun sent bass to the shaded bottoms.

"Let's take a look at the 'deadening' that you're always talking about," suggested Williams as we snaked our way over logs and limbs.

The deadening referred to comprises a third of Grassy's area and is literally covered with stark dead tupelo and cypress. Storms have felled great numbers of these trees and their scattered limbs and trunks add to the general confusion caused by the live aquatic growth. Coupled with the fact that its waters are usually shallow, progress through the deadening is almost impossible and it was with considerable misgivings that I turned the boat in its general direction.

After twenty minutes of heavy going we reached the edge of the deadening and moved to within its sun-baked premises. I noted with consternation that the moss, if possible, was even thicker but far out across its brassy stretches I could see a few dark spots that might prove fishable. As rapidly as possible we made our way to the nearest and largest of these openings, and as we reached its edge a bass struck noisily toward the center of the pool.

Quickly we strung up tackle and, as I threaded line through guides, my companion whispered: "What bait?"

"A semi-surface plug with plenty of red," I advised. "These Grassy Lake bass have a hankering for big bright colored lures."

"What about a top-water bait?" he demurred. "That heavy plug will catch a lot of moss."

"Do as the Old Man advises," I haughtily replied. "Man and boy, I've fished this lake for eighteen years and Grassy Lake bass won't hit those little plugs."

In a moment we were ready and together we dropped our lures in the center of the pool. My plug, an ancient redhead affair, struck with a splash but as I prepared for a slow, erratic retrieve, I found to my dismay that it was heavily fouled with moss. Quickly I snaked it in, bringing along a pound or two of the slimy stuff and as I picked it from the hooks I noted that my companion was experiencing the same difficulty.

"This is silly," he complained. "That heavyweight lure falls so hard that it submerges and grabs the moss. Think I'll put on a light, top water bait anyhow."

Being obstinate, I ignored his remark and again dropped my lure to the center of the pool. This time, by casting very low, I managed to keep it afloat, but after two or three successful jerks it sideswiped a floating wisp of green and I was again well fouled.

Cussing audibly, I reeled in the bait and began the monotonous job of cleaning the hooks. In the meantime, Williams had snapped on the lightweight floater and as he made his initial test I watched with envy as it bubbled back to the boat, completely free of foreign matter.

"Look at that baby go," he gloated as he held it aloft. "No moss; see?"

Failing to take his hint, I cast frenziedly across the pool, becoming immediately fouled. Gritting my teeth but saying nothing, I watched as Williams made a suicidal cast far across the open water. A cypress had fallen into the edge of the pool and with utter disregard as to consequences, he had dropped the lure in a small opening, completely blocked off by two waist size limbs. These limbs lay flush with the surface of the water and as he began the retrieve I muttered sarcastically: "You've played the wilds now! What would you do if a fish did strike? You'd never get him over *both* of those limbs."

Suddenly, as if in answer to my query, the fish slashed upward and engulfed the floating, churning bait! With a yell, the angler sat back on the rod, the viciousness of his strike bringing the bass clear of the water!

"What would I do?" he yelled. "I'd put him in the boat; that's what I'd do!" and as he spoke these words he began horsing the fish through the vegetation, bringing him up to the first of the limbs. Then, with a jerk of the rod, he raised the fish to the surface and immediately slackened the line. With a frenzied leap the bass cleared the barrier by a good two feet, landing with a splash on the opposite side! Quickly the angler regained the slack, but as the fish reached the second limb it bored straight downward, hanging the line between a crevice in the cypress bark.

"Paddle to the limb," yelled Williams and, needing no second bidding, I hurried the boat to the spot. In the meantime, heavy surges of water testified that the fish was still on, but as we neared the spot a surging roll from well to the left led us to believe that he had fought his way free. Suddenly, however, the vibrations of the line increased, and as we reached the limb we discovered an almost impossible fact. As the line came free not one but *two* bass rolled to the surface, both neatly pinned to the miniature floater! The commotion to the left of the line had undoubtedly been the strike of the second fish and as the fish were boated I merely stared!

Three casts later, Williams hooked and landed a two-pound fish, and, tossing pride to the winds, I removed my heavy lure and groped through the contents of my box for a mate to his surface bait. Failing to match its snow white color, I begged a loan from my companion, and on the second cast with the new lure I raised a fish, only to lose him as he dived beneath the moss.

Having exhausted the pool, we moved along, threading our way through bushes and logs and keeping a sharp lookout for open water. At the edge of the green timber we found an open spot and slipping easily to within casting range we dropped our baits side by side. As they struck, a fish rose hungrily and downed Williams' offering in a shower of spray. Quickly I brought in my lure and with rod tip high my companion worked the bass through the vegetation and finally to the side of the boat. As he held the fish motionless on the surface of the water I snapped a picture of the defeated warrior.

"Hold that fish out to the side so he'll show up plainly," I ordered as Williams began removing the hooks. "I want to get another picture."

Misinterpreting my orders, the angler gently dropped the fish overboard, holding the rod high, thinking that I wanted another shot of the fish coming in.

"Not that way," I barked but the order came too late. With a last desperate flip the fish turned over on the surface and literally spit the lure from his jaws! Turning easily, he disappeared beneath the boat, and, as Williams glared, I remarked casually:

"Bet that's the only bass in Grassy Lake that ever had his picture taken and then got away!"

Williams glared again.

As the sun grew warmer bass became less inclined to strike and out across the deadening rising fish became few and far between. As we approached a huge old borrow pit that made up Grassy's eastern boundary I suggested that we paddle ashore and rest for a while. Williams readily agreed, and after pulling the boat ashore we stretched our cramped limbs.

Breaking out our lunch we spent a pleasant hour recounting the morning's events, but after a while Williams remarked: "We ought to go back out about noon. Those fish will feed again and we ought to pick up a couple more easy."

"You're crazy," I murmured. "Grassy Lake bass won't strike in the middle of the day, hot as it is. Best thing for us to do is to take a long nap and then try 'em again late in the afternoon."

He made no reply, and, having missed my sleep the night before, I was soon in a state of semi-consciousness. Presently, however, I was awakened slightly by a nudging foot, and dimly I heard Williams speak: "Say, boy, I'm going out again."

"Go 'way," I muttered. "Grassy Lake bass won't strike in the middle of the day—"

"Suit yourself," he replied, and as I again drifted off into slumber, I heard the grate of the boat as it slipped away from the landing.

When I awakened, the sun had passed its zenith, and, as I sat up, rubbing my eyes, I saw the boat, parked exactly as we had left it. Turning, I found my companion stretched beneath the willows and sleeping the sleep of the just.

Rising, I nudged him with my foot, and as he sat up, frowning and stretching, I remarked: "Well, Bud, where are your 'middle of the day' fish? Come, come, let's see 'em."

Without a word he raised himself, stretched grandly and walked to the water's edge. Bending over, he fumbled with the stringer, and as I noticed his expression I wished devoutly that I had remained silent. Slowly he raised the string, and there, in plain view, resting atop our morning's catch were two bass, worthy of the name! Not too big, just right in fact, and I mentally estimated their weight at four pounds each.

Turning to me with a smug, complacent smile, the angler spoke: "Fish'll always hit a little in the middle of the day, Grassy Lake fish just like any other fish. Come on though boy; we're burning daylight. I want you to give me some more pointers on fishing this lake. I'll swear, *I never would learn how to fish this thing!*"

The Clearing Buck

By JOHN S. MARTIN

THE MOONS THAT RIDE OVER THE ADIRONDACKS LOOK, I SUPPOSE, just as they always did—soft and warm when the brook trout are rising to an evening hatch of May-flies, cold and hard when the bucks' necks are swelling and the shadows are like fine black lace along the silvery beech ridges. The people who move around in the Adirondacks have not changed so much, either. Vacationists escaping the grind of their cities are motivated not much differently from the first trappers and settlers who came there to escape the grind of colonial poverty; to consume the wilderness and, by taming it, to quench the ache that its savagery put in their hearts.

But I think the Adirondack deer have changed. When the Indians were there, deer were only deer, for then there were elk, too, and moose, and the little fellows, with white tails were minor characters. Today they are the region's biggest wild creatures, barring a few bear.

I know one deer that stood for something eternal in the Adirondacks. He lived at a time when Lake Placid was already loud with college kids and Lake George and Schroon and Long Lakes were already lined, on one side, with hot-dog stands and gents' clothing stores. He lived back in a sheltered country, west and a little north of Brandreth Lake, ranging between North Pond Flow and Deer Pond in the section drained by Shingle Shanty Stream. Folks used to see him or find his track around the long clearing that lies two-thirds of the way in to the lake from Brandreth Station. The clearing was made for a logging camp when they cut the soft wood off that section for the first time, more than a generation ago. This clearing was grown with hay, sparse but sweet, and across that long forest meadow at dusk sometimes people traveling the wagon road would see a huge deer, gray with age, feeding in the open at the far edge.

If the traveler stopped to watch, this buck—a true stag in size and dignity—would not flounce away like the young bucks and the does and fawns. He would just raise his head, which was crowned with what looked like the top of a dead chestnut tree, and gaze back majestically. Then he would move slowly off into the timber—royalty whose privacy had been invaded. A true monarch of the wilds.

They called him the Clearing Buck. Jim Hall, the head guide, used to call his track "as big as a bull's." Reuben Cary, who had been at the camp ever since the late General Brandreth got the township as his bonus after the Civil War, used to say gently, into his snowy whiskers, "He's been around there a number of years." That was going some, from old Reuben.

No one had ever had a shot at him.

Our guess was that the Clearing Buck nooned on the high, steep beech ridges that ran southwest of the old logging track. He was so wise and alert that he probably picked spots to spend the day, even in rutting season, where he could hear or smell a man coming for half a mile. Then he would just slip over a ridge and move away unseen without your knowing he had even been there.

Maybe, too, he had a much wider range than most deer—all the way to the foot of the big lake and 'way out to Panther Pond. Anyway, we used to drive his section every now and then and never see anything more of him than that enormous deep hoofprint, more than four inches long and splayed in front as wide as your rifle butt. In soft ground you could see where his fetlocks had pressed in. Two hundred pounds, dressed, is heavy for an Adirondack buck. The Clearing Buck would go nearer three hundred. Even old Reuben thought so.

But we never saw him except when he showed himself at the clearing. We felt about him as you feel about the spirit of a place, a spirit too shy to be conjured. Nor could you lie in wait for this spirit to appear. We tried that many an evening at the clearing, and he never showed. Either he knew we were there, or he came and stayed invisible. We had this feeling about him: that he was just a little bit supernatural.

Some people get sentimental about wild things. They think you should leave them entirely alone, let them live out the lives they were born to, even though you know they won't live so long and though man, when he hunts them, is only reverting to whatever wild is left in him.

We were pretty lusty young animals in the Clearing Buck's day, and fancied that our killing was more aboriginal than most hunters'. We stalked our game ourselves and dressed it out and carried it in with only a little help from the guides, or so we thought. But about the Clearing Buck even we had something of that soft feeling, almost a reverence. He was so superior to all other deer that it would be a crime to shoot him if you did get the chance, so mysterious and patriarchal that to kill him would be to rob Brandreth of its most important unseen presence.

And yet, we realized, he could not live forever. He must be so old that, any season now, he would lay his great body down in some deep tamarack swamp and go to sleep for always, leaving behind him nothing but his legend. And even that would become thin and unbelieved as the people who knew it stopped coming to Brandreth. The Clearing Buck's head belonged in the Colonel's big game room at the main camp, up on the stones over the ten-foot fireplace, to stare proudly across at the long rows of lesser bucks which Brandreths and McAlpins and Potters and Pyles had shot through the generations. At least, that was our way of rationalizing the challenge, almost the scare, that the Clearing Buck's shadowy existence put into our predatory young hearts. We didn't hunt him often, but every once in a while some one of us would say, "Let's go out to the clearing and see if we can get a crack at him." And then two or three of us boys would go out there together, talking very little and only in whispers, because going for the Clearing Buck was really awesome.

I lately flew over the Adirondacks and didn't see much of them. The overcast was thick, and the Montreal plane went high above it. We flew far east of Brandreth, but I knew about where it lay as we passed, and I thought how different it all looked from up there. The autumn sun was hot on the clouds below us and through the cabin window. Down under the clouds I knew it was drizzling through the Adirondacks, the way it drizzled and then froze and sleeted and finally snowed the day Don and I hunted the Clearing Buck, and saw him close to, and fired lead into him.

That was one of those days when it rained so hard just before dawn that it wakes you up, and you turn the other ear to it and forget about hunting. But something got me up, and I made breakfast before rousting Don out.

Then I broached the idea of going out the track past the clearing as far as the old Potter camp, rain or no rain, if only to pick up a few partridges. We were due to go home in two days, and he hadn't killed his buck yet; so he would carry a rifle, I a shotgun, or, rather, old Reuben's three-barreled gun with buckshot in the left side and a .30-.30 bullet underneath, just in case. The weather ought to fair off about eleven o'clock, I figured, and we could hunt a buck for him coming back.

Don went, but he grumbled a lot and said I was crazy, and he was right. It certainly didn't fair off. We were soaked through by the time we reached Potter's. But the wind died out and the rain became a fine drizzle and the woods went dead. They had that damp, dark silence that makes the trees sound as though they were mourning when a breath does stir them. Even their steady dripping stopped as the air turned colder and the drizzle congealed into fine sleet. No bird or squirrel moved. The only thing alive in the woods was Shingle Shanty Stream, raised by the rain, pouring down its course into the ghostly swampland below the ridges.

Wet as we were, we might as well make a swing along the ridges, for now stalking conditions were perfect. Under our feet the dead leaves lay limp, turning to forest mold. You could move like a wraith, and in the still air all scents carried nowhere, but hung heavily where they were—our tobacco, our sweat, our guns' oil and our wet wool and leather. We worked up over one ridge and found the big trees on its top groaning softly like an organ. Down in the next hollow all was still again, and entering a blue-spruce thicket was like pushing through damp velvet curtains. The sodden carpet of needles was centuries deep.

Don and I had hunted together so often this way, one ahead with birdshot, the other behind with a rifle, that ordinarily we scarcely exchanged glances. But today was somehow ominous. We knew we would likely be right on top of deer before seeing them, and just lately one of the guides had been charged by a rutty buck when he surprised it with a doe. I kept looking back at Don to see if he saw in the trail what I saw—old prints of the Clearing Buck. After so much rain it was hard to tell how old they were. But we were on his range, all right.

I remember I had on a red worsted hockey cap which got brushed off on to my knees by a twig as I crouched suddenly at an exclamation behind me from Don. I looked around and saw him staring pop-eyed, his gun half raised, after a fawn which had jumped up right beside him and was bounding away without a sound through the thicket. I must have passed its bed within two paces without its stirring. It startled Don so badly that he was panting as he lowered his rifle and grinned at me sheepishly. I grinned, too, pulled on my sopping red cap, straightened up, and started along the trail again toward where it climbed a small hummock. I had to chuckle at Don, letting a fawn panic him.

When I was halfway up the little rise, I squatted suddenly a second time, and now it was my turn to pant. Every bit of breath had gone out of me, every nerve and muscle had gone instantly taut, at what I had seen just beyond the blue-spruce hummock. I had seen, without his seeing or hearing me, the biggest, grayest deer in the world, with a head of horns like chestnut rampikes. He was lying right beside the trail, not twenty paces away, broadside to, with his head turned away. It could only be—it was without any question—the Clearing Buck!

I have never had such a moment in the woods, before or since. There lay the fabled monster, and there crouched I, with his certain death in my hands. All I had to do was cock the gun, rise, aim and fire. But I didn't do any of those things. I crouched there frozen, getting my breath in and out in gulps as silently as I could.

I knew the buck was absolutely unaware, undisturbed. But Don hadn't seen me yet, either. He was feeling in his breast pocket for a cigarette, after the fawn episode, coming along slowly behind me without looking. The great buck was right there for him to shoot, but I had to get Don's eye to make him crouch and creep to where I was. The seconds were torture until he looked up, saw me gesturing, grinned again and said right out loud: "Damn that little critter! He made me jump almost out of my skin."

Then he caught my excitement, put his hand over his mouth and hunched down where he was. But he stage-whispered, "What's the matter?" still smiling. He still had that fawn on his mind.

I made the words "Clearing Buck" with my lips and pointed to the hummock. He didn't understand, but began stealing toward me; so I turned to cover that astonishing quarry, sure now that he was ours. I stayed down until Don reached my shoulder, and by the time I could whisper to him I was cold calm once more.

I know now that I should never have named that awful name to him just then, "The Clearing Buck." For those words shook him apart again, into the state the fawn had started, and as we both straightened up—much too fast—for Don to let him have it the great animal sprang to his feet and whirled away in one incredible blur of motion. Don, who is a crack rifleman, missed him cleanly with one, two, three shots as he crashed off to our right. I cut loose with the buckshot charge and never even slowed him up.

Then he was gone, and we stood looking at each other as though the world had come to an end. The silence of the dead forest closed in around us. We just looked at each other, trembling, and then one of us said, "My God!" We sank down on the spruce needles to whisper it over.

He may not run too far, we said, and in these wet woods we can follow his track easily. The thing will be to see him first, because he is as old as these hills and twice as wise. He will stop and look back, listening, smelling. It's dark enough today so that maybe we can get up on him, with no wind and such quiet going. But now Don had better go first, for a snap shot. And we'll both move mighty slowly.

I took off the red cap. We gave the buck the time it takes to smoke one cigarette. Then we took his trail.

Up the beech ridge it led, in bounds so far apart you wouldn't have believed an animal his size and weight could make them through thick timber. We followed stealthily for a mile before we came to the place he had stopped for the first time. That made us feel better. Beyond this spot, on a high knoll, the broad, heart-shaped hoofmarks fell into line where he had walked off instead of running. They led to and around a brush pile which he had skirted instead of leaping. They paired again and lengthened out where he had bounded across an opening, but on the far side he had stopped for a second look back

From there on the tracks were a stately march, ever toward higher ground. He was over his first fright, but an old-timer like this would be extra alert for days to come.

On the higher ground, the sleet turned to wet snow. Big flakes swirling down so densely they made you feel they had pressure. This would be a help, if we hurried, because we could go forward farther apart, and still keep the buck's trail in sight between us. But it cut down the visibility, and the motion of the snowflakes sometimes imparted itself to rocks and stumps, so that we paused more often, peering breathlessly ahead at nothing.

When I did see the Clearing Buck again, Don wouldn't believe me. He was halted a good hundred yards away, with head and horns concealed from us, behind a thick beech butt. My eye must have caught one twitch of his tail, which he did not repeat for the longest time after I got Don to see what otherwise looked like a tall gray boulder coated with snow. We stood together, straining for verification. I was on the point of agreeing with Don that I was "seeing things," that no deer's body could possibly stand so high and massive. Then that tail twitched again. Don drew a long breath and laid his wet cheek again the stock of his rifle.

Lots of bucks spring into the air when you hit them, or crumple right to the ground. This one just sagged a bit, then straightened, moved out beyond the beech trunk and sank deliberately to his knees, as though lying down by choice. But his incredible head went on down too and he rolled over on his side, and when we saw that we started walking in.

You always see afterward how easy it would have been to do the right thing, and how that hurts! We hadn't gone five steps before that buck was up and away over the next knoll as though nothing in the world had happened.

How badly he was shot, how strong a beast he must be to run at all, we could only judge by a two-foot splatter of dark blood where his side had been and by more splotches on the underbrush for fifty yards.

Old Reuben, of course, later rubbed it into us cruelly about what we should have done then: hold still for an hour and let the buck lie down wherever he would, until the wound stiffened. Then trail him; he would never get up again. But I doubt if anyone who had seen and shot that magnificent, ghostly animal, and judged from the sign how deeply he was wounded, could have exercised such patience.

Besides, it was snowing hard, and it was getting late. In a few minutes the trail would be blanketed, first by those cascading snowflakes, then by evening gloom.

We pushed ahead feverishly, both of us ready to fire the finishing shot when the Clearing Buck should surge up, as we were sure he would, from a windfall or rocky pocket or clump of beech switches. We pursued those tremendous leaping hoofmarks, now punctuated on the off side by splotches of blood, just as hard as we could, without caution. Instead of uphill, the tracks now led down—another sign that the buck was mortally hurt. He was heading for water to kill his scent, and a swampy tangle to hide in.

Twice we heard him start up just ahead of us, both times out of sight. He blew furiously when he winded us and crashed off into the gathering dusk. We hurried on faster, stumbling and slithering on rocks and down timber.

Where a rivulet cut under the hill's shoulder, we found that he had slid down a long, steep gravel bank, too steep for us to take without risk of grit in our guns. We had to descend a longer way. At the bottom we knew he had followed the stream bed, undoubtedly downward toward the fastnesses of Shingle Shanty Swamp.

We splashed down the watercourse after him, and dismay got its first clutch on us when we came to a long pool, too deep to wade, that beavers had backed up with many yards of wabbly bog on either side. We were twenty precious minutes floundering through and around that obstacle. Meantime, somewhere ahead of us, into the wilderness and the night, struggled the greatest buck we had ever heard of, the high-headed monarch of these mountains, wounded, dying, never more to be seen.

Don and I didn't get into camp that night until long after the rest had finished dinner. Finding our way back to the logging track was a job in itself, after our matches gave out and we had to admit we would never find that deer in the dark. We told everyone in camp our story, over and over, suffering intensely when old Reuben poured on us his gentle scorn.

But I think we suffered even more lying in bed that night with the awful thought that the Clearing Buck lay dead somewhere and that we who had killed him had done it clumsily, ignobly. Unless we found him the next day that shaggy, hoary hide would never be tanned soft and spread across a gun room table for hunters to admire. Those magnificently spiked and palmated antlers would be meanly nibbled by mice, or would just rot in the swamp muck, instead of gleaming in a place of honor for years to come.

We never did find him. The whole camp turned out next day and combed that run, right down into Shingle Shanty, until sundown. It had stopped snowing in the night, so that everyone saw the deep blood stains. Old Reuben said we had simply "hit him in the short guts," which would let him travel a long way, until he lay down and stiffened. But it must surely be fatal.

Maybe it was, for he was never seen alive again, and his great track was gone from the Brandreth region. But I like to hope that somehow he survived, to live out his days in some distant range, and I almost wish that I had never seen him alive at all. It's a fearful thing to know that the wild held something so splendid, and that you spoiled it.

The W. D. A.

By JOHN ALDEN KNIGHT

THERE IS AN AFFLICTION THAT LAYS ITS HEAVY HAND FROM TIME to time on those who indulge in the outdoor sports. A by-product of nervous tension, it sometimes has the capacity to reduce its victim to an exaggerated condition of inarticulation, wobbly knees, and all-round jitters. Although the symptoms are the same, to a greater or less degree, this unfortunate malady manifests itself variously, its expression varying both with the temperament of the individual and the situation in hand. Generally, it is known as buck fever, but it does not confine itself to deer hunting. Even in so mild and delightful a sport as woodcock shooting, it is apt to rear its ugly visage—often with deplorable results.

The opening day of the woodcock season had dawned clear and crisp and we were in our choice cover, finding the birds there in soul-satisfying quantity. My friend's son, having completed his years of apprenticeship in the field under the watchful eye of his father, had been admitted to the clan and now was enjoying his first "opening day" excursion on even terms with his elders. His father had urged me not to favor the boy in any way on the day's shooting, feeling that the youngster would learn his wing shooting more quickly and thoroughly if he were allowed to go it on his own. There are many tricks of the trade that come with experience, and his father wanted him to learn them for himself—the hard way.

As I say, there were plenty of birds in the cover. Almost from the time we had left the car, the dog had been busy making game, standing birds, or retrieving. Since we were handing out no favors, it is not surprising that all of the shooting had been done by the two more experienced guns. The dog would come on point, the man in the center would walk in for the flush, and the other two would flank each side. Out would go the bird and the youngster would bring up his gun, only to have the bird crumple and fall just as he was about to pull the trigger. Not that we were deliberately stealing his shots; he always seemed to be out of position or on the side away from the direction of flight.

It was not long before we had two or three woodcock apiece in our game pockets, but still the boy had not fired his gun. To his credit, he voiced no complaint, but his face grew serious and lost its customary grin. At last his chance came. The big setter had come down on a staunch point between two low hemlock trees, directly ahead of the boy. With his gun at ready, he walked in for the flush while we skirted the trees on each side for the possible quartering shot. Unfortunately the bird happened to be a "flutterer." It twittered up out of the grass a few feet from the dog's nose, towered for a yard or so, and then set off at a leisurely pace only a trifle off the straight-away line. Up came the boy's gun and he covered the bird. He knew that the shot was too close and that he should wait. But he knew, also, that there were two guns, one on each side, that waited only until the woodcock had cleared the protecting hemlock trees. The pressure was too strong. Bang! The bird folded and dropped into the grass.

My friend walked over and picked up what was left of the little woodcock—two wings, the head, half of the backbone, and the upper part of the bill. All else had vanished. Folding the wings around the tattered remnants, he handed the pitiful little bundle to his son.

"There's your bird," he said. "Remember, that one counts in your limit. How often must I tell you to wait until your birds are in proper range, particularly when you have a wide-open shot. You know better than to do a trick like that. One woodcock—wasted."

I knew what the youngster was thinking, but he took his reprimand without excuse or alibi. For a moment he regarded the worthless bundle of feathers in his hand; then he placed it under a clump of grass and we went on.

After that I noticed that his parent's gun did not come up quite as fast as it had earlier in the day, and I must confess a certain tardiness on my part. Two of the next three woodcock fell to the boy's gun, and the familiar grin came back to stay. Once his father glanced at me sideways and I saw the suspicion of a wink. Other than that, all went as usual.

On the way home in the car, it was inevitable that a bit of kidding should be in order.

"There's nothing like economy of motion," I remarked to my friend. "It takes the succeeding generations to develop new and better ways to get things done. I have been under the impression that all was well if I could only manage to *hit* my birds. But not that boy of yours. He not only kills his birds—he dresses them right in midair."

"That's right," agreed his father. "Speed and efficiency are the watchwords. Don't ever tell me that it's impossible to do two things at once—and do them thoroughly. Well—we live and we learn."

Hardly a week had passed before I found myself in much the same predicament as that of the boy on opening day. Three of us were shooting the same cover, and it was one of those unfortunate days, that happen to every sportsman, when everything goes wrong. First off, I missed two birds, twisters that zigged when I zagged, or vice versa. When a bird got up I would be on the wrong side of the dog, or the woodcock would flush behind the screen of a tree, too dense to permit a shot. Once a close sitter flushed after allowing me to walk by within three feet of him, taking advantage of thick cover before I could swing about and get my gun on him. By the time four o'clock rolled around, I had but one woodcock in my game pocket. My sympathy for the boy became even more heartfelt than it had been a few days earlier.

The climax came when the setter came down on point under an old apple tree. As I walked in past the dog, out twittered the typical "flutterer," and it ambled off across the field, taking its time about three feet above the tops of the weeds. I covered the bird and swung with it. At the last instant, I checked my gun in an attempt to throw the bird off-center in the pattern, but I didn't check it quite enough. The head and part of the breast remained intact, but the rest of the woodcock vanished with the report.

"Well, well, well," chortled my friend. "So you've joined the club. Just wait till my son hears about *this*. I think you went him one better—that woodcock is killed, dressed and partially cooked."

For the next six months, those two badly shot woodcock furnished the basis, off and on, for not a little persiflage. The club was given a name and I had the dubious honor of becoming its president. President of the Woodcock Demolishers' Association. Then the long arm of the war reached out, and both of our boys left for active duty, mine to fly for the Navy and the other accredited member of the W.D.A. to see to it that the motors of the Army Air Forces kept turning over.

We two relics of a bygone era, too old to be of any use in the armed forces (at least, that's what they told us when we tried to sign up), hunted together most of the time during the next woodcock season. From the first I noticed that my friend was shooting inordinately well. The bird would flush, there would be a single report from his gun, and then would follow the command to the dog, "Fetch, boy!" Birds were scarce that season and he had to take his chances when he found them. Still he didn't miss.

Things went on this way without much of note coming to pass until he had killed his seventh straight woodcock. Seven birds flushed —seven shots—seven dead woodcock. The seventh had flushed from under his feet, without warning from the dog, in an abandoned apple orchard. He had pulled the trigger an instant after the bird had dodged behind the tangled branches of one of the old trees and, failing to see it fall, he was not sure that he had killed it. I joined in the search for the dead bird and we two, with the help of the dog, covered every inch of ground where it should have come down. Search as we would, we could find no dead woodcock.

My friend walked back to the spot under the projecting limb of the old tree where he had last seen the woodcock in flight.

"It should have dropped right here," he said. "Too bad. That would have made seven birds with seven shells. Well, let's go. I guess I missed him."

Just then I happened to glance down at the grass between us.

There, camouflaged perfectly in the lights and shades of autumn browns, with its wing tip almost touching his shoe, lay the dead woodcock.

The eighth bird was one of those impossible, miracle shots that a man makes once or twice (if he's lucky and fast with a gun) and remembers for the rest of his life. We had left the hillside for a while and were hunting through a bottom swale of tall black alder. The dog had been making game for perhaps twenty-five or thirty yards, but the woodcock refused to lie and kept moving ahead of us. At last the dog went on point at the edge of the swale where the alder merged into a heavy growth of hemlock.

The woodcock flushed, fast and strong, to the left of my friend as he walked in. For only twenty feet was the bird in sight before hiding itself among the protecting evergreen limbs, but somehow my friend managed, lightning fast, to get his gun up and on the bird as it vanished. Boughs and twigs showered down with the report of the gun and with them fell the mortally stricken woodcock. A truly magnificent bit of snap shooting. And that made eight.

The ninth bird was hard to find. As I have said, woodcock were scarce that season, and we worked for what we killed. Two birds fell to my gun while we hunted out the remainder of the alder swale, but my friend was out of position on one bird and out of range on the other. Then we climbed the hill and, at long last, the dog went on point in a thick patch of blackberry briers.

As is so often the case in thick cover of this sort, the bird lay close and refused to flush. The brier patch grew on top of a bank that bordered a country road, so we circled and came in from the rear so as to drive the bird across the road into the open. As we fought our way through the briers toward the pointing dog, I glanced at my friend. His face was serious and he held his gun high up over the briers, ready for instant use. His attitude and every movement told me that his nerves were tight as fiddle strings.

Not until I had passed the dog and kicked around in the briers ahead of him did the woodcock flush. It was a tiny bird and, re-grettably, a "flutterer." As it twittered away across the road, I brought up my gun part way and then waited for the bird to move into shooting range. Even as I did so, my friend fired. One moment there was a woodcock flying across the road; the next, the bird miraculously disappeared right before my eyes, while *one wing* floated down to come to rest dead center in the dust of the roadbed. It wasn't a question of being unable to find the remnants of the bird. What was left of the bird fell in the road in plain view. Never, in many years of shooting, have I seen such a complete example of total disintegration.

Tenderly I picked up the lone wing, with a pendent shred of skin and feathers, and laid it to rest at the roadside. Then I picked a bouquet of dried goldenrod and ragweed and presented it to my friend with appropriate congratulations.

"Orchids, my boy! Meet the new champion. One bird killed, dressed, cooked, and predigested. I'll be over to get the boy's address tonight. He should be informed that the Woodcock Demolishers' Association has a new president."

We hunted the hillside cover a few days later but, no flight birds having dropped in, we eventually gravitated down to the bottom swale where the alder grows dense and high. It makes the toughest kind of shooting, but we felt sure that there must be a few birds left in its maze of tangled branches. Here and there in the small wilderness a wild crab tree has made a space for itself at the edge of the swamp on the higher ground, forcing back the alder growth and creating a small clearing carpeted with lush, green grass. In normal times these spots almost always hold woodcock, but now they were deserted so we pushed our way into the thick tangle of the swamp itself.

The stream that winds through this bottom land flows deep and slow, with undercut banks and few riffles. To get from one side to the other is not easy, so we usually hunt the place lengthwise, with a man on each bank. When we were about halfway through the cover, my friend called to me that the dog was on point. Not being able to cross the stream, I stopped in a place where I could move with freedom, made sure that there were no branches that would stop the swing of my gun, and waited for what might happen. A few seconds passed and I heard the bird flush, twittering as he towered; then came the single shot from my friend's gun. For the first time since the season had opened came the cry.

"Hey, Jack! Comin' your way!"

As he called, I saw the woodcock, high above the alder tops and winging it across the swamp for all he was worth. Swinging through with him, I pressed the trigger as the front sight passed him in his line of flight. He crumpled and fell.

"Good shot!" called my friend. "Fetch, Lief!"

Although the bird was hard hit, he had enough left to hide himself before he died. He did a thorough job of it, but the big setter found him at last, out of sight in a clump of bluegrass at the edge of the stream.

No more birds turned up in the thick cover, so we stopped at the old beaver dam to have a smoke and talk things over. That's the nice thing about October shooting in Pennsylvania. It's always warm enough to allow pleasant relaxation in the welcome sunshine when you feel like resting. We dangled our legs over the edge of the high bank and smoked for a while in silence, both of us content to drink in the crisp mountain air while we watched the changing riot of color in the foliage on the hill across the valley.

"By God, I'm glad that's over," said my friend.

"What's over?"

"That one bird—one shell business. Nine straight. That's not bad. I wanted to make it ten, but what the hell. Now I can relax and enjoy myself for a change."

"And so can I," I agreed. "For a while, I thought I must be shooting with Superman."

My friend smiled and lay back in the soft grass. "Ever get buck fever?" he asked.

"Sure," I replied, "so have you."

"I know it," he laughed. "Now I can tell you something. Before that last bird got up I was saying to myself, 'Careful, now. Take it easy. Put your gun on this one and don't stop your swing. Make it ten straight.' I had myself wound up so tight before that woodcock flushed that I know damned well I missed him by three feet. So you think that's buck fever?"

"How else can you account for the Woodcock Demolishers' Association? We all know better than to shoot our birds too close. We know we should relax and swing through with the bird instead of stopping the swing as the trigger is pulled. What makes us do these things? Nothing but buck fever in one of its milder forms."

"I guess that's it," he agreed. "Well, it's all over now. I've had my buck fever for this season. Glad you got that tenth woodcock so long as I couldn't." Sitting up, he stretched his long arms, picked up his gun from the grass, and stood up. "Come on; let's do a little relaxed woodcock shooting."

Don't Tell Judy

By CLARKE VENABLE

THIS IS JERRY WARD'S STORY. NOT MINE, MARK YOU, BUT JERRY'S. It's a fine state of affairs when a chap is compelled to become a press-agent for the truth, but that's the way things stand. If I am to get a pup from my old friend Jerry, I can't wait for truth, crushed to earth, to rise again; I must give the old girl a boost. That's why I am asking you to listen to Jerry's story. However, since I know a bit about Judy Dare, and a bit more about old Gabe, Jerry's trainer, I hold the private opinion that Jerry has met up with artifice and stratagem. But don't quote me. And above all, don't tell Judy. After all, I am working for a pup rather than trying to establish a personal opinion.

Word reached me that Jerry was going out of the field-trial game. I had heard this often enough before, not less than a dozen times from

Jerry himself, but this time it sounded like the real McCoy. I was shocked. Good old Jerry! Always a bit obstinate, always a trifle confused, always easy to circumvent; but always in there trying like a nobleman and a sportsman—and usually in there with some most excellent dogs. Now he was going out.

In this bit of seemingly authentic news I saw a chance to get a good puppy prospect. I motored down (remember the day of unrationed gasoline when one could quest for a dog?) and I found Jerry at home. Very much at home. He was doleful, almost tearful. He waved me to a chair and yelled to old Gabe to bring a julep. Gabe was trainer, major-domo, julep-mixer and about everything else at Jerry's.

"So you've heard, George?" he said, looking at me with sad eyes.

"Heard what?"

"Why, about Judy. About me. About the dogs. Confound it, about everything."

"I only know that I heard you were quitting the field-trial game, and I thought I might pick up a good prospect from your lines. What about Judy? And you and the dogs and everything?"

Jerry sighed with evident relief. "Thank God, here at last is an unpoisoned ear that can harken to the truth. Listen, George; you're one of these writing fellows. You can help me out. Get the truth on record, so to speak, and let all the facts be known."

"I'm after a pup, not a story," I reminded him.

"All right. You want a pup; I want truth to have a little circulation. Go to bat for me in this hour of trial, old man, and I'll give you your choice—yes, even the choice of the litter when we mate Bright Tomorrow with Double Dare."

That was news! "Since when did you begin going to the Dare kennels for blood?" I asked. "I thought there was a sort of feud between you."

"Ah," Jerry sighed. "Now I know you haven't heard this parcel of lies. Confound it, George, even Judy might hear what the dim-wits are saying, and she might give it credit. She might think I pulled a fast one on her, outsmarted her, so to speak."

"She might," I said significantly, "and again she might not."

"But I'll arm you with the truth, George. The truth is mighty, George—if it gets a little play. You'll noise it around, won't you, old man?"

"Spill it," I said. "I noise things if they are worth a noise; and judging by the state of mind I find you in, I have a hunch this will be."

That was the signal for Jerry to take off.

"Yes, George, it's true that I'm quitting the field-trial game—cold. Not just yet, of course, but soon. Another year, maybe, but no more. And yet, do you know what they are saying? They're saying that I'll stop at nothing to gain possession of a bird dog better than those to be found in my own kennels. Nonsense! There aren't any. Yet some wag, with a muddled sense of wit, said that I'm about to marry a bird dog. Fancy that! And yet, if that lie should come to Judy's ears, she might suspect me.

"I'm fed up. I'm exhausted from listening to those who, before the race, are forever extolling their dogs; and I'm equally weary of the invented excuses that come flocking in when the judges see it otherwise.

"Fortunately, I don't have to talk about my dogs. You know that, George. Good thing, too, for it's getting to the point where a chap with real dogs can't get a word in edgewise. But we've fallen on evil days, old man. The time has come when a real dog can be beaten by something that has the general conformation of a goat and nothing to recommend him save his ability to get from here to yonder in less time than it takes to blow a whistle on him.

"Nowadays you can win with a bolt of lightning if you can manage to get a little hair on it—and you can't win with much less. It's the wrong school of thought, George. I've grown weary of competing with crosses between Australian ant-eaters and African gazelles, and I'm going out of dogs. Definitely.

"Yet the ridiculously absurd story has gained circulation that I'm going to marry Judy Dare just to become at least half owner of that great setter, Double Dare. You hadn't heard? I know you hadn't George, and that's why I'm telling you the whole truth. And please remember that I never had to turn to the Dares for blood. Why, doggone it, man, where did Double Dare come from? Everyone who knows anything at all knows that he was by Merry Man, out of Sultana, she by Handy Andy. And where did Handy Andy come from, I ask you? Line bred to old Sultan, that's what. And Sultan came right from these kennels—bred by my father, twenty-five years ago. Man alive, we don't go to the Dares for blood. It's just the other way around. But that's between us. Judy might not understand. As a matter of fact, Judy is just a little strong-willed—too strong-willed, like most breeders.

"The truth of the matter is that I'd have gone out of dogs a long time ago if it hadn't been for the fact that Judy was always waving some red flag in my face. And I'd be out right now if old Gabe had kept his hands out of my affairs. But Gabe indulged in some of his noted mental work, and as a result I'm stuck, for the time being, with some dogs.

"You know, when I fell heir to these kennels I fell heir also to Gabe. I expect you'd say Gabe fell heir to me. Maybe so. He ruled me as a boy, just as he ruled the kennels. Sometimes he had to resort to finesse, but he always ruled. I tell you, that fellow could give a five-man committee composed of three Chinamen and two horse-traders a 24-hour head start and still outsmart them.

"Hang it all, George, I should have known I was in for something when that old rascal began to spend a lot of time over at the Dare place. I certainly had more than enough dogs to keep him busy, yet he would spend hours with some of Judy's more difficult prospects, and then have the gall to come home and regale me with tales of their progress.

"As a neighbor, I suppose that was a cross to be borne. But it got too heavy when he began to argue that we should go to the Dare kennels for some sharp out-crosses. That was too much! Why, everyone who knows anything at all knows that the Dares have been running second to us for years—that is, until recently. Oh, yes, I know that in the last few years Judy's dogs have outfooted us a few times; but they never outmannered or outfound us, and between foot and manners I'll take manners. Besides, as you know, Judy thinks just as highly of short-haired dogs as she does of setters, and I just don't hold anything in common with such opinions. Pointers are for hound men, and with some good setters in her kennel Judy should have known better.

"But I try to be liberal in my views, even when things are running against me a bit. And I'll admit that something was happening to us in the matter of wins. I decided one morning that affairs might be better with us if old Gabe spent more time with our dogs and less with Judy Dare's. I wasn't jealous, you understand; I just thought that Judy should rely more on her own trainer, Rance Rathbone. I never thought much of him, but is it my job to train all the trainers?

"One day I told Gabe, rather bluntly, I fear, that I would like to hear more about our own dogs and less of Judy Dare's. Naturally, Gabe has his answer. He always does.

"'The Book says'—you know how he always falls back on The Book when in need of force for his arguments—'The Book says to love yore neighbor, and I reckon that takes in his dawgs. Besides, this neighbor has some danged good prospects, which we ain't.'

" 'Ours might look better with a little more work,' I suggested.

" 'Mebbe. And a leetle foot blood wouldn't do us any harm, neither. 'Bout time fer some out-crosses in our kennels. Maybe a mite past time. Some of our bitches put to Judy's Merry Man, or that comer of hers, Double Dare, would be about right, I figger. Be too late some day soon.'

" 'Why too late?' I asked.

" 'Judy's fixin' to sell out. Quittin'.'

"That was news. 'Who told you that?' I demanded.

" 'Judy did. I reckon she knows.'

" 'Why, she can't do that! Not after all these years,' I protested. 'Why is she quitting?'

" 'Says she reckons dawgs is sorta standin' in her way,' Gabe answered.

" 'Way of what?' I asked.

" 'Dunno. Just her way. Wimmen is funny, 'specially dawg wimmen. You never can tell when they're doing just plain foot-work or actually makin' game. But I know this: her kennels would be a right good prop'ty to own, considerin' what would get throwed in to boot —to the right man.'

" 'What do you mean to boot, to the right man?' I demanded.

"You know how Gabe worries his cud of fine-cut when he gets in a tight place. He ruminated a while before he said: 'It's this a-way. When the right feller comes along, he'll git Judy, and with her the kennels to boot. Count it either way—her or the kennels as the boot— and it'll be better than an average bargain. When you was just a saplin', I used to think that mebbe you was goin' to do some fair foot-work in the right cover, but Judy made the mistake of beatin' you in that juvenile handlers' stake over in Rappahannock County, and danged if it didn't make a blinker out of you! Blinker and potterer, by gravy!

" 'I thought at one time that mebbe so Judy would do a leetle choke-collar work on you herself, but I reckon she knowed you had no nose fer game and was bird-shy to boot. She's beat you several times, fair and square, with some mighty good dawgs, and it's made you blinder than a mole at midnight. Judy's a fine girl—though I must say that fer a female person she ain't acted very smart. Been a different story if her dawgs had run second to yours.'

" 'I'll hear no more about Judy or her dogs,' I told him bluntly.

" 'That's what you think,' he came right back at me, 'but as The Book says, "Man proposes and God disposes"—that is, He does iffen a female don't git in His way. And I 'spect Judy'll be in our way with that Double Dare next month down at the Tidewater Open All-Age.'

" 'How good is he?' I asked.

" 'Well,' Gabe said, 'he ain't no faster than lightnin', and he ain't no solider than a rock, and he can't smell birds any further than from hell to the Pearly Gates. Outside a few things like that, he's just a dawg.'

" 'Bright Tomorrow will beat him,' I said. 'She beat him twice in the Derby age.'

" 'She can beat him,' Gabe said, 'if you can manage to put her on roller skates and let her carry her own birds in a basket.'

"That's where Gabe went too far, George. I couldn't take that. But you know, I'm beginning to wonder if the old rogue didn't prod me that way on purpose. He thinks mighty fast at times. Anyhow, I rose to the bait. I'll wager anything that Bright Tomorrow doesn't run second to him,' I flared.

"Gabe worried his cud a minute. 'Anything?' he asked.

" 'Yes, anything. The sky is the limit.' I felt that strong about it, George. I was really hot.

" 'Um-m,' Gabe mused. 'Might work out that way. I'll tell Judy, and like as not she'll lay you a leetle bet. You know how the Dares are.'

" 'Yes, I know how the Dares are,' I flared, 'and you'll tell Judy nothing. You keep out of this—and if you are already in, then get out.'

"I could see that sort of hurt Gabe. He put on that injured look of his. 'All right, I'll keep out. You don't seem to have enough huntin' sense to know that sometimes it takes an old potterin' dawg like me to draw heavy cover where the briers is thick. I'll fool with a well-bred pup a long time, but when I lead him to game and he don't even make a halfway p'int then, by gravy, I'm through!'

"I haven't the foggiest idea what he meant by that; I'm only reporting what was said between us. Putting the whole truth on record, so to speak.

"A few days later, maybe as much as a week, Gabe and I were out working Bright Tomorrow on the lower end of the plantation down near the Dare line. We were riding her pretty hard, and she was stepping. We came upon Judy, sitting on horseback at the head of a draw.

Rance Rathbone was dismounted, standing in the broom-sedge with uplifted hand. Judy's Double Dare was on point, but it was about the sloppiest point I've ever seen. It didn't look like he had any game in front of him.

" 'He's been fudging a little on his honoring,' Judy explained, 'and Rance is giving him some rehearsals on his manners.'

" 'That's no way to do it,' I told her quite frankly. 'I've seen false pointers made by holding a dog on nothing. At least Rance should know that.'

"Now, George, I ask you, what was wrong with that? Just neighborly advice, that's all. But Judy blew up. Just like the Dares. A little pig-headed, and set in their ways. But don't tell Judy I said so. She really went after me, and her chin went in the air like a good bench type in a pose.

" 'When we begin taking defeats from you, Jerry,' she said, 'then we'll begin taking lessons from you in training.'

" 'That will be right after the Tidewater All-Age,' I came right back at her, 'and please come in the afternoon for your lessons and try not to be tardy.' I laid it on pretty thick.

" 'You feel quite sure of yourself, don't you, Jerry?' she said, and her voice had honey and vinegar mixed in it.

" 'No, just sure of Bright Tomorrow,' I told her.

" 'How sure?'

" 'Oh, anything you like.'

"For a moment I thought that the no-limit offer had given her pause. I should have known better. Sweet as sugar, she said: 'I hear that you're getting out of the field-trial game. Is it straight goods this time, or just talk while you are in a peeve?'

" 'I'm not in a peeve,' I told her, 'and I'm going out, definitely.'

" 'So am I, just as soon as I can get out. Don't ask me why; I'm just going out. Since both of us are quitting, this might be an excellent time for one of us to make good. So here's my offer: my kennels against yours—every dog, every puppy, every matron in whelp—on Double Dare against your Bright Tomorrow in the Tidewater Open All-Age. With this one important proviso: our trainers are to handle.'

"Whew! There was a bet for you—a typical Dare bet. I heard Gabe gulp. Swallowed his cud, he told me later. He must have doubted what my reply would be, for he glared at me and said, 'It's a covey find, young feller, and I hope you show good manners.'

"'It's a bet,' I said to Judy, 'but will you tell me why you wish Gabe and Rance to handle?'

"'Gladly,' she replied, sweeter now than ever. 'It's an open stake, and you're too clever a handler for me, Jerry. You've learned so many things.'

"An admission like that from Judy should have put me on my guard. But, like a dope, I said, 'The conditions are fair enough. It's true that I've had more experience.'

"'Oh, yes, Jerry. So very much more experience!'

"And that was that. You can imagine my state of mind by the time the trials came off. Other than Bright Tomorrow, we didn't have much to run—a couple of puppies and one derby, I believe. They weren't very hot. This was just giving them experience, you know. So I'll skip the puppy trials and the Derby. You say that might be a part of the story too? Well, hang it, Judy won a second in the puppy stake. Our pups merely waddled around out of the money. We did better in the Derby, though. We won a second there. Who won? Blast it all, George, you writing chaps are hounds for all the facts, aren't you? Well, if you must know, Judy won the Derby. But I tell you that has nothing to do with the story. Judy runs in luck, that's all.

"To prove how she runs in luck, how do you think she came out in the drawings for the All-Age? First dog out of the box—that's how! It would give him early-morning going. And to make her dog look all the better, he was braced with a tangle-footed short-haired dog that couldn't overtake a land terrapin. And how did Bright Tomorrow come out in the drawings, do you think? Fourth brace—that's where. It would put her down in the heat of the day. To make matters tougher for her, she was braced with an ill-mannered setter that some goof must have found at the side of the road. You know, George, at times I wonder if I live right. However, I put on a fine front and congratulated Judy on her luck in the drawings. But I didn't sleep much that night. I felt that the tide was running against me.

"Naturally, I was on the line the next morning to ride that first brace. Courtesy, you understand—purely courtesy to Judy. And, as always, Judy delayed the start a few minutes by staging one of her cool and lofty late entrances. But I'll say this: I had never seen her look better. Pretty—downright pretty. Boots, riding breeches, windbreaker—she had been poured into them.

"I distinctly recall how I thought it a bit odd that I had never before noticed how all of Judy's curves came in exactly the right places and in the right proportion. Good conformation—darned good conformation. But for heaven's sake, don't tell Judy I hadn't noticed these things about her since we were—well, just youngsters. I dare say I hadn't noticed them before simply because she was forever doing something most upsetting to my peace of mind.

"She held Double Dare on the line for Rance, awaiting that thrilling moment when the judges say, 'Gentlemen, let 'em scat!' She and the dog made a picture—I'll say that. Hard to beat a pretty woman with a good-looking dog—if it's a setter dog. I do think that Double Dare was just a trifle short on muzzle, George. Just a shade, mark you, but it was a pretty picture.

"And I wish to say publicly that I saw a bird dog that morning. He was all that Gabe had reported—but Gabe hadn't reported all. He found all the birds on the course and refound them for good measure. He made his brace-mate look like slow motion in reverse. As for manners, no judge could require better. Rance handled him well, and the dog handled kindly. I knew then, as did every other owner, what dog we had to beat. And to tell the truth, George, I doubted if he could be beaten.

"At the end of the heat Judy asked me what I thought, and I must confess that I was just nasty enough to tell her that her dog was by all odds the better of the brace. I wasn't exuberantly happy.

"But I am happy to tell you that when Bright Tomorrow was put down she rose to the challenge and ran the greatest race of her life. She is a bird-wise old dog, and she can tell the time of day. She knows more about a quail than a quail's papa. She headed for cover, and she laid with it. She made her finds brilliantly, she was wide enough to suit any judge, her manners were perfection, and she finished going away. It was the race she had been bred and trained for, and old Gabe turned out a swell job of handling. But was it good enough? Honestly, I didn't know.

"Neither did the judges. When at last all braces had been run, the judges went into a prolonged huddle and came out with the announcement of a second series—Double Dare against Bright Tomorrow. It meant, of course, that the run-off would be held the following morning. Good! At least things were equal all around. I tell you, I was feeling better.

"We were on the line at seven the next morning. All but Judy. She was there at 7:10—another nicely timed entrance. And what an entrance! She was in a brand-new turn-out—at least I had never seen it before. But when you put a chestnut-haired woman in a forest-green riding habit, and then top off the whole with a jaunty Alpine hat with a cocky bright feather, anyone is bound to notice. At least I did. And it seems odd, but for the first time in my life I noticed how lithely at home she was in the saddle. Most women ride clumsy, but not Judy.

"Have you ever seen small cloud shadows race across a field on a blue-blowy May day? Well, that's the way that brace went when we cut 'em loose. Stride in stride, headed for cover. It was a pair of dogs, I tell you. And for once with Gabe and Rance handling, Judy and I were merely out for a ride. But what a ride!

Bright Tomorrow was the first to lock up on a covey. Lofty, head high, statuesque, she was in great form. Double Dare came charging in. Now, I thought, we shall see about that fudging that Judy had reported. Doubtless this was precisely what the judges wished to see, since neither dog, in their first braces, had done any honoring; they had done all the finding.

"Fudge my eye! Double Dare was as lofty and rigid as the finder herself. Had Judy been pulling my leg?

"When the dogs were sent away again, it was plain to see that Double Dare did not intend to spend the morning honoring. He really went away. That didn't bother me. I figured that sooner or later he would over-run his nose. But again I was wrong. He made two slashing finds in quick order, and then it was my bitch doing the backing. With dogs like that it is a waste of words to report on manners. Of course, both were steady to wing and shot.

"Then Bright Tomorrow stoked the fires, turned on the heat, and came back with two covey finds that were honeys. I tell you, George, we were seeing a race—a race for the books. It was what you writing fellows call high drama and suspense; it was what dog men live for. I give you my word that I completely forgot what the stakes really were.

"At last we came to a part of the course that held many possibilities for disaster. On the right a deep and heavily wooded ravine offered fine sanctuary for birds, but it was also a splendid place to lose a dog long enough to be declared out of judgment. Beyond the ravine was a piny wood, thicker than dog hair.

"It was here that Double Dare, again fed up with two consecutive honors, decided to go it alone. He headed for that deep ravine and piled into it like a fish-hawk going after an eel. Rance rode after him hard, but he made no effort to turn the dog at the cover line. It was bad handling—very bad. You couldn't see a dog in there, or find him if he were ringing a bell. Five minutes in that wilderness, and the dog would be ruled out of judgment. I didn't want to win that way—I'll give you my word I didn't. I made the only decent offer I could.

" 'If you'll permit me to handle Bright Tomorrow,' I said to Judy, 'I'll send Gabe over to help Rance scout for the dog.'

" 'That's nice of you, Jerry,' she replied, 'but Rance should have turned him. If he doesn't come out in the time limit, he'll simply be your dog, won't he? Then you can go look for him yourself.'

" 'Tommyrot!' I said. 'This is no time to be pig-headed,' and with that I ordered Gabe to ride after Rance.

"I took over Bright Tomorrow, and she hadn't gone far along the edge of the ravine when she nailed a single. Manners perfect again, of course. Then almost immediately, from deep in the ravine, though much further along, we heard old Gabe bawl, 'Po-int!'

"We rode along the edge of the ravine, peering in, trying to locate Gabe. Again we heard the long-drawn call of 'Po-int!' but this time it was Rance's voice. Finally we caught a glimpse of the two handlers, standing together, Rance with uplifted hand. But we couldn't see the dog, he was that tight in cover.

"You couldn't get a goat down that bank, much less a horse. The judges rolled out of their saddles, groaning. They had had three hard days of riding, and I assure you that judges are not as hard of seat as they are supposed to be of heart. Ask any judge.

"I sent Bright Tomorrow in, and we began our scramble down the steep bank. Then it happened. Judy slipped, went down in a heap, and slithered to the bottom. She tried to get up, but fell back again. She grimaced in pain and clutched at one of her ankles. Naturally, I hurried to her.

"She tried to wave me away. 'Go on to the dogs,' she ordered.

" 'But you're hurt,' I protested.

"With that lofty Dare manner—you know how she can be at times —she tilted her chin and said to the judges, 'Gentlemen, do me the favor of going to my dog. I'll be all right.'

"The judges obeyed reluctantly, but I've never been managed or bossed around by Judy Dare. No, sir! But don't tell Judy I said that! She might not understand.

"I kneeled beside her, but I couldn't do much. The riding boot prevented any examination, and Judy's pain likewise prevented its removal. 'I'll carry you out,' I said.

" 'You can't do it, Jerry. The bank is too steep.'

"It was steep, but something had to be done. I told her that if she would put one arm around my neck and hold tight while I picked her up. . . .

"Well, confound it, George, she did, and a wisp of that chestnut-colored hair blew across my face, and I sort of lost track of things—time, the world and everything. We'd better skip right up to the point where I heard one of the judges say: 'Ahem! I hope we do not intrude, and we regret to report that Double Dare just made a false point. Now you may continue.'

"I was still holding Judy up in my arms. She didn't seem a bit fussed. 'That's odd,' she said to the judges. 'Are you sure nothing was there?'

" 'Gabe and Rance were there,' Judge Watkins replied, 'and to me it did look a mite like the dog was pointing one or the other.'

" 'You see,' I stormed to Judy, 'I told you what might happen if Rance didn't stop that foolishness. He's made that dog over-cautious. The idiot!'

" 'Don't be in a peeve, darling,' Judy answered. 'You've won the old cup, and the money stake, and me, and my dogs—both setters and pointers—all in one day. What do you want out of a single race?'

"I sat down heavily. It was a sudden and overwhelming realization —positively overwhelming. Especially about the pointers!

" 'My gosh!' I moaned. 'I thought we were going out of dogs.'

" 'And so we are, dear'—Judy was sweet enough about it—'just as soon as we can mate Bright Tomorrow with Double Dare and see how the puppies turn out. I think it would be a wise mating.'

"Now, that is precisely the way it was—honestly. You can see for yourself how it happened. What's that you say? Oh, yes, the ankle. Well, sir, Judy is a hardy girl, and she made a surprisingly rapid recovery. With a little help she even managed to hobble out of that ravine. Plucky of her. And yet, you know, George, sometimes I wonder. . . ."

That's Jerry's story. Not mine, mark you, but Jerry's. Sometimes I wonder too. But not about the same thing. I'm wondering if I will ever get that pup. If I do, I shall name it "Finesse."

But for heavens sake, don't tell Judy! She might not understand.

Brindle Cow

By BUD JACKSON

ALL DURING THE DAY I HAD BEEN IMPATIENT FOR SCHOOL TO be out that I might get home. There was a watchful silence in the early fall air, as though the sere hills and the columns of trees that marched across them here and there were waiting for the season to change. But my patience did not match theirs.

For I was nine—that very day. Nine years old. Looking back to it now, nearly a quarter of a century later, I find a veritable jumble of confused impressions, chief of which is the recollection of the vein of happy anticipation that runs through the thoughts of any normal child on his natal day. I had watched the crawling clock on the schoolhouse wall and trembled impatiently through the snail hours until last bell. I knew that, at home, as in any home, however small or unpretentious, the great day would be properly feted.

At last came the welcome clang of the bell that freed the army of eager feet, none more quick than mine in the dusty road that led to our house on the bald hill behind town. It was late August (school started early in our small agricultural community—still does) and warm.

I was panting when I came to the stile across our pasture fence and legged it on up the long hill to the house. No one was astir, but with the wisdom of nine I was not fooled. Dave, my older brother, lagged far behind as I grasped the knob to the back door, having remembered in time that dusty feet came in *only* through the kitchen, and opened it on a smiling father, a gentle mother, a loving, chubby little sister.

For a second my eyes grappled with the dimness of the small kitchen after the brilliance of the light outside in the pasture. Then, in their groping, they found what they sought and I stood, a tongue-tied small boy, in the presence of a great moment.

On the table lay my birthday gift and, shyly, half-embarrassed, I scanned it, length and breadth, before reaching out a hesitant hand. That shattered the spell and the shouts of "Happy birthday," "Happy birthday," from Dad and Mom and the chubby four-year-old, and Dave's belated "Birthday" from the door, broke around my shoulders.

On the table lay a fly rod, its burnished, shining length set off by a new nickled reel, attached to its butt! And flies—a dozen of them, spilling in glittering profusion from the little packet in which they'd come! A few bass bugs, a quartet of shiny spinners, a coil of leader, and, yes, new line on the reel.

The sparkle to them was almost more than my eyes could hold, as I caught the rod. Many, many times I had, under Dad's speculating eyes, handled his own carefully preserved fly rod. I had not begged for its use. It was all he had and I sensed somehow, even then, that I hadn't the right to use it.

But now, my own fishing rod sprang alive in my hand, the tip springy and strong, the mid-section resilient but well-backboned, the butt comfortingly solid but still giving with the play of my hand.

"Tomorrow," said Dad quietly, "we'll go fishing."

Tomorrow would be Saturday—a full day, free of school worries. But tomorrow was yet years away and there was still light today, and instantly I came to think of the rock quarry. As though he had read my heart, my daddy's gray eyes reached flickeringly into mine and he said: "Better put it away for now."

A half mile behind our house lay an old pit, a rock quarry, abandoned when the workmen opened a spring beneath the rocks. That spring had filled the pit to overflowing and sent water spilling down through the big meadow into Salt Fork Creek south of town. In years past, fish had come up out of the creek into the quarry. We often had fished there and, on rare occasions, had brought out good catches of bass, sunfish and crappies.

But there was one inviolable rule at our house. We children were never to go to the pit unaccompanied by either Dad or Mom. The quarry was deep—how deep we didn't know. And danger lay in the caving edges. Teetering rocks lay carelessly tumbled about there, ready to plunge crashing down at a mere sneeze.

To go to the gravel pit—the quarry—meant but one thing, a good hiding, when I was found out. Besides, my day's end job, as always, was fetching Brownie, our old brindle cow of jersey leanings, which obstinately roamed the heavily wooded, 80-acre patch behind our house. The old witch favored a tactic which frequently nettled me unreasonably. She always seemed to know I was coming before I got there. And she'd stop stockstill, her cud quiet beneath her tongue, not even an ear or her tail flicking to give her post away. Many, many times my supper grew cold while I looked for Brownie. And until Brownie was fetched to the barnyard I got no supper!

I gripped tighter the new rod in my hand, and glanced again at the treasure that lay on the kitchen table. In that instant Brownie lost— and the rock quarry won. Sweeping up the hoard, I turned toward Dave's and my room. Once there, I closed the door, stepped quickly to the window, thrust the rod through it into the lilac bushes outside, put flies, leader, spinners, bugs into my overall pocket, then climbed out.

Five minutes later I skirted the shoulder of the hill behind the house with wary eye on the kitchen, then, with trees between the house and me, turned angling toward the quarry pit.

Memory fans into quickness again the delight with which I sighted those clear waters. I went to the shallower side of the great gouge in the hillside, knelt, and immediately became absorbed in mastering the task of attaching leader to line. That goal achieved, I fastened on a small spinner, and then a black gnat. With no one to watch, I shook line out through the guides and began to cast.

For a little time it was enough to toy with the rod, to be satisfied merely with fishing, without thinking about the possibility of catching anything. Then a cruising green sunfish (he was a black perch to me then) boiled from beneath a huge boulder at the pit's edge, smashed the gnat, then turned, angling, back toward his nest. The rod's smart, brown length became a sudden slender arc in the fading sun.

I checked that first angry run, overcame the second as rod tip toe-danced on the water, then confidently brought the fish around to my feet. From one pocket of my jeans, amongst an assortment of shiny nails, a broken watch, bits of colored glass, a taw marble, a rabbit's foot and other miscellany, I untangled a short length of grocer's twine.

Seconds later the sunfish, strung, fanned the crystal water beside the rock that had been his home. I watched him intently. For a full minute he lay quietly, ignoring the string through his gill and mouth. Then, like a dog who by burying his chain pretends he is no longer tied, he dashed suddenly for the green depths. But he snubbed up abruptly when he reached the end of the slack.

On the other side of the pit a loud splash now cried for attention. Against the deep, shaded west wall of the quarry, a widening ring on the surface of dark water betokened the presence of a good fish. He had risen to nail a cricket or a grasshopper, perhaps, and he could only be a bass, I thought, as the heavy wavelets of his wake washed the damp rock wall.

Decision in my heart, I clutched the rod. But, how to reach him? The distance was much too far for a cast—at least for any cast of mine. In the center of the pool lay a possible answer. Where the south bank had sometime caved lay a cluster of great rocks extending a foot above the surface of the pool to form a tiny island. The deeper water lay between that island and the west bank, but the part between the island and me was deep enough. Still, if I could get to those rocks.

My overalls and blue shirt fell in a tumbled heap as I wriggled free of them. Then, as mother-naked as the day I first saw light, and with the precious rod held above my head, I waded toward the rocks—and made them! The water, at its deepest point, came just to my chin. It was icy, and I shivered as I crawled wetly upon the little mound of rocks.

Standing there, I measured the distance to the spot where the fish had boiled. The sun was gone from me here. The long shadows reached nearly across the quarry from the towering bank to the west. I got out line, a little at first, then more. The first cast was yards short. I knew nothing then of "shooting" a line, so I peeled a little more off my reel as I lifted the rod for the backcast. The fourth cast, shot forth with all my chattering strength, dropped the fly, as lightly as any thistledown, in the exact spot where I wished it to be.

In that instant something smashed it with a savagery and a decision that literally frightened a cry of alarm from my blue lips, while the goose-bumps pimpled my bare hide. Setting the hook was instinct, I suppose, and the fish, stung to sharp anger, drove deep. Quicksilver drops of spray hung suspended in the air behind him, as the new rod bent like a reed in a gale, while the line slipped through my fingers and cut the water. Down, down, down he went, until my anxious heart tapped in my throat and my pulse pounded like a piston.

Suddenly, deliberately, he stopped and lay sulking, so still that I thought at first he must be free. But when I tightened the line he still was there and I gathered my baby strength for the battle I knew was to come. With a confidence born of the play of the new rod itself, I forced that fight by prodding the fish with a quick lift of the rod.

This declaration of war moved him in a fashion for which I had not bargained. Swift as an arrow he surged along the wall of the high bluff, then slanted upward with a rush that carried him a good two feet clear of the water, where he hung for a thin fraction of a instant, his gills flared to show the angry red, his jaw set, his eyes glaring. The following run I checked with difficulty and again he took to the air, this time shaking his head savagely and tail-walking across a yard of water before falling with a crash and a swirl back into the depths.

Surprisingly, I took a little line from him, but it was a minor concession on his part as he turned leisurely, like a hound on a leash, and swept regally past me, only a few feet away. A movement of my hand sent him surging down against the trembling strength of the rod, then up he came in another mighty leap, rocketing crazily out of water. Again he smashed for freedom, fighting for the sky while I stood helpless and half-frightened.

The memory of those few minutes when the fish repeatedly summoned his strength to lift himself clear of the water never comes back to me without my feeling some scorn for so many of our modern-day experts (who ought to know better) who contend, seriously, that the smallmouthed bass is not a jumper!

At last, after another of those frenzied trips into the air, he fell back heavily and lay for an instant, tiredly, on his side. And all at once, amazingly, it was over. I put steady pressure on him with the rod and he came to me, weaving from side to side, but coming still. With one brown arm I reached for the spot where he lay near my feet, got a thumb in his mouth, closed the fingers down and hefted him out, wriggling, still willing to fight, but spent.

I realized suddenly that the sun was down and it was twilight. The black water between the little pile of blue clothing on the shallow bank and my island looked somehow menacing. But with rod in one hand, fish in the other, I dared it with all the lip-quivering courage of nine.

The sunfish, once I'd slipped into my clothes, I found still fighting the grocer's string and, in magnanimity, without ever releasing my hold on the bass, I freed the little fellow and watched him race into the deep. Then, picking up my fly rod, I started up the hill toward home. As I did, Dad's breeze-borne whistle reached my ears: "Whee-whee-whooo-ee-e-e-e. Whee! Whee!"

That was *my* whistle. One "Whee" was for Dave, the oldest, two were for me, three for Sister Lucille.

Again it shrilled down across the meadow in the gathering gloom, as I shagged it for home. The licking would be waiting, I knew, but somehow I didn't care. Dad had put the lantern atop the barnyard gatepost, a sure sign of worry and anger. And when I puffed up to the gate, he came forward from the deep shadows next to the barn, a switch of lilac tapping impatiently against his strongly-calved leg. His voice literally took me up by the nape of the neck and shook me.

"*Where* have you been?"

It was in that instant that his eyes fell on the fish which, tail dragging in the dust, I carried by the gill. My father's eyes, black in the lantern light, widened, and I was spared the need of answering his first question by a second.

"Where did you get that—the rock quarry?"

I nodded, submissively.

"In heaven's name!"

He dropped to his knees there in the dirt and grime of our barnyard, reaching for the fish, while I discreetly kept my silence.

He examined the fish, talking softly, almost to himself.

"A smallmouth, eh? Mmmm-hmmmm! And on what? A spinner and fly, likely. Good heavens, he must weigh all of 4½ pounds. Mmmmmm. Fat and healthy, too."

Swiftly then he rose to his feet and one huge arm dropped companionably across my shoulders.

"Let's go show your mother," he said, and there was in his voice a softness, a pride, that brings tears to my lashes yet.

The warm, friendly rectangle of light from the kitchen window drew us as a magnet. Mom, smiling that serene smile, exhibited the expected amazement and approbation, then withdrew, still smiling a little secret smile, as though she knew this was man's business. We knelt on her new linoleum floor (itself a brag-thing in those days) and sullied it with ourselves and our fish, conducting a minute examination that could wait no longer.

The scales were got down from the kitchen cabinet and we waited eagerly for the nervous needle to stop its quivering. Four pounds, two ounces! There was awe in Dad's voice.

"I have never caught one that big!"

Together we opened him, investigating every fascinating thing about him. His stomach yielded two huge grasshoppers and a great-clawed crayfish. Dad pointed out to me with his knife blade the organs which identified the smallmouth's sex as male, cut away the heart and showed it, still throbbing, to me.

Then he showed me how to fillet the fish. I saw the huge, still-defiant head cut away, the bronze skin peeled away from the heavy layers of white meat. The job done, we tucked away the fillets in a great stone crock on the back porch. We'd have them for breakfast. Pointing to the fish's head, my father said:

"If you'll wrap that up in cloth and save it, I'll show you tomorrow how to clean and cure it for mounting."

Then:

"Mother will have your dinner on the back of the stove. I've got to get back to the chores."

There was warm meat pie on the back of the stove, fragrant, fresh country bread in the oven. Beneath the dish towel spread on the table were my plate, a bowl of beans dripping bacon fat, rich country butter, homemade pear marmalade, a huge boiled potato, and a pitcher of thick Jersey milk.

The milk made me think of Brownie. But first things first, and I fell to eating. Then I found myself suddenly in bed, sleepy, incredibly tired. Dimly I remember Mother coming to tuck me in before I slipped into oblivion.

It was not until 15 years later to the very day that I found out the rest of the story of that day—my ninth birthday.

I was then 24. I had come in from my work—in a city far removed from the quiet little house on the bald hill—to find a birthday dinner on the table and a lovely silken muffler, wrapped in spotless tissue, at my plate.

Dad, his kind gray eyes the same, even though the shock of black hair long had gone, looked up from his paper to say: "Happy birthday, son!"

Mom's gentle voice said it in almost the same instant and, somehow, my mind swept back across those 15 years to the towheaded little fellow of nine who stood barefoot and dusty in a small kitchen, gazing unbelievingly at some fishing tackle, while cries of "Happy birthday" echoed through the room.

Dad bowed his head and said the simple blessing that has prefaced every meal I ever ate in my father's house. And then we talked.

"The best birthday of all," I said, "was when I was nine."

Mom looked me level in the eyes.

"Did you ever wonder how Brownie got home that night so many years ago?" she said. "The day you were nine, and caught the big bass? Did you?"

I shook my head, confessing that I hadn't.

She looked at Dad, her eyes soft with reminiscence.

"Your father," she said, simply, looking straight at him. "At midnight that night he drove her into the barnyard, and milked her. You never knew!"

Could any man have failed, with initiation like that, to be a fisherman?

The Stork and the Pintail

By IRA BRIGHT

AUNT FANNIE HAD OFTEN SOUGHT MY PROFESSIONAL ADVICE RE-garding the health of her numerous grandchildren. She usually had in custody the particular offender who happened to be ailing and would shuffle into the office, pushing the reluctant patient before her. The impression was given that it was due to pure cussedness amounting to nothing less than a downright reflection on Aunt Fannie's personal integrity, as well as the efficacy of her home remedies, that any child under her care would get sick enough to need a doctor.

And so it was with some surprise, one December morning, that I received her unaccompanied by any of her responsibilities. After the usual respectful inquiries concerning my health and that of my family, she came to the business in hand.

"Doctah, I'se got er friend whut's gwi' have er visit wid de stork, an' us want you to take de case. Cose you knows I'se er ol' han' at dat bizness, an' I'se gwi' be dar to help wid de 'rangements."

There had not been a birth within five miles of Aunt Fannie at which she failed to be among those officiating. Also, she had nine children of her own; so I readily agreed that she certainly had more than a passing acquaintance with the stork and assured her of my pleasure over the prospect of her able assistance.

A somewhat detailed discussion of her friend's complaints followed. Also, a searching analysis of just how Aunt Fannie knew when to expect the happy event. These matters settled, apparently to her satisfaction, she finally gathered the various bundles and well-filled paper bags from around her chair in preparation for departure. Then, pausing in the doorway for a moment, Aunt Fannie diplomatically clinched the deal.

"Den if hit's all right wid you, Doctah, Sally gwi' come see you nex' Sat'day."

A week of heavy winter rains followed which resulted in washed-out bridges and impassable plantation roads. Sally's visit to the office failed to materialize and had been forgotten in a rush of work when a telephone call at two o'clock one cold, rainy morning served to refresh my memory. The humming and crackling which came in over the wire warned me that I was talking over a county line and that connections might cease at any moment.

"Doc, that you?" came in faintly.

I assured whoever it was that this was Doc, though I am afraid I did not sound at all enthusiastic about it.

"This is Chaney out at Racetrack Plantation. You remember Sally Brown old Aunt Fannie came to see you about?"

I said I could never forget Aunt Fannie, but had yet to have the pleasure of making Sally's acquaintance, although I remembered her troubles with the stork.

"Well, Sally's husband is up here at the big house and says Aunt Fannie needs you on the stork deal. You can drive your car to the commissary, and I'll have old Nick meet you in the truck."

I told him it was certainly a proper and fitting night during which to meet old Nick and that I would be there. Before the stork, I hoped.

"Say! Aren't you a duck hunter?" he added casually, as if the matter were not very important.

"Sure am! Why?" Chaney and I had shot quail together on Racetrack Plantation, of which he was manager, but we had never discussed ducks.

"Well, we got those old brakes we hunted birds in last year cleaned up and drained with tiles into the river. The main tiles are stopped up, and Clarence says all the brakes are full of water and some kind of ducks."

"What kind of ducks?" I inquired, trying hard not to give the impression of having become suddenly so genial over the prospect of a night call.

"Clarence don't know. Says he never saw any like them before. Why don't you bring your gun and see for yourself? You have to go near there anyway. Maybe a duck hunt will improve your disposition."

"Never mind about my disposition," I said, still trying not to sound too pleased over the ducks. "I'll be at the commissary in an hour."

On a large Southern cotton plantation the commissary is like the general store on a country crossroads, everything from lemonsnaps to brogans being carried in stock. In addition, it often contains the plantation owner's office, where settlements are made each fall and the weekly Saturday business is negotiated. On such occasions it is surrounded by laughing, talking negroes.

When I drove between the two oak trees standing in front of the commissary porch, I saw a lone negro sitting with his back against the wall. His presence there made the place seem somehow doubly deserted. I strongly suspected that he had been asleep, but before the car came to a stop he had gotten up and was ambling out to meet me, hat in hand, his black face, beaming in the glare of the headlights.

"Dat you, Doctah?"

"Clarence?"

"Yassuh."

I was certain I had recognized him. "I thought old Nick would be here to go with me," I said as I got out of the car and began unloading gun, shells and medical bags.

"Naw, suh, he at town visitin' wid his boy. Mist' Rainey don' sont me 'stead er him anyhow 'cause I'se de one whut see de ducks."

I thought it best not to go into the logic of this statement, but busied myself helping Clarence load our equipment in the truck.

We drove off between the commissary and the cotton gin, swerving around a wagon still half filled with cotton and covered by a tarpaulin. Then we bounced around the corner of the gin and headed out down a plantation dirt road.

It was turning colder, but I was so fascinated by Clarence's truck driving and the possibility of getting stuck in each of many mud holes we passed through that the falling temperature completely escaped my notice. When we reached the ridge road, the tires began to catch on good, sandy loam. I took a deep breath, settled back and began once more to wonder about those ducks.

"Clarence, what kind of ducks were those you saw?" Clarence was a highly successful squirrel and rabbit hunter, but I was uncertain about his knowledge of ducks.

"I doan' 'zactly know, but dey's some er dem green, mallet-headed ducks runs wid 'em." To Clarence and many of his kind a mallard drake was a "mallet-headed" duck—"green" sometimes being added. "Dey got long necks an' tails whut come to er p'int. Some er dey breasts is white. Dem ducks flies sort er lady-like an' kinda whistles."

I was thinking that here was what could be called a description of the pintail duck when Clarence pulled off the road onto a bare patch of ground, turned off the motor and lights and admonished a barking dog running about the truck to be quiet. I could not see a house, but judged one to be somewhere near by, for the air was laden with the fragrance of wood smoke.

As I got out of the truck a door some seventy feet to my right swung wide. A negro woman stepped out on the porch of a cabin, and firelight from the log fire inside transformed her into a flickering silhouette.

"Hyar de doctah now," she said over her shoulder to someone.

"Aunt Fannie?" I called.

"Yassuh, dis me."

Clarence and I started toward the cabin. By the aid of my flashlight we made our way through the yard and climbed the high steps leading on to the porch. Clarence carried my bags to the door and carefully turned them over to Aunt Fannie, then made a hasty retreat around the rear of the cabin to the warm kitchen. It was plain to see that he was not interested in the further practice of obstetrics. Aunt Fannie and I entered a small room, and the wind rattled a window somewhere in the cabin as she closed the door behind us. I followed her across the firelit room to the bedside of my patient.

When I returned to the porch several hours later, the wail of a baby girl new to this world filled my ears. Aunt Fannie had followed me outside.

"Dat's sho' er fine, fat baby!" she said with satisfaction, her tone somehow implying that she and I were solely responsible for its weight of eight pounds. "Doctah," she added, "ah bet you sho' is hungry after all dat work an' it dis close to breakfus'. You got to eat some breakfus' 'fo' you goes huntin'!"

Before I had time to agree with her on the state of my appetite, she was headed for the kitchen, where Clarence and I soon had a regular country "breakfus'" spread before us. Later I changed to my shooting clothes while Clarence borrowed an aged double gun with hammers from Sally's dazed husband.

A home-made weather-vane on top its pole in the yard was creaking softly in the north wind when we left the house. There was just light enough to see our way across cotton rows and ditches. After a short walk we came to the crest of a slight ridge. The ridge sloped gently down before us to the edge of a long and fairly wide body of water. Clarence stopped and eased the sack of decoys to the ground. There was no sound save the faint, soft rustling of leaves on near-by corn-stalks.

We stood and watched the heavy cloud bank in the east turn to pure gold and a deep red glow spread over the still surface of the water. Clarence coughed and started to speak, but said nothing as the roar of wings came to us across the wind. In a few moments the rush and whisper of wings moved closer, and seven pintails passed over against a crimson sky.

"Dat's dem," Clarence whispered. "Hear 'em whistlin' at us?"

From somewhere in the east a mallard hen hailed the coming day and a chorus behind us answered her. I began to wonder if there were more mallards than pintails.

"Clarence, where can I hide? Is this the best place?"

"Yas, suh, dis er good place. Dey uses in some er dese other ol' brakes, but I'se gwi' walk erbout an' run 'em out." He paused and then went on somewhat apologetically. "Dey's er hollow stump 'cross de brake." I gathered that having to suggest that his guest ensconce himself in a hollow stump caused Clarence some embarrassment. He seemed relieved when I suggested we go see what the stump had to offer.

We waded the pond without seeing another bird and examined the stump. It stood at the water's edge on the south side of the brake and was hollow down to the ground, which formed a muddy floor. Inside, it was easily four feet in diameter, and when I stood erect the rim struck me about right, coming not quite up to my shoulders. On the whole, it gave promise of being an ideal blind except for the all-important wind. When the decoys were out, they would be up-wind. I knew that some men preferred this arrangement for goose shooting, but this would be my first attempt of the sort with ducks, and I shuddered as I thought of what some of my duck-shooting friends would have to say if they caught me with such a decoy set-up on an open, wind-swept pond.

At any rate, it seemed to be this or nothing, as the banks were as clean as a lawn as far as we could see save for a few scattered corn-stalks. There was nothing with which to dig a pit. We might have scraped together enough corn-stalks, but time was pressing, as I was due back in the office that morning. By liberal use of the call and taking circling ducks, I felt I could at least get some shooting.

Clarence assisted in placing the decoys to my satisfaction, borrowed a box of shells to add to his meager supply and then started off on his rounds of the other ponds. I climbed into the stump, meanwhile making a resolution that I would always carry a small, light spade on similar trips and thus be prepared for digging pits when the need arose.

The light was good by then, and the entire length of the pond was visible. Not over three hundred yards long nor over eighty yards wide and running roughly east and west, it had once been a swampy brake with gradually sloping banks. It was one of a chain of such depressions, or low brakes, which marked a former course of the Tallahatchie River. Having been cleared of its cypress, tupelo gum and undergrowth and drained by an underground system of tile pipes into the river, this particular brake had been planted in corn and soy-beans. With the usual richness of soil of newly cleared ground it had also produced a luxuriant growth of grasses. Along the bank near the blind I noticed some scattered patches of smart-weed.

I was on the point of looking about further when three teal sneaked up on me from behind. They buzzed by to my right, banked against the wind like giant bumblebees and started up the pond. I swung rapidly with them, striving to get those gun barrels ahead. The last two birds fell in the middle of the pond, and I tried once more for the lead bird with the other barrel, but missed him again. In spite of the two teal floating on the water, I felt sheepish. Twenty years a gunner and still shooting behind! I had to admit that bagging those two had been purely accidental.

My spirits were quickly revived, however, by the sight of ducks flying toward me out of the north. Flight appeared effortless as they rode down the wind stream. Their fifteen trim, slender bodies and manner of flight made it plain that they were pintails and interested in the pond and decoys. I let them pass over. Then a loud hail on the call hastened their decision to make a return trip. They veered to the southwest and began a wide circle. It looked as though they were going to come in directly over me.

I decided to try them if they were not too high, but I had very little confidence in that decoy set-up. The white breasts and other markings of the drakes, seen distinctly in the early light, indicated clearly that they were in range. I guessed at thirty yards, yet could have sworn they were nearly fifty. Overhead ducks always seem so much higher than they actually are.

In this uncertain state of mind I picked out the rear bird and left the rest to past experience. The sixes caught him dead-center, and with a surge of increased confidence the second barrel took a flaring, climbing hen.

Wading out in the knee-deep water, I inserted pointed stakes made out of heavy wire under the skin of the breasts and necks of my four ducks and staked them out as additional decoys. I had formed the habit of carrying six of these wire stakes, three feet long, in a tubular container of nearly semi-circular shape for ease in packing in the decoy sack or bottom of a boat. The pliable wire stakes were easily bent to proper shape when placed in the case or when in use.

While thus engaged I wondered when, if ever, I was going to learn to judge the height of overhead ducks and feel confident that I was correct. In timber shooting with tree heights to go by it was easier, but the open marsh was a different matter. In view of the absence of trees on my pond, I decided that I could at least experiment with the more exact judgment of horizontal distances. Having heard of the procedure, I paced off a spot forty yards from the blind as accurately as I could, and there I stuck a slender pole about five feet high which I had cut from a willow sprout near my stump. I could not find material for other poles; so I had to be content with this one, which was in the approximate middle of the pond and straight out beyond the farthest decoy.

As is usually the case when placing or rearranging decoys, several pintails had passed and caught me standing in the open water. Two shots from Clarence across the ridge hastened my trip back to the stump. In short order the air was full of pintails circling and beating up and down the pond. I watched them closely—and their relation to my stake. None seemed anxious to decoy, and all were too high. They were evidently still mindful of Clarence's shooting.

After considerable calling, I coaxed two drakes and a hen to drop to a lower level. They finally headed up the pond at what I took to be a height of twenty-five yards and passed just beyond the willow pole. They looked easy over the gun muzzle, but nevertheless I felt better about judging distance after making a double.

As the morning wore on the wind died completely in favor of a clear, cold day with an almost cloudless blue sky. Then my willow pole and the heavier loads came into interesting and instructive use as more birds passed up and down the pond. That pole certainly served to confirm an opinion in which most wildfowlers will concur: that crossing ducks flying rather low often seem closer than they are, while overhead incoming ducks usually seem higher than they are.

The changing lights and shadows on the water caused the distance from my stump to the willow pole to seem close at times. Then again it seemed much farther. It was wonderful shooting I enjoyed as the pintails returned in twos and threes or larger droves. I could have sworn there was no wind, but occasionally a pair or more would swing in from the north and circle back as they had done earlier in the morning, causing me to turn and take my shots on incoming birds. If I let them pass over, they showed a tendency to alight beyond the decoys near the north bank of my pond and out of range when flushed.

It was with regret that I checked on the time and realized I must leave for the office. I whistled for Clarence and climbed out of the old stump to begin gathering the blocks and my ducks. Clarence turned up in a few minutes with a pintail and two rabbits. I had heard him shoot only three or four times and guessed that he had taken no chances on flying ducks, as he wanted to make the shells I had given him last through the Christmas holidays and the frequent plantation rabbit hunts.

The rabbits must have been collected while sitting, as Clarence, in common with his brethren, had a sharp eye for game. I think he had experienced considerable difficulty in sneaking up on more than one sitting duck, as the clean banks of those ponds certainly did not afford cover. At any rate, he would have a whole box of shells left for rabbits Christmas week.

"Doctah," he said as he waded out and began to help me take up the decoys, "you sho' got after dem ducks!"

I agreed with him that I had frequently been after them—in fact, was very often away behind them.

Clarence and I were both in high good spirits when we finished our walk back to the truck. Aunt Fannie was standing on the cabin steps when we arrived.

"Doctah," she said, "I knowed you gwi' get some er dem ducks. Dey sho' is plentiful." The thought occurred to me with a twinge that it was certainly a plenitude of ducks that had made up for the misses. "Whut kind er ducks is dey?" she asked.

"Pintails, Aunt Fannie," I said.

"Sho' 'nuff, Doctah? Dey sho' is pretty!"

"They sure are, Aunt Fannie. The pintail is one of the world's most beautiful ducks. And his beauty is surpassed only by his gracefulness." Still feeling in fine humor, I was inclined to joke Aunt Fannie a bit. "This duck is known to the ornithologist as *Dafila acuta tzitzihoa*," I added. Aunt Fannie looked puzzled. "Whut's dat word you say, Doctah?" she inquired. "Dat doctah word?"

I knew what she meant. "*Dafila acuta tzitzihoa*," I repeated. "That's what the men who study about birds named this duck."

"Dat's sho' er pretty name," Aunt Fannie said, frank admiration in her eyes.

I forgot the entire matter until the ducks were packed safely away in the truck and I had made a last examination of Sally and her new baby girl. Seated in the truck, we were ready to leave when Aunt Fannie sidled up to the open window. "Doctah, I wants you to write dat name on er piece er dis paper."

Feeling flattered and rather self-satisfied over stirring Aunt Fannie's interest in ornithology, I carefully printed "Dafila acuta tzitzihoa" on her piece of tablet paper in large simple letters.

Several days later, as I sat in the office, the sound of the north wind whispering over the rim of that old stump and the way those pintails looked against the morning sky came back to me as I opened a letter from the County Health Office and took out a neatly folded birth certificate ready for my signature. Sally Brown on Racetrack Plantation had registered the birth of her baby girl, born that windy December morning. And it was easy to recognize the fine touch of Aunt

Fannie's when I looked at the baby's name, typed out in full black letters on the certificate before me: "Dafila Acuta Tzitzihoa Brown, born to Sally Brown. . . ."

Certainly the stork and the pintail worked well together that morning!

Odd Bedfellows

By WILFRED S. BRONSON

FOR YEARS, LIKE MANY A NATURE STUDENT, I HAVE KEPT NOTEBOOKS filled with detailed dated data. Recently I have been reading, for the first time, in the Nature notebooks of Thoreau. It is fun to compare his written thoughts on wood frogs, accumulating over several springs, with entries of my own.

In thus turning to the 19th Century, one is reminded of how much more the classics counted then in the thinking of an educated man than they do today. I had to turn much farther back, to 405 B.C., really to understand one reference of Thoreau's regarding frogs. And so, in studying *The Frogs* by Aristophanes, I gleaned yet another writer's thoughts about these animals, for even more comparing.

This comparison makes the oddest bedfellows of Aristophanes, Thoreau, and me, and it is drawn, not with any notion that my own crude scrivening has a place, as such, beside the work of the great Greek humorist and playwright, or beside unplayful, humorless Thoreau's, but only as one may compare the qualities of Pentelican marble, Plymouth Rock, and shale. Conditioned as each was by the age in which he wrote, uninfluenced by the others, what were our several reactions on observing frogs?

Differences of course there are, but, in our recording of the voices of frogs at least, some striking similarities. Our efforts are often complementary. Sharp scientific accuracy, unimportant to the poet of old, is achieved by the 19th Century philosopher—up to a point. And where Thoreau's pen may have been halted by the properties of his time and place of writing, the quill of Aristophanes has been considered over-free in many a line, even in our day. But, less free than Aristophanes and less fastidious than Thoreau, I shall, in this 20th Century, attempt to tell not only of voices, but "more that can be told" concerning wood frogs in the spring.

Of course, Aristophanes never heard the flat, dry cackling of the American wood frog, *Rana sylvatica*, although some Mediterranean species may have an almost identical voice. Compared to the green frog's "Dunk, dunk, dunk," or the bull frog's "Rum, more rum," the wood frog's cry sounds very dry. So also did the frogs of ancient Athens, if we rely on Aristophanes, the English translator carefully preserving the sounds indicated by the Greek. Animal cries are difficult to describe or imitate in writing in any language. But note the surprising similarity between the imitation of frogs by Aristophanes, and a description of the wood frog's cry entered in my notebook several years ago. What I described on April 22, 1939, as a "rackety, ratchety, cackle, or quack," Aristophanes gave as "Brekeke-keks, co-ak, co-ak" in 405 B.C. The fact that, in his play, the frogs were in the Styx, and therefore croaking in Hell, would not account for the notable dryness of their voices, for the pagan Hell of ancient Greece was far from being a region of fire and brimstone only.

Only in a play would a choir of frogs taunt and defy a noisy, violent human being, let alone a god. Yet as some of the verses show, Aristophanes knew a good deal of actual frogly habits. So is it not reasonable to believe that, in writing a chant for them in the play, he also gave, as best he could, an approximation of their actual cries in the refrain? Although capable of talking back to Bacchus, the frogs continually repeat their "Brekeke-keks, co-ak, co-ak," much to his annoyance. Briefly, at the point in the plot where the frogs take a leading role, here is the situation. There is a temporary shortage of

good poets in Greece, and Bacchus takes upon himself the task of
going to Hell to bring one back to Athens. A very vulgar god, he is
ordered by Charon to row his own passage over the Styx, in a boat
inadequate for his blubbery bulk. Much discomforted by the un-
accustomed exercise, he seems to sense insult added to injury in the
voices of the frogs, and lashes out at them with tongue and oar.

> "Brekeke-keks, co-ak, co-ak."
>
> Bac. "Oh, the Frogs, consume and rot 'em,
> I've a blister on my bottom.
> Hold your tongues, you tuneful creatures!
>
> Frogs. Cease with your profane entreaties
> All in vain forever striving:
> Silence is against our natures.
> With the vernal heat reviving,
> Our aquatic crew repair
> From their periodic sleep,
> In the dark and chilly deep,
> To the cheerful upper air.
> Then we frolic here and there
> All amidst the meadows fair;
> Shady plants of asphodel,
> Are the lodges where we dwell;
> Chaunting in the leafy bowers
> All the livelong summer hours,
> Till the sudden gusty showers
> Send us headlong, helter, skelter,
> To the pool to seek for shelter;
> Meagre, eager, leaping, lunging,
> From the sedgy wharfage plunging
> To the tranquil depth below,
> There we muster all a-row;
> Where, secure from toil and trouble,
> With a tuneful hubble-bubble,
> Our symphonious accents flow.
> Brekeke-keks, co-ak, co-ak."

There is more, but this is plenty for the purpose of comparison.
Thoreau was much impressed with the dryness of the wood frog's
cry. Here are some of his notes on it, beginning with the one that
sent me studying Greek comedy.

"March 15, 1860. Am surprised to hear from the pool behind Lee's Cliff the croaking of the wood frogs.... Their note is somewhat in harmony with the rustling of the now drier leaves. It is more like the note of the classical frog as described by Aristophanes.

"March 23, 1853. A remarkable note with which to greet the new year, as if one's teeth slid off with a grating sound in cracking a nut." An English walnut probably would give the best approximation.

Another time he tries to imitate the sound in writing, but succeeds mainly, I think, in demonstrating the difficulty of doing this. It would read more dryly had he written "wurak or wu-ak." But he writes:

"March 24, 1859. Now when the leaves get to be dry and rustle under your feet, the peculiar dry note wurrk wurrk wurrrk wurk, of the wood frog is heard.... A singular sound ... associated with the first warmer days when you sit in some sheltered place in the woods amid dried leaves....

"He pitches and tunes his voice to chord with the rustling leaves which the March wind has dried....

"... A single dry hard croak, like a grating twig,... such is the earliest voice of the liquid pools, hard and dry and grating."

Still considering this quacking dryness in wetness, let me quote a few notes of my own.

"April 22, 1939. The combined quacking of the males makes a mighty racket. Each one, sounding somehow impatient after a winter's inactivity, keeps croaking his rackety, ratchety, cackle, or quack; and all this vocalizing, accompanied by the instrumental music of two spring waterfalls, plus the crash of heavy ice pillars collapsing into the pond from the quarry walls, creates a deafening din....

"April 13, 1938. I worked at the stone table in the sun. The frogs were very noisy, their voices sounding oddly dry, but with so many overtones and echoes in the quarry that half the time I was not sure that Sonia wasn't calling from the house below....

"March 29, 1938. They utter another sound today as well as those described above. It is simply a very short flat 'Ach!', higher pitched and louder than the other sounds." "Described above" refers to:

"March 25, 1938. A secondary sound, amidst what sounds to me like a million poaching eggs, is a sort of moan-groan, like somebody suffering from toothache." The ache of the frogs, of course, is closer in character to the pangs of love. Perhaps the "poaching egg" idea is fairly apt, for every quack is accompanied by a sudden bloating of the frog's throat and sides, as though he were impersonating a steam-blown bubble, and certainly eggs is the big idea the frogs are cooking up.

Referring back to the secondary "moan-groan" sound, let me quote Thoreau once more:

"April 3, 1853. There is not only the incessant lively croaking of many together, as usually heard, but a lower, hoarser, squirming kind of croak, perhaps from the other sex." Here is the only instance in which he shows that he knows sex has anything to do with the noisy conclave in the pool. Restraint is important in life and in art, though in science one should state everything. The sounds Thoreau so painstakingly described were merely the music to a wood frog wedding he was watching, the extraordinary, interesting, even at times amusing details of which he must have witnessed as regularly as I. Possibly, himself so unrequited in his human need for love, he was too like the numerous superfluous bachelor frogs, too altogether unfamiliar with success in love, to discuss even in his private records this part of Nature's plan.

But the inexorable fact of the matter is that in every frog there is enough of an ego needing the individual satisfaction of success in matrimony so that the species as a whole is ensured a future. Eggs laid in the water do get fertilized by sperms likewise liberated, turnkeys unlocking cells to free the lives imprisoned there through embryonic growth to hatching time. Although males clasp females, it is nonetheless a hit-or-miss performance except that, in the case of wood frogs, Nature makes more sure by producing every spring a vast majority of males, something like six or twelve or even more, to every female. The resulting polyandry presents a spectacle to astonish, but a scene varying from year to year only as the spring is late or early, and in the ratio of females, males, and supernumeraries.

"April Fool's Day, 1938. Wood frogs so far have laid a square yard of very black eggs. As I guessed, males outnumber females five or six to one. Every female I saw (some had gone, having dropped their responsibility) was straw color with brown markings, the males all very dark and purplish.

"Two terrible scrimmages, in one at least a dozen males all trying to embrace one female. She sank amongst those who actually had grasped her, a blonde beauty with swarthy suitors. Her body was strained back and how she could live I cannot see.

"April 21, 1939. I thought I saw something singular in the plurality of male wood frogs last year and the resulting polyandry due to the scarcity of females. But this year five purple-brown males clung to one big light tan female. She couldn't kick her legs at all but floated in apparent contentment, propelled in circles and figure eights by the spasmodic kicks of her beaux, first one, then another, then several together. Then they'd come to a full stop until one or another, unable to get a good grip with so much competition, would kick out again, futilely, except that it may have eased a mounting feeling of frustration.

There is always a long stag line at the Annual Wood Frogs' Wedding Ball, and much cutting in. Are the females aware of, and do they enjoy this popularity at all, each truly a belle of the ball surrounded by eligible males and certain of becoming a bride at last in instantaneous duplicate? Each is a belle, not only of the grand ball itself but of her own particular ball of consorts revolving around her. Whether or not she realizes and relishes her personal glory, it is hazardous. "Safety in numbers" does not here apply. In the midst of the melee she may suffer accidental injury and she may die, her ribless body stabbed by the too tightly pressing thumbs of one or more competing males.

"April 26, 1944. I found a female wood frog dead in the water, her chest punctured and eggs slowly oozing from the injury.

"April 27, 1944. I found another dead female wood frog, not punctured but possibly hugged to death, and she also had not lived long enough to lay. Then I spied a female with six males and scooped her with three of the males into a scap net. Out on the bank two let go immediately but one held on for several minutes. I removed him and he transferred his strong instinctive grip to my finger. 'Love is blind' and thoughtless here. 'Frog he would a'wooing go' whether you would distract him or no, 'Ko-ak' says Rana."

It is said that Aristophanes wrote The Frogs to distract men's minds from public affairs. Perhaps susceptibility to distraction is proportionate to a man's or animal's intelligence. The wood frog male under the influence of spring is almost nondistractable. The one public function he attends temporarily shuts out all other interests. But, as shown by his clasping my finger, he is a blunderer. For a moment he may grip a last year's cattail stalk or, as often happens, another male. Not the latter's quacks and efforts to break away, but the disappointing absence of a certain firm rotundity as of a gravid female, impels him finally to loose his hold to go on seeking blindly elsewhere.

This spring I found a gravid female spotted salamander, half dead from the unwelcome attentions of six or seven wood frogs. Rescue came too late. She must have been injured internally from frenzied clutching, for in a safe aquarium she grew rapidly enormous with gas till I had to finish her lest she burst.

The wood frogs' wedding winds up with enough eggs laid correctly to ensure an ample crop of tadpoles soon to swim. The frogs, all passion spent, turn to a life of leisure on the forest floor, tempestuous times behind them. No, all is not idyllic charm and sheer perfection in the woodland ponds in spring, although the drama that Thoreau most surely witnessed there is as important as the actors' lines that he transcribed. Act I at last is ended; Act I of the four-act play entitled "Spring, Summer, Fall, and Winter." Nature shifts the scene, more certain of a successful second act than even the great Aristophanes could ever be. But the wood frogs in the cast will not be back until, in its never-ending run, the drama is repeated.

Bruisers of the Weed Beds

By BEN EAST

THERE WAS AN EVEN YARD OF HIM IN LENGTH, LEAN AND STREAM-lined as a torpedo, and he weighed about 12 pounds. That's a lot of fish if it's put together right!

He took the red-and-silver wabbler at the edge of a patch of weeds, just beyond a waterlogged old birch-top a hundred feet from our boat. He smashed into it without hesitancy. The minute he saw it he had marked it for his own, and he wanted the world to know it. He hit the plug with everything in the book, and his emphatic smash telegraphed across a hundred feet of tight silk and five feet of arched steel and stabbed into my arm like a left to the chin.

We sparred for a minute, and I could feel the solid shock of his blows, one by one. Then, away out there by the birch-top, the water boiled in an angry swirl, and the rod bent like a bow. He was making for the weeds, and I knew it. I set my wrist and my will against him and turned him, caught him off balance and took ten yards of line away from him.

Then he stopped, threshing and fighting like a wild steer on a rope, and I gave part of the ten yards back. He detoured, and the silk cut a little wake through the water like a midget periscope. Feeling for the weeds once more, he went deep, sounding in a short, savage rush. Then he remembered the lair he had left, back there in the sunken birch, and tried for it, but the live steam was going out of him and I made him walk at heel again.

Grudging and sullen, he gave what line he had to, flared suddenly to the top and jumped, bent double like a living horseshoe and leaving an empty crater in the water where he came out, twisting and rolling to break the gut that had him fast. He smashed back and drove himself down toward the weeds again, but his punches had lost their power, and I held him and let the rod deal out its steady punishment.

A boat-length away he made his last-ditch stand, flailing in a welter of water. When I snubbed him up short, he streaked for the boat and went under it, but I dipped the rod tip to keep the line clear and led him back where I wanted him, foot by foot, until he rolled his belly up beside the boat, white as a flag of truce, and I knew I had him.

Muskalonge? No. Pike—great northern. A fish that packs brass knuckles on his jaws and a blackjack in his tail. Old Longnose, the bruiser of the weed beds. *Esox lucius*, the books call him. It ought to be Lucifer. There's a lot of hellfire and brimstone in his make-up.

Maybe you don't like him. Well, we'll have no quarrel on that score. It's every man's privilege to pick his friends and his favorites. But before you blast the bruiser wide open with a long burst of scorn and derision, let me ask you one honest question: have you fought him in good water, up in the country that gave him the name of "great northern"? Have you taken his measure, toe to toe in the center of the ring, in a way a game fish deserves to be tried?

Sure, he's no muskalonge. Nor Atlantic salmon, small-mouth bass or speckled trout. He's a pike, and no apologies are called for. The world is full of worse. His cousin, the muskie, is the big tiger. He's the little tiger, and guts aren't always measured by weight or by length.

Fishermen have known him for a long time, on both sides of the Atlantic, and mostly respected him wherever they came together. Old Izaak Walton is rated something of an authority, and he admired Longnose enough to devote an entire chapter to him. There's something in his make-up—in his lean and sinister shape, his gaping jaws, his endless hunger and murderous disposition—that has stirred the imagination of men as have few other fish. Somebody has said that more fantastic tales and plain lies have been told about the pike than about any other fish found in the fresh waters of the world, and the statement is likely true.

There was a pike somewhere in England, for example, that grew to be 19 feet long and weighed 350 pounds. Whoever started that rumor let his imagination bog down pretty badly on the weight. A pike 19 feet long would go better than a ton unless he had the general outlines of a python. There were other pike that swallowed dogs, one that made away with an infant child. One bit a boy's hand off, and still another "seized the foot of a young woman while she held it naked in a pond." Let's hope it taught her a lesson.

English anglers and the folk who lived by English streams took the bruiser seriously in the old days. They had some reason, if it comes to that, for at his best he reaches a length of 4 feet and a weight of 40 pounds. That's big for a fresh-water fish, but it doesn't account by itself for all the weird, outlandish tales they told of him. It was his manners, not his size, that gave him his early reputation.

Incidentally, the pike of those English rivers is the same one that inhabits the weed beds of Wisconsin lakes. *Esox* is a globe wanderer, a circumpolar fish, equally at home in the north of Europe, the north of Asia and the north of this continent. They named him well here in America when they called him the great northern.

They might with equal reason have called him the weed pike, as his dwarf kinsman that rarely exceeds a foot in length is known as the grass pike. The weed beds are his hang-out. What a brier patch is to a cottontail, weeds are to old Longnose. They shelter and feed him, hide him from his foes and give him cover when he hunts. He is rarely found far from them.

In the warm-water lakes in the south of his range, the big-mouth bass lakes, look for rushes and weed beds, and you will find pike if they are present at all. In the rivers, weeds waving in the current like fresh-water kelp mark his home precinct. In the cold rocky lakes of the North you waste your time trolling for him above the weedless reefs or in the black deeps. Seek out a bay, moderately shallow, and scout for weed beds if you hope to keep a rendezvous with the bruiser.

Some of the greatest pike fishing that has come my way I've had in Lake Superior. Now, Superior is literally one mighty, overgrown spring, crystal-clear and sparkling cold. Old-timers who live by its shores will tell you that it never freezes over in winter and never thaws out in summer. Which is to say it has a year-round temperature of not far from 45 degrees. That's hardly pike water. Lake trout and whitefish and big speckled trout (the famed coasters of the Nipigon country and Batchawana Bay and points between) along the rock-paved shores, yes.

Longnose doesn't want his environment that cold. But there's a big island up in the northern bulge of the lake—Isle Royale, youngest National Park in the United States, dedicated in 1936 and opened four years later. Its rugged shoreline is indented with long, narrow harbors that wind back between the timbered ridges like low-walled fjords. At the inner end of those harbors sluggish little rivers come loafing out of the alders, on the last leg of their jaunt down from the ridges. Moose like to wallow in the black muck on the banks of those lily-fringed streams, and off their outlets there is warmish water and the harbors are grown up with weeds.

What do you find in those weed beds? Pike, of course—big sullen devils with tempers like a wildcat's and an appetite like a cannibal's. I've seen 'em in Brady Cove, on the north shore of the island, on a still evening when the water was as flat and unstirred as polished glass, hunting their prey in the weed tangles like a pack of vest-pocket sharks.

We drifted down the cove one July evening just after sundown, and in half an hour we counted twenty or thirty big pike within sight of our boat. The weeds are sparse in that bed. They come up from the bottom in long green strands like frayed ropes, and the clumps are two or three yards apart. The pike were moving slowly and lazily in the open lanes between the weed fronds, no more than a foot underwater, like lean dirigibles scouting low about a farmer's wood-lot. In the dim green light they were a black, ugly and hungry-looking lot, and I was glad I didn't live down in that cold-blooded, pitiless world of theirs.

We had a couple of rods in the boat, and we ended the hunt for half a dozen of 'em. It was the oddest and easiest pike fishing I'd ever done. We cast to our fish as a trout fisherman casts to a rise.

We would spot a pike drifting along thirty or forty feet from the boat. We'd lay a plug four or five yards beyond him and a little ahead and twitch it back so that it crossed his course literally under his nose. We could see his sudden interest in the lure; see the strike and his frantic flurry as he felt the hooks and the pull of the line.

We could watch every rush and turn he made, whether at the top or deep down among the weeds. It was the best ringside seat I've ever had on a fishing trip, until the light failed and dusk gathered.

No two of them took the plug in the same fashion. One went into it with a rush—jaws gaping, pouncing like a leopard, hitting with a wrenching smash, starved and savage, making dead sure the prey had no chance to dodge into the weeds and get away.

The next was in no hurry at all. He lay idle, watching while the bait swam into sight and weaved nearer. He waited as if suspicious of trickery or uncertain whether this flashing, silvery thing was on his diet list. Whatever the critter was, it had no chance, and he knew it. It was small and hurt, and too far from the bottom to take shelter. He was a pike—a greyhound of the weeds, long and slim and fashioned for speed. There was no need for haste. He slid forward a yard, paused briefly to watch the bait at closer range, moved again without effort. His long jaws opened almost lazily, and the plug was gone and there was sudden strain on the line.

I learned something that evening. I had lived all my life in pike country without knowing the great northern would strike in the dusk of late evening, even in the last twilight when the western sky was turning gray and ashen and the water was like black velvet.

Those pike fed long after it was too dark for us to see them moving above the weeds. We used a flashlight to unsnarl a back-lash before we took the last one, and it was full dark when we rowed back and tied up at Birch Island.

I caught my first pike when I was a kid about ten. He wasn't big —a little better than three pounds, but he looked big to me. I took him on a minnow—or, to be exact and truthful, on a fingerling blue-gill about three inches long. The bluegill fooled around a worm I was using for grown-up members of his own family, and when I brought him in I transferred him to a bigger hook on another pole and dangled him over a weed bed while I went on with my worm fishing. I hadn't much hope, but the pike came along, and the rest just happened.

He was my first fish bigger than a rock bass or a half-pound bull-head, and he made me a pike fisherman for life. Using that kind of bait would be illegal today—undersized pan-fish in possession, the warden would say—but I still can't think of any better use for a small bluegill. The point is, I caught my first pike on a fish smaller than himself, and I've been taking 'em that way ever since.

The bruiser is a sucker for a minnow. He's a plug-ugly, a toughie, and he revels in the role. He likes live bait, and he wants it red-blooded. Let softer and better mannered fish have the caddis larvae and the flies, the crawfish and garden worms. He wants his food made in his own image, *Esox* does. He delights in picking a victim under his own weight class, assaulting it and sending scales drifting down through the water in a silver cloud. Show him another fish small enough to be swallowed, and his eyes brighten with the pure light of murder. It takes several tons of little fish, scattered through his voracious years, to turn out the finished product of twenty-five pounds of pike. All of which makes Longnose exceedingly vulnerable to a chub or shiner deftly impaled on a barbed hook and dangled in his home range on a silk thread.

Give him a minnow first if you would accomplish his downfall. If your taste does not run to live bait, give him something that resembles a minnow. A strip of pork rind is a fair substitute. So is a spoon or spinner or wabbler, or any of the countless patterns of wooden, plastic, rubber and metal minnows. As a matter of fact, any trolling or casting lure that is minnow-like in shape, size or action will take pike, some more frequently than others, of course.

But stay away from surface baits. The bruiser doesn't go for 'em. His dining room is deep down among the weeds, and he waits there and lets his meals come to him. Most of the time he shuns the top of the water, and the deeper your plug or wabbler runs the more deadly it will be on great northerns.

Esox seems partial to red in artificial baits. It goads him as it goads a bull, and so most pike fishermen incline to a dash of red on whatever lure they offer him—a red-headed plug, red feathers on a treble hook behind a spinner, red lining for a metal spoon, red and white stripes on a wabbling gadget. That last one is hard to beat, incidentally. Maybe he favors red because it's the color of blood.

On one of the bruiser's traits all fishermen are in accord: that's his appetite. His harshest critic will admit it's second to nothing in its class. There are times when fish won't feed and there's nothing you or anybody else can do about it. You may stand in the best pool on the most famous salmon river that empties into the Atlantic and lay your Black Dose down with consummate skill a hundred times at the head of a dark hole where you know not fewer than six great fish are lurking, and if they aren't rising you'll quit empty-handed in spite of all you can do!

A fish's will is his own, and when he's on a hunger strike no man can coax him out of it. That's as true of old Longnose as of any other fish—but his times of fasting are few and far-spaced. Most of his life he devotes to foraging, tireless and single-minded. On top of that, he's an opportunist. Even when the pangs of honest hunger are dulled, the lust to kill is on him and he is prone to gratify it if the chance offers.

There are times when all the pike in the lake quit striking, to be sure, but such times are rare and brief in their duration. If you are on good pike water with the right bait and fail to get action, rest your rod for an hour or so. The odds are good you'll not need to wait longer than that.

On another of the bruiser's traits all fishermen are not agreed— that is, his fighting heart.

There are those who will tell you he has no guts when the hooks are home and the blue chips are down. Up in Canada they call him the jackfish and despise him as most fishermen despise the carp. They are honest enough in their opinion, too, but they malign old *Esox* for all of that.

He's no salmon, as I admitted earlier. He lacks the dash of a trout, the finesse and showmanship of a small-mouth bass. He hasn't the weight of a muskalonge and for that reason his performance isn't the knockdown-dragout affair which the musky stages. I know men who have taken both, and they argue that he's a fair match for the musky, pound for pound; but I've too little evidence to defend that.

But whatever his shortcomings, the bruiser is no quitter. He fights, and he does it in his own devilish way and by his own rules. Fair play has no place in his tactics. He slugs and gouges, puts his knee in your groin, hits below the belt and after the gong has rung. He's no gentleman and makes no false claims. He's a bully, and he battles like one because he knows no more likely way to save his own skin.

He has little taste for flashy sparring at the surface. Most of the time he stays deep and makes his punches count. Give him weeds, and he'll go down like a corkscrew and foul your line to gain the slack he needs for throwing the hooks. Give him rocks or logs, and he'll snag you if he has a tenth of a chance. If all else fails, he'll do his damnedest to saw through your leader with his awl-sharp teeth, and plenty of times he succeeds.

While the last hand is being played he'll take cover under the very boat he dreads and tangle you or smash your rod if he is able. And when he's licked and knows it, he'll lie doggo at the top, floating on his side, and then spend his last ounce of hate in a vicious lunge, coming at you as you reach for his gills, and slashing your hand if you're unwary or slow.

He's no trout, old Longnose isn't, but he's quite a fish for all that. Those who say he won't give a good account of himself at bayonet range have never tried him in proper water, or they deny the evidence.

In the northern midlands, where I know him, he plays one part that's out of character: he's a mortgage-lifter of some consequence. The vacation industry is big business in more than one state nowadays. Anything that brings outside visitors and outside money is important, and the weed-bed bruiser brings 'em in a big way.

One other role he fills outstandingly well. He livens the long, dull weeks of winter for a host of anglers in the snow belt. He's one of the big five on the ice fisherman's list. In Northern lakes and rivers the black bass virtually hibernates for the winter. He retires into sunken logs, crannies among rocks, holes beneath water-logged trees and stumps. His appetite as good as disappears, and as a result bass fishing, waning through the autumn, dies out about Thanksgiving in the North.

Trout, which spawn in the fall or very early spring, would not be available to the fisherman even if the law permitted, which it doesn't. So the ice angler falls back on pike and walleyes, perch and lake trout, and in recent years bluegills, to bridge the lagging days from December to April. Of the lot the pike ranks first in the affections of winter fishermen. But that doesn't win him any place in paradise with the average summer angler.

Ice-fishing is, to begin with, an odd sport. Those who follow it put it ahead of eating. Those who don't contend it should not be talked of in the same breath with honest fishing. Certainly it's no pastime for pantywaists, but for the outdoorsman willing to take a little discomfort with his fun it affords plenty of entertainment at a season when the wide open spaces are snowbound and fishing of any kind is a rare privilege. I'll admit that catching a pike on a hand-line on a wind-swept, frozen lake bears little resemblance to taking brown trout on a dry fly in the warm dusk of a May evening. But each has its time and place, and luckily all men do not seek the same things in angling.

The fisherman who wants to avoid the bulk of the hardships that go with winter fishing turns to an ice shanty. It's a small, dark, weatherproof shelter, heated with a stove no bigger than a three-gallon can, and in it the angler is as comfortable as in his own living room. The winter wind may sing its dreary song outside, but a fire of dry pine or cedar pops cheerfully in the tiny stove and all is snug and warm within.

The shanty is windowless, lighted only by the reflected pale-green light that shines up through a hole cut in the ice to match a hole of equal size in the floor. The warm darkness is in sharp contrast with the bright underwater world below. All that moves within the shanty-man's range of vision, to a depth of ten or twelve feet, is seen as clearly as in an aquarium tank. He waits in endless patience, ready with a short iron-shafted spear fastened to the shanty wall with a stout line, in the fashion of a harpoon. Down in the water a big chub or shiner, hooked on a lighter line, swims in slow circles above the dull-green moss and water weeds, serving as a decoy.

The minnow gives ample warning when a pike, or other fish big enough to be feared, is coming in. It shows sudden activity, swinging far out under the ice in an effort to escape danger as yet invisible to the spearman. Then, from the opposite side of the hole, an ugly long-jawed head slides into sight. *Esox* is coming to lunch. He lies idle for a few seconds just beyond the spear's range, watching the struggles of the crippled chub. Then he drifts ahead, gathering speed.

But the spear is moving down through the water now, unhurried and deadly, trailing a few silvery bubbles. A foot above the bruiser's back it checks for a split second. The spearman is making sure of the target. When he lunges, it is swift and hard, and the barbed tines go deep behind the ugly head. He lets go the spear instantly, and it sinks down and carries the impaled pike with it, holding him on the bottom with its weight.

There's a wild flurry for a minute, and a cloud of mud floats up. When the wounded fish subsides, the spear can be drawn up. The shantyman kicks open the door and backs out on the ice with his catch, and never sees the snow eddying across the white level of the lake, never feels the bite of the January wind.

So long as he keeps that same location a little handful of pike scales will shine bright on the lake bottom to remind him of his kill. Deride it or not, ice-fishing is far from a dull sport.

It all adds up this way: wherever and however I have taken *Esox* he has given me my money's worth, paid his own freight. He's even good on the platter. Not, of course, if he comes from warm, stagnant, mud-tainted water. Take him from a cold, clear lake if you want him for table fish, and let the skin go with the scales. After that, treat him as you would a trout.

"He is choicely good," Izaak Walton summed it up a long time ago. "Too good for any but anglers and honest men."

Who are you and who am I, my friend, to question the judgment of such a sage? Longnose has his faults, to be sure, but he has virtues as well, and he gets my vote any place and any day!

Sportsmen's Thanksgiving

By JACK VAN COEVERING

FOR THE GROUSE THAT DRUMS IN THE SPRING WOODS, FOR THE bobwhite that whistles in the cornfield, for the pheasant that crows along the fencerow, for the whippoorwill that sings in the late evening, for the kingfisher that rattles along the streamside, for the chickadee that visits our campsite, for the bluebird that cheers our garden, for the robin that builds its nest in the eave trough of our home, for the wildfowl that travel uncharted sky lanes as they come and go with the seasons, O God, we thank Thee.

For the white-tailed deer that inhabits our North woods, for the raccoon that makes its home in the dead trees of our South woods, for the beaver that builds its dams on our rivers, and for its little cousin the muskrat that inhabits our pond holes, for the bunny cottontail that thrives on the farmlands, for the snowshoe hare that lives in the cedar swamps, for the bobcat and the coyote, for all the creatures of Thy hand, O God, we thank Thee.

For the trout that play in our clear-watered streams, for the bass that lurk in our lakes, for the great pike that swim like destroyers in our waters, for the palatable perch and the bluegills, for all the life that exists in the water: the fish, the frogs, the clams, the crayfish and the turtles, O God, we thank Thee.

For the pines that grow on our northern hills, for the giant oaks that thrive on our ridges and plains, for the tamaracks that bud in the springtime, for the cedars that clothe the swamps, for the fire cherry and popple which hide the scars of forest fires, for the June berry and beechnut, the hemlock and alder, for all the trees and shrubs of the forest, O God, we thank Thee.

For the waters that run clear and clean, for the waves that wash our shores, for the lakes which dot our landscapes, for the beauty of the wild flowers, for the opportunity of life out of doors, for the inspiration of the stars, the challenge of the storm, the comfort of the babbling brook, and for the opportunity of helping to preserve Thine Own handiwork against that blundering juggernaut we call civilization: God of our great outdoors, we pause and give Thee thanks.

Caravan in the Pines

By JOE BROOKS

"QUAIL AN ACRE—TWENTY COVEYS A DAY—NUTS! THERE aren't that many quail anywhere in the United States!" Jim snorted when I told him what we had coming.

"But Jim," I told him, "I've been there. I've seen 'em."

The guy was still skeptical. "Show me," he said. "That's all I ask; just show me."

At the time Jim Weaver and I were putting in a week's quail shooting around Thomasville, Georgia. Somehow or other Jim Campbell, who manages a big plantation in the southwestern part of the state, heard we were in his neck of the woods, so he invited us to come down for a day of big time stuff. Having shot with Campbell before, I jumped at the chance, for this kind of quail shooting is something every man should try at least once before he dies.

That's how-come Jim Weaver and I were climbing into Campbell's shooting wagon, with our host and three colored lads riding on ahead. It looked like a big day, whether Campbell could deliver twenty coveys or not.

You'll want to hear about that shooting wagon. This mule-drawn vehicle was the darnedest thing. It was especially designed for quail shooting, with a large wire box built into the rear for the dogs, seven or eight of them, and railings on the top of the box for shells, clothing, lunches and sundry shooting gear. Built into each side of the wagon were lockers for carrying guns, and in front of old Sam, the dusky driver, there was another compartment for our dead birds. All in all, it was a de luxe rig—and a highly practical one, too.

We headed out through the tall Georgia pines. The quail is king here—pampered, watched over, protected. His favorite food grows in abundance to hold him here throughout the year. Scientific burning of the fields prevents lush vegetation from running riot. A close watch keeps predators from getting out of hand and regulated shooting insures sufficient seed for future gunning.

You need wide-ranging dogs for this country, pointers mostly with the blood of field trial champions coursing through their veins—finished bird dogs, sure on point, steady to shot, smart bird-finders and good retrievers.

Jim turned in his saddle. "Sam, put down Jack and Jill and Frank."

"Yessir, boss," replied Sam, pulling up his team.

The dogs broke out in front of us and, picking up speed, ranged out of sight. Once again the caravan got under way. It wouldn't be long now. Weaver spoke just about then.

"To think," he said, "we're actually here. We're ..."

"Point!"

The magic word floated back to us through the pines. Old Sam broke the mules into a trot and we rattled and bumped toward the dogs. There they were—Jill had them pinned tight. Jack and Frank, like statues, honored her find. Sam pulled up about fifty feet in back of the dogs and Weaver and I jumped down, snatching our guns from their rests. Jim Campbell and Josh, his number one boy, dismounted and stood aside as we loaded our guns.

"John and James," Campbell directed, "you two ride up on the ridge and mark down the singles."

When they reached their objective, Jim gave us the "go" signal and we moved in for the flush. A quick glance at Jill and you could just see the scent of birds streaming into her nostrils. We walked in and talk about a covey bursting! The air filled with them and when I'd finally recovered my senses, I picked out a bird off to my left and dropped him. This first covey startled me so I didn't have time for a second shot. Weaver reacted more quickly and made a double. The dogs still stood rooted.

"Fetch," said Jim, and in a flash they were off to retrieve the dead birds. "Three, eh? We only take four from a covey so let's pass up these singles and go after another covey."

Josh handed over the dead birds to Sam to be put away in the game box. Weaver and I climbed aboard the shooting wagon and Jim and his boys rode on ahead with the dogs ranging well out in front.

Birds came thick and fast now. Jim's cry of "Point!" rang through the pines. Each time we went after singles, Jim would take up the covey-finding dogs and put one dog down to hunt them. Every so often he would put down fresh dogs. It was streamlined quail shooting; fast and furious.

Four to a covey—that's all—let's get another. Sometimes we took only one bird; they ran and most of the covey would flush wild. Point! Point! Birds, lots of birds. All the birds in the world. . . .

We stopped to count our bag—only two more for the limit. We looked at our watches—out only two hours.

"Boy, where's Jill?" asked Jim Campbell.

"Don't see her, sir," answered Josh. "Guess she's pointing."

"All right. Ride back where you last saw her. You, James, search out that ridge over there and, John, you look over in that bottom. I'll ride out ahead. Sam, you stay where you are till we find her."

Far off to the left, we caught glimpses of Josh as he moved through the cover. Suddenly we saw him stop.

"Point!" he whooped. "Point!" He seemed to put all the points of that day into his cry. I felt my scalp tingle.

"Giddap!" shouted Sam.

Riders converged on Josh from all sides as we raced along, bouncing and shaking and hanging on as best we could. Josh sat his horse on the other side of the field, looking into a dense stand of waist-high broomsedge. As we rattled nearer, we saw Jack come tearing up and start into the cover. Two leaps and he pointed, tail up and head high.

"Look at that li'l ol' dog point!" cried Weaver.

Just about then, Frank tore past us and, seeing Jack pointing, seemed to stop in mid-air and freeze. Sam had to do a quick piece of maneuvering to keep from running him down. As we stopped he broke and moved up directly behind Jack where he froze again. We got down and loaded our guns.

"Remember boys," Jim Campbell cautioned, "only one more bird apiece for your limits."

We walked in and two birds rose. We downed them. Suddenly the rest of the covey rose. I watched and about fifty yards to the left another covey got up. Still looking, I saw a third bunch take wing farther down the field. Three coveys in the air at once! I looked at Weaver; he looked at Jim and then turned and walked back to the shooting-wagon without a word. Carefully, he put his gun in its place and, climbing aboard, sat down. Suddenly, he jumped up as though coming out of a trance.

"No...no...it's not so!" he babbled. "There just weren't three coveys in the air at once. Take me away...take me away!"

With that he slumped down in the seat and stared vacantly into space.

"Well," Jim Campbell said with a grin, "what about a spot of lunch?"

We sat in a circle eating cold quail and dove and drinking piping hot coffee—a fitting climax to as fine a quail hunt as one could possibly have. Over us towered the giant loblollies with a backdrop of Spanish moss laced against a blue Georgia sky.

"Joe," Weaver inquired gently, "how many coveys did we find?"

"Oh, about nine," I replied.

"Fifteen, boss," broke in Josh, "fifteen counting those last three that were in the air at once."

"Fifteen coveys in two and a half hours," said Campbell. "Not bad, eh?"

"Not bad?" I echoed. "It's unbelievable. Furthermore, it's not possible."

Weaver stirred and looked around. "I just can't believe it. But it did happen, didn't it?"

Jim Campbell munched on a piece of quail and leaned closer. "Now," he said, "I'll let you in on a little secret. We have ten other courses on this plantation every bit as good as this. We usually find eighteen or twenty coveys in half a day's hunt."

"Stop it," Jim moaned, "It's just too much to stand."

Weaver muttered something but I couldn't make out what he was saying. I did hear the end of it, though..."a quail an acre," he muttered. "And how!"

1,000,000 B.C.

By FRANK DUFRESNE

I T WAS MIDSUMMER IN THE ARCTIC. THE ESKIMO NAPAUK AND I HAD come a long way to visit this remote spot on the bleak shore line of Kotzebue Sound, in northwestern Alaska. From where we stood under the receding glacier, you could look out past our schooner riding at its anchor and see the pea-green expanse of the polar ocean, dotted with sparkling jewels of ice, curving away over the top of the world. Bright-plumaged eider drakes flew by in small groups; a school of milk-white pygmy whales puffed and sighed beyond the breakers.

Just above the swirl of the surf, we had been exploring for teeth and bone fragments of Pleistocene creatures. The spreading horns of an extinct bovine had already been balanced across the Eskimo's kayak and paddled out to the schooner.

A fossilized molar the size and weight of a cobblestone had been dug out of the sand, and I was prying at a thighbone big as a small tree trunk, when Napauk's gaze suddenly riveted on a spot above the thudding water.

"No use diggum any more," he said. "Here comes a whole one."

It looked just like that at first. It looked like a curiously deflated elephant in the very act of breaking through the walls of its icy prison. Two enormous tusks of stove-pipe diameter, curled back against themselves like giant fishhooks, hung suspended in the air. Part of a huge skull was in sight. A poised foreleg gave the impression that this long-dead beast was probing cautiously for a foothold before taking another step. You caught your breath in the wonder of it! Here was a woolly mammoth—something out of a legend. It just didn't exist any more. It belonged to another age. Yet here it was, moving out into the sunlight of today.

There wasn't much to be done about it. For one thing, we had no way of scaling the slippery white wall, and there was little we could accomplish if we succeeded in reaching the animal. We could only keep our rare discovery under observation during the short summer; see it project farther out like a mounted specimen on the mantelpiece as the ice melted away from it; watch it collapse gradually for lack of support, and see pieces of it come toppling into the sea. We gathered handfuls of long dark hair; picked up chunks with flesh and hide still attached to the bone.

Napauk even chewed on a grisly dark joint. "Plenty old!" was his only comment, and he didn't reach for a second helping.

Perhaps we were fussier than the Siberians across Bering Strait, or maybe they grew a better grade of mammoth over there. Anyway, it is claimed that cold storage specimens recovered from Siberia were devoured by dogs and bears. In a pinch maybe a man could have eaten this ancient flesh, though I am inclined to believe he would first have consumed all the dogs and bears in sight.

On the Alaska side of Bering Sea, the news of the discovery of Ice Age creatures filtered into Nome largely in the form of complaints from the gold miners. To begin with, it was trouble enough to cut down through a hundred feet of frozen muck in order to reach the gold-bearing gravels on bedrock. Streams of snow water gathered in ditches dug around the mountain slopes were led down into the valley through flexible canvas hose, and shot through tapering nozzles to thaw and wash away the overlying debris. But when the sluice boxes were in place and the long-awaited "clean-up" at hand, more troubles appeared.

In a few instances long strands of black hair and rust-colored wool clogged the riffles of the sluice boxes. Strange-looking skulls bigger than the camp cookstove, too bulky to be carted off in wheelbarrows, had to be pushed and rolled out of the way. Ivory tusks longer than any sported by modern elephants required the strength of two men to carry them from the pits. And over the whole area was the penetrating odor of decaying flesh thawed and shredded by the giant hydraulic nozzles.

But it was in the Fairbanks region that paleontologists really hit the jackpot. Here in central Alaska, gold mining was conducted on a grand scale and by newly discovered wrinkles that permitted extensive areas to be stripped of endless tons of muck and ice. It was here, far below the present earth's surface, that one of the greatest game fields of all time was laid bare. The miners found a setting that obviously had swarmed with wild life. They found abundant remains not only of mammoths and bison, but also of horses and camels and giant cats.

Contemporaneous with a long list of vanished species were practically all of our existing forms. Both in numbers and variety, the Pleistocene life excelled anything left on the continent today. Only in the heart of darkest Africa may living man hope to see its equal. Actually, what we have in America today is only a remnant of that which occurred before the glaciers moved down from the polar regions to blanket the top half of the New World.

Not only once, but probably four times, the ice advanced upon temperate America. Originating in Canada, it reached roughly down to a line drawn from New York through Cincinnati to Saint Louis, then swung sharply northward to near the Canadian border and west to Seattle. Mountain valleys as far down as mid-California were covered. Greenland got such a heavy dose of glaciers that it hasn't recovered from the shock yet; geologically, it is still in the Ice Age.

When did it all happen? Probably a million years ago, and it lasted to within twenty-five to eighty thousand years of the present time. The glacial epoch of the Quaternary period, known as the Pleistocene, played no favorites. A large part of Europe and Asia fell under the steamroller of advancing ice. The south polar region reached out from down under; even Africa had a touch. None of this implies a catastrophic change in climate. An average drop in temperature of ten or fifteen degrees might bring the ice far southward, a corresponding lift would start it back for the arctic. Not fast, though; you can't hurry a glacier. It counts time in thousands of years.

There are two reasons why Alaska is such a good hunting ground for long-dead animals, and why it may hold the key to many questions, including that puzzling one about when man first made his appearance in this country. In the first place, Alaska forms one end of a land bridge that once connected America with Asia across Bering Strait. The walking is poor up there right now; there are thirty-five miles of water separating Cape Prince of Wales on the Alaska side from Russian Diomede Island, and it is about the same distance from there to East Cape, Siberia. But back in a far distant age, it is believed, it was a wide and fertile valley across which came the ancestors of our moose, elk, caribou, wild goats and sheep, bears and many other animals. Probably even man with a stone club on his shoulder trudged along this trail.

Another good reason why Ice Age fauna is so easy to find in Alaska is that excellent cold storage is provided in many, but not all, parts of the Territory. Because of its prevailing colder climate, full recovery from the last advance of the glaciers has not yet been reached. To this day, over wide expanses of central and northern parts of the Territory, the soil is thawed only a few inches or a few feet.

All you have to do on wide stretches of the tundra to find solid ice is scrape away the matted roots of dwarf vegetation with your hands. There is your ice, more than a hundred feet thick, covering thousands of square miles of the old earth's surface. Any animal pinned down by this cold weight is quite likely to be right where hard luck overtook him, and just about as well preserved. What apparently happened was that the animals became buried in mud, muck and silt, the water in which then froze.

That was why collectors got on the job soon after the hydraulic nozzles at Fairbanks blasted the first mammoth out of its icy crypt, incidentally scattering the precious pieces far and wide over the landscape. This was soon remedied by an arrangement whereby the miner swung his nozzle in another direction whenever he spotted a new creature showing up in the ice.

Following this bit of co-operation, no scientist ever had better equipment at his command for removal of overburden—such equipment as thawing devices, scrapers and giant electric dredges with chains of buckets reaching a hundred feet down into the earth. It took the incentive of gold to warrant such extensive equipment— scientists are notoriously poor—but at any rate the mounds of recovered bones grew to astonishing proportions. They were hauled away by the truckloads.

Not only bones, but bits and patches of hide, hair and tendons were recovered. Mammoths and regal bison were among the commoner types found, although it wasn't long before the antlers and skulls of giant elk-moose, caribou, musk oxen, horses and bears came to light.

Then came a mastodon, which is like a mammoth but with different type molars, a saber-toothed tiger big as a grizzly bear with six-inch fangs used in stabbing its prey to death, and an enormous cat that could chase any African lion off the veld. One of the queerest finds was the great dire wolf. Smaller animals were harder to pick up because they got lost in the silt, but enough parts were recovered to show that this million-years-old game field had its full quota of foxes, lynxes, squirrels and other rodents.

You have to imagine what it looked like then; no one can tell you. You have to see in your own mind's eye the trumpeting mammoths big as so many loads of hay, their 12-to-15-feet-long curled tusks swinging from side to side as they shuffled along in these forests of long-ago Alaska; see them reaching with their trunks to wrench tasty vines from the tall trees, or maybe tearing a smaller one up by the roots just for the fun of it. They would have caught your eye first of all, but you couldn't very well miss seeing other creatures; the now extinct giant elk-moose pushing its massive antlers into view through the thick underbrush, perhaps on its way to a deep, dark pool constructed by beavers as big as our common black bears.

Away from the gloom of the forests—the biggest trees there now are mostly waist-high willows—herds of yaks and camels covered the meadows, sharing space with bulbous-nosed antelopes and horses; preyed upon by tigers, lions and wolves.

Life in the Alaska Pleistocene period was a strange blending of animal forms, some of them soon to succumb to the grim decree that only the fittest may survive. Gone are the mammoths, mastodons and the giant elk-moose, and with them they took the fierce smilodon, or saber-tooth tiger, and the carrion-eating dire wolf.

By an odd twist of circumstances, the horses and camels that once loped over Alaska's plains are credited with siring present-day types, even though they had to leave the continent to do it. The horse was gone from America many thousands of years before the Spaniards brought it back in the 16th century, all dolled up with armor and trappings to frighten the natives.

Did man live here when all this was going on?

Well, they thought they had the answer to that one when the skull of a mammoth calf was brought out of the ice at Fairbanks with an object like a jadeite axhead lodged in the lower jawbone. It was finally concluded that no human hand had delivered the lethal blow, that the young mammoth had instead fallen onto a ledge. But this was negative evidence; it didn't prove anything. The search still goes on, based on a number of interesting if conflicting theories.

One eminent anthropologist denies the existence of the Ice Age man in America, holding firmly to the tenet that the forefathers of all our native tribes came across to us from Asia by way of the Aleutians at a much later date, using the islands as steppingstones from one hemisphere to the other. This top-ranking authority has an imposing collection of Aleut mummies and low-browed skulls to back up his contentions. He's a hard man to argue with. But it cannot be denied that there have been persistent reports of American Indian culture fully as early as the Aleutian migration.

They're still searching for the mysterious Folsom man whose distinctive weapons and other artifacts were found in New Mexico. These have given rise to another theory: namely, that immigration to Alaska from Siberia might have taken place anywhere from eight to twelve thousand years ago. The Peking man, found in Pleistocene caves of China, and from whom this pioneer stock may have sprung, almost certainly existed a quarter of a million years ago. This ties in with the prevailing supposition that the first American was a Mongoloid invader.

Even this has been disputed, though not too successfully, because the published theory that America originated its own human life seems to have died with the author of it. This student took us down to the other end of the Americas for his proof, contending that human life sprang from the pampas of Patagonia. While this idea appears to have few supporters at the present time, nevertheless there is a belief that some of the humans found in the lower Argentine might date back to the Pleistocene.

It's all very confusing to the layman and may not be so clear even to the experts, but so far as the records show, no human skeletal remains have been found in American Pleistocene deposits. We can go a step further: No anthropoid ape fossil has been found here. That's why Alaska's vast deposits of frozen muck are important. Not only may now unknown species of animals come to light, but there is always the possibility that the red letter day will arrive when America's number one citizen may be found resting in his icy shroud. New developments in this field may be delayed because of war conditions that put a stop to most gold-mining activities.

Hand-Line 'em for Fun

By BILL ACKERMAN

BEFORE THE FIRST WORLD WAR, WHEN I WAS JUST A YOUNGSTER, I cast my lot with some of the Atlantic City skippers who were winter-chartering out of Florida's Indian River Inlet, three miles north of the present Fort Pierce ship channel. It was late September. The muggy thickness of the hurricane season was apparent even in the daylight hours, but it was far more noticeable in the long, still twilight.

Ben Sooy was getting along in years. He didn't like the hard days of scraping and varnishing. The weather this day had suggested an evening look-see at the cuts, and maybe a run out over the bar if the break wasn't bad. Anything to shorten the day's work met with my approval.

Now the near two miles of the river was behind. We had threaded our way through the last tortuous channel in the shifting sands of

Nigger Cut. The broad expanse of water between the headlands inside the bar was in full sight.

I was busy rigging a line, and it was the faint whistle in Ben's quickly indrawn breath that brought me to attention. I stood tense in the realization that the roar I had thought was the surf was made by thousands of panicky mullet seeking escape from foraging fish. Darting triangular patches were cutting the surface everywhere. Sharks!

When Ben turned the nose of our little boat toward the shore and cut the engine a moment before the bottom grated and it slid to a stop on the sands, I knew there would be no try for a blue at the bar that evening. We walked the edge of the north channel to the outer beach. Close to, the sickled dorsal fins were unbelievably long—the shadowy bodies beneath them enormous.

Oil now covered the water so thickly that it was damping down the combers on the bar; but the sickening carnage continued unabated. It was the most awe-inspiring half hour I had experienced in all my eighteen years.

"They were man-eaters," Ben said when the tiny single-cylinder engine was once more pushing us along toward home. "Only one other time have I seen them so. You might find an occasional pair out in the Stream. Usually they are solitary hunters. It was here, too. Seven or eight years back, when I was fishing with the Senator. We was using the little skiff and had a tarpon on. It was late in the evening, just like now, when they struck in, under the south point.

"You know, kid, those so-and-sos hit at anything moving in the water. My oars were nearly splinters 'fore we reached the beach. They had taken our fish on the first go-round. Threw my bailing can at one, and it was gulped down as soon as it hit.

"I had a big hook aboard the launch and plenty of line for a rig. Just speared the barb through the middle of the biggest sheepshead in the box and threw it out. It disappeared, with the hook and most of the chain, in a split second.

"The Senator wasn't a youngster, but he carried a lot of meat on his frame, as you know. Even so, it was only enough to keep us hung to that thrashing brute till a couple of market boys, on their way in after a day on the reefs, pulled up to lend a hand. They turned the tide, too, and we soon had him out on the beach."

With that Ben lapsed into silence.

His wife later showed me a picture of the shark, taken the morning following the catch. Penciled data on the back provided the information that it was more than 22 feet long, had a girth of 91 inches, and was estimated to weigh 1,500 pounds.

It isn't often given to a man to see the strange ways in which Mother Nature works—to learn first hand, actually to witness how precarious life in the world under the surface of the sea, the life of the little fellows of the shoals, can be when the big bullies of the deep waters put upon them. The sight brought a feeling of hatred for every shark and all his kind and the desire to kill them when and as often as the chance was presented.

It was the second winter before I could do anything to satiate that desire, to catch and kill the really big fellows. I was fishing out of New River Inlet with Mike English. The runs of fish were few and far between. Time hung heavy.

We acquired a single length of three hundred feet of quarter-inch manila and a hook of such proportions that it was the cynosure of all eyes along the Fort Lauderdale waterfront.

Our first efforts were unproductive. Maybe it was because the boat scared them off in the shallow waters. But eventually we learned the right presentation of the bait. It required a float, placed in the water at a point where the sweep of the tide would carry it well around and down the middle of the channel.

There was only one way to place it so: to swim out with it. I have wondered many times since what would have been the choice of a shark had he met me before I had let loose of the bait—one relatively small bonito or 150 pounds of prime meat under a sun-tanned hide?

After that we caught nurse sharks no end and browns—even an occasional hammerhead of noteworthy dimensions. We killed them with satisfaction and cast their carcasses back to the little fellows, but we never ran across the long, slim length of a tiger, which Ben had mistakenly called a man-eater, the name usually attached to the white shark.

We ranged the Gulf Stream, too, and used rod and reel with the star drag, which was just then coming into general use. For a while we counted that fun, until our lust began to wane. Finally we failed to respond at all to the urge. After all, it wasn't an intriguing pastime.

Later, at St. Lucie Inlet, I was fishing the reefs with Somers Hick-man. The going was good. So densely populated were the rocky offshore ridges that any day's catch was just about the ultimate of diversification, from luscious blue grunts of scarcely a pound to enormous jewfish of five and six hundred pounds.

The size of our fleet increased, for the market men, in a midwinter lull between the runs of blues and mackerel, were finding it a worthwhile fill-in, but the sharks also were increasing in numbers and size. There came a time when it was next to impossible to snag a fish and get him up whole.

The boats rested that stretch of the reefs for a while, and then returned. Within a day the sharks were back too. It continued always so. Finally we decided something must be done about it.

Toward that end, on the first flat day, each boat rigged up an extra-long kingfish line with a 20-foot leader to keep the rough hides from fraying or cutting the line when they rolled. The lines were coiled handy in the stern-sheets, and everybody went to bottom-fishing until they would be interrupted.

And it wasn't long before first one boat and then another picked up a customer. Shortly almost everyone of the twenty-odd had their hands full.

It so happened that it was my grouper which our shark took; so I was the one to put the big line over. I had my hands full when that baby was hung, and it was lucky that his first run was short. The dry tarred line burned through the equally dry cotton gloves, and it was impossible to reach down the few inches necessary to souse them.

I doubt that shark knew he was hooked, for he doubled of his own accord, seeking additional tidbits in the way of hooked fish. It gave us time to wet down our gloves and line, recoil it on the bottom boards, take a turn around a thole-pin, and start the battle on our terms.

The next thirty minutes were nip and tuck. I paid off through the snub on the pin when I had to, but just hung on most of the time. Now and then I got line in so fast that Som would lay off and coil it in back of me against the next run. The times I had him under the boat were uncountable. I could see that he was big.

Then suddenly he was up, close alongside—not beaten, maybe just bewildered. Resting. Balefully glaring at us through tiny yellow eyes. And there were the tiny openings in back of those eyes—the spiracles denoting the tiger shark.

Som hollered to take another turn or two around the pin as he reached for our hatchet, always honed to razor-edge. As I did so he sank the blade to the handle in the fish's gill-slits. How he hung to the haft in the burst that followed I'll never know, possibly because the long hulk seemed to rise straight up.

One of the pectorals smashed our cockpit coaming. Part of its tail hit heavily against our bow. It was hard to believe the planks were not splintered. Som's torso was running red with blood—shark's blood. I was standing dumbly, with a short section of the wire grasped in my hands, following the course of the freed shark—free, yes, but hurt mortally, and attacked within seconds by his kind.

We watched enthralled as others swung in to the kill. It appeared as though hundreds of them came up to slash at one another, to hit anything that moved in the reddened waters. The blood-lust was terrifying.

For many days thereafter we followed our fishing undisturbed.

The experience freshened again the thought of hunting with the big hook and the quarter-inch manila line. We stowed it aboard, but it was not used until a friend aboard the *Mary Ann* expressed the wish to tangle with a big one. Toward that end we cruised the Stream in search of a solitary roamer.

We found one too, so large that I, lying across the bow with hook baited with a sizable bonito, was frozen to inaction. I was actually afraid to drop it over, knowing somehow it would be taken and that the resultant battle would be more than we could handle. Our 19-foot skiff was not as long as that shark! I figured it to be a tiger, but it might have been a true man-eater. If so, it is the only one I ever encountered.

Shades of Izaak Walton! To find that which you seek and lack the guts to take it on.

It was several years before I tried my hand again at the game. I had found a few weeks to take a Southern fishing holiday, and Som had made all the necessary arrangements. We were anchored for the night in the dredged cut through Featherbed Banks in the lower end of Biscayne Bay after a brawly afternoon with the big barracuda. Our wives were shaking up the evening meal in the galley. Som and I were sprawled on deck, lazily talking over old times.

Both of us heard a rumpus toward the north beacon. We knew it was caused by sharks, but failed to do anything about it for a while, until suddenly we realized the size of them by the telltale fins, now cutting the surface close under our quarter. Finally we just couldn't take it any longer lying down.

I overhauled a hank of tarred line while Som was making up his favorite rig, a long-shanked 10/0 hook run through the eye of a short-shanked 10/0. It was in my mind to make this as near a sporting proposition as possible, to give these fish the fifty-fifty chance which many talk about but so seldom extend to finny adversaries—the strength of the shark against that of the fisherman armed with no more than light cotton gloves.

Soon there was a sizable chunk of 'cuda floating off into the sunset, suspended just under the surface by a preserver cork fastened lightly with cotton thread so that it would break off easily. Nothing happened.

The calls from below now were mandatory to come and get it. Reluctantly we heeded them. We were nearly finished when the water bucket, skittering across the cockpit, gave warning that we had something on. Soon I knew it was my size.

How? Because as fast as he would take line out I could turn him and get much of it back, but for a long time I just couldn't get him to the boat. That, also, was eventually accomplished. It was a brown of maybe ten feet and weighed possibly several hundred pounds.

I counted that fish not on a par with a jumping marlin, or even with a small tarpon, but lots of fun nevertheless. With rod and reel it would have been a set-up—soft going.

Try it that way sometime on any species of shark anywhere, but don't take a turn of line around a handy bit unless you're sure he's whipped you down. Then no holds barred, for in all waters a shark is worth a little for oil, a little for meat and a lot for the fun he can provide on the end of a fishing line.

We Get That Way

By HORACE LYTLE

J UDGE HARRIS NUDGED HIS HORSE WITH A HEEL AND RODE FORWARD several paces to where the two handlers were holding their dogs on lead—ready for the order to let them go.

"Gentlemen," he said, "we're not going to ask you to run this second series yet this evening—unless it's perfectly agreeable to you both. We could probably do it—but there's not going to be much more than just enough daylight left to let us squeeze through. And the little setter bitch is pretty heavily marked, an' hard to see anyhow. However, the weather looks bad for tomorrow. So it's entirely up to you men. If either of you objects to starting now, we'll not run."

The two handlers looked at one another, a bit tense. Neither of them spoke up at once. It was well known on the circuit that they were not friendly. But most of us never had known why. Then Jim Hanson said:

"Well, I'd rather run 'em now—better chance for birds this evenin'." No doubt about the truth of that statement—and the big white pointer would not be too hard to follow under graying skies, as what daylight remained would begin gradually to fade. The dog, too, was noted as easy to handle.

Judge Harris turned to the other handler. "How about you, Mr. Wilson?" he asked. "We'll run if you say so—though I doubt if I would were I in your place. However, tomorrow may be even worse."

Jack Wilson spoke quickly: "Le's go, Judge. If you're willin' to ride 'em, I'm ready to run."

That's how it happened that the second series and final heat of the Southern All-Age Subscription Stake was concluded under trying conditions of waning daylight that hung on just barely long enough to let us finish. But what a dog race it was! One those of us who rode it will never forget. Most of all will we remember that smashing climax, just before the judges ordered them up.

At the end of 50 minutes, with the bird score all even at two finds each, and not much to choose between them in performance, no flaw in the work of either dog, the little setter bitch was seen to pass the pointer as they rounded a thicket and go sifting on and out, still racing like the wind behind her magic nose—until she faded away in the enveloping sedge.

A rider near me exclaimed: "Oh—oh! She's g-o-n-e now." And, indeed, that might easily be.

Shortly thereafter the ever-thrilling call came drifting to us from ahead—"P-O-I-N-T!" And, as on four previous occasions, we galloped up to witness the work.

There was Hanson, his hat held high as the signal of a dog on game. Judge Reed was the first up. "Where is he?" he asked, feeling the tension of it as did we all.

"'Tain't him—it's *her!*" Hanson exclaimed. "Get Wilson up. His bitch is right in there by that bush." Then he galloped on to handle his own dog followed by Judge Harris. Judge Reed held back to cover the setter's work, as did also the gallery. This find, if no flaw in its consummation, must show us the winner—we all sensed that. We *knew* it when, after Jack had flushed the birds and fired, Judge

Reed said: "Take her up." It was one of those rare finds worth 10 of the common kind.

Early that evening the storm that had threatened struck with violence and vigor. It was well that we'd finish the stake. The cold rain turned to snow and hail, which tick-tacked against the window panes. This was a good night to be indoors. I was occupying the same room with Judge Harris. When we retired, I noticed that Jim Hanson and Jack Wilson were sitting together by the big log fire in the lobby, laughing and talking together as only fast friends can.

There was a merry fire of red coals burning brightly in the grate in our room. Judge Harris pulled up a chair before it and sat down, stretching out his legs for greater lounging comfort. And he sat for some time without saying anything—just gazing into the flickering flames, which gave the room all the light we needed. It was good to be alive! Good, too, to be inside and so cozy. Let the wind whine and the cold come on. The prediction was for zero in the morning— and that's real weather in Tennessee. But we didn't care.

Finally, the Judge said slowly, not turning to me, but still just looking straight ahead as if fascinated by the fire: "D'you know, young man, what happened out there today was one of the finest things I've ever seen a man do—dunno but 'twas the very *finest*, all angles considered. And I'm sure glad of it." Somehow he seemed to be talking almost as much to himself as to me.

"You mean Hanson calling point for Wilson's dog?" I asked. "Isn't that right often done?"

"Yes, it is these days," he said, "though 'twasn't always so. However, the case today was different. Those two men have hated each other for several years. Hanson just happened by accident to spot that bitch on birds—more'n likely Wilson might never have found her. He wasn't even looking for her in the right place. Had Hanson passed on and not called the point, he'd almost surely have collected the thousand-dollar purse with the pointer—while the little bitch was lost on point out of judgment. Yet he proved man enough to do the right thing—and that dumped the win right into Jack Wilson's lap. The reason it was so big is 'cause, if he hadn't, no one but Hanson himself could ever have known. It was big because, as it was, he tossed away a thousand dollars that he needs, and gave it to a man he didn't like. Anyhow, Hanson will be a happier man for what he did today. After all, a man's got to live with himself—an' a clear conscience helps mightily."

"Of course, sir, it was the only *honest* thing he *could* do," I ventured. And Judge Harris came right back at me with: "You'll never say a truer word than that, young man, but even so you saw a fine thing happen."

Neither of us said anything more for a while. It was too fascinating just to watch the fire. And we seemed to have forgotten the idea of turning in. Finally, I asked the Judge why Hanson and Wilson had hated each other. The whole setting being as it was—with the fire an' all—and Wilson and Hanson having now patched it up forever—Judge Harris told me the story that night before we "hit the hay," while the grate coals smoldered on.

It seems that, several years before, Jim Hanson was studding his famous setter, Mo' Gold. And Mo' was siring large, healthy litters that trained on well to All-Age performers. So that Mo's puppies came to be much in demand. But there's just nothing in the world with so many possibilities for complication as most any kind of a dog deal—and Hanson found that out.

Mo' wasn't of the too eager, amorous type—he was too much the aristocrat for that. If a matron sent for service wouldn't stand, Mo' Gold would simply try to woo and win her in a gentlemanly way. There was no rough crowding—but his method took time. There had been no real difficulty, however, until—

A gentleman from South Carolina shipped for a service and there was nothing doing. This patron had his heart set on this particular mating for Futurities. Jim Hanson knew it and he became desperate. Finally, in discouragement, he gave up all hope and so wrote his customer, returning the fee in full. However, before the return shipment, although convinced it would do no good, Jim left Mo' all night in the kennel with the visiting matron. Then the lady went back to Carolina along with the returned fee and an explanation of deep regret.

And was that customer mad! Of course he never blamed the bitch—but wailed to Hanson of his frustrated hopes and cursed him for offering such a dog at public stud. This caused Jim to cancel Mo's advertisement and to decide to withdraw him. Which, had things ended there, would have precluded this story. But things didn't end there.

In some 63 days the lady from Carolina whelped eight beautiful setter puppies and her owner then wrote Hanson a letter that made his former seem mild by comparison. Poor Jim—he now was convinced that Mo' had done it, after all. But he hadn't *seen* it happen. He even went to see the puppies and his patron. He tried to explain how it all had occurred—but the owner was too provoked to listen. So sure was Jim they were Mo's that he offered to sign the certificate if the customer would refund half the fee to help defray his expenses for the trip to see them. This was refused. Then Hanson got mad himself—and left.

But his faith in Mo' had been revived and the stud advertisement was reinstated. The demand for Mo' Gold's get demanded it. Yet Jim had learned a lesson. There continued now and then a fractious female. In such cases Jim just left Mo' alone at night with them—and trusted him. The certificates for unseen service always went out—the fees were kept—and Mo' never let him down. There were puppies for every occasion but one—and even in that case they materialized from a free return service.

So all went well until Mo' Gold's ultimate retirement; and his popular puppies were winning everywhere and training on. Came, then, an inquiry one day from Mississippi begging for one last service by the grand old dog. After some deliberation, Jim granted it. First, however, he emphasized the dog's age to his customer and secured his full permission to select and use an outstanding son of Mo's if conditions demanded it.

And, as it turned out, the substitution was required. And Jack Wilson owned the dog that Hanson selected to use—one of Mo' Gold's finest sons. The two men were close friends then. Everything was arranged and in due time there arrived in Mississippi a litter of fine grandsons and granddaughters of Mo' Gold, sired by Jack Wilson's dog.

But Jim had not yet gotten the certificate from Jack to send to Mississippi. The day he went to get it Jack had been drinking and was in a questionable mood. He made a crack that he didn't believe Jim intended to send the certificate at all—that he'd wager Jim already had sent one certifying the pups as by Mo' Gold.

Hanson passed that off but flew off the handle when Wilson added: "Well, I took the man's name and address from the bitch's collar an' I'm goin' to write him an' tell him they're by *my* dog—which I'll bet you haven't done."

"Write an' be damned," Jim explained. "But d'you think I'd send that bitch to a fool like you with the *right* name and address on the collar! Not on your life—I changed her collar 'fore I ever let you even see her. So you don't know to whom to write."

With that parting shot (which, of course, wasn't true) Hanson left, and they've been enemies ever since, till today. Jim was wrong there. He should have seen Jack the next day and straightened it all up. Jack hadn't really meant what he said—it was just "liquor language." But neither of them ever tried to right the uncalled-for damage to their friendship.

The puppies were registered by affidavit, which, of course, Wilson later found out when they started winning and *his* dog was duly recorded as sire. And that's when Wilson should have gone to Hanson with abject apology. But he didn't. Not, at least, until this very night, after they'd been braced together in the finals of the Southern Subscription.

Judge Harris looked at his watch. Our fire was getting low. "Land alive," he said, "it's later than I thought—we'd better turn in."

"Well," I said, "thanks for telling me the story. I'm sure glad they're friends again. They should be—I now say more firmly than ever that was a wonderful thing Hanson did."

"We get that way in this game, I guess—or get out," said the Judge, as he started to pull off his boots.

Suddenly he stood up. "Say!" he exclaimed. "I never thought about it till just this very minute—and it doesn't take a thing away anyhow from what Jim did—but that little setter bitch today is one of those very granddaughters of Mo' Gold!"

"Well, I'll be damned," he added a minute later, as he sat down again. "She's of the very litter that made all the trouble—and now it's she who's helped patch it up!"

A Red Dog of Ireland

By JOE MacGAHERAN

WE WERE MISSISSIPPI BOUND, FOR T. W. JONES HAD WRITTEN: "Looks like the best quail season in years. Come down for a week or two. The dogs are ready and r'aring to go. Even young Bennie will surprise you. Believe it or not, he's steady at 15 months."

So, in answer to Bobwhite's ever-recurring call, three fellow hunters—Martin Hogan, internationally known dog trainer and sportsman, Art Welch and myself—were driving slowly over the sleet crusted highways of southern Illinois. Hour after hour, through intermittent snow flurries, we crept on, the monotony of the country occasionally being broken by villages and crossroads settlements. Although the afternoon was not yet half gone, snow-darkened skies made headlights necessary.

At one village, due to the murk, we came close to hitting a bedraggled Irish setter that darted into the street. Fortunately, Art pushed the brake pedal in time. The dog leaped to the curb, frightened but safe.

"What a sorry looking Irish setter," I remarked. Knowing that Martin Hogan is one person with a good dog story always up his sleeve (if you can get it out of him), I continued: "Martin, tell the truth now; did you actually ever see a *good* Irish setter—one that could hold his own against the pointer?"

"Indeed I have," he replied. "In fact, I'm not at all certain in my own mind but that the greatest bird dog I ever saw was not an Irish setter. She was owned by an Irish peasant farmer of County Kerry with never as much as a pound of cash in his purse at a time, yet he refused my offer of 100 pounds for the bitch."

I immediately rejoined, with sarcasm: "Oh, yes; well, tell us about this bitch. Where did you see her run—what made her so great?"

Half-turning in his seat, Martin began his tale...

It was back in 1904 that I went to the County Kerry in Ireland in the employ of the Marquis of Landesdown. The Marquis had a magnificent sporting estate of some 20,000 acres and was having trouble with his tenants about poaching. My job was to run the sporting department, manage the dogs and horses, improve the hunting and fishing and to stamp out poaching. Two of my predecessors lost their lives in rather mysterious accidents. Feeling was running high amongst the tenantry. I decided to proceed slowly and with every consideration for the peasants. Trying to drive the Irish would be a fool's game, anyhow.

This estate, by the way, was one of the greatest sporting properties I've seen, whether in Ireland, Scotland, England or this country. The huge acreage comprised a narrow strip of land and followed a valley between two mountain ridges. At its widest, the valley was not over three miles across, and extended 17 miles in length. In the streams, we had wonderful salmon fishing; in the lakes, plenty of trout and on the moors, exceptional grouse shooting.

The mountains towered to 2,000 feet in height, topped by the beautiful heather. Spruce and larch trees grew up the mountain sides to the heather line. Holly and birch trees bordered the valley streams and made a natural home for woodcock and snipe. The first day we hunted, six guns brought down 211 woodcock in a few hours. We employed men and boys for beaters, and I shall long remember the thrill of hundreds of woodcock darting zig-zag from the cover, the beaters moving in line through the valley, chanting "Hi, cock!" in unison.

My first assignment was to eliminate the salmon poaching—and that *was* a job. The peasants were apparently using some sort of poison in the streams, because we found many dead fish floating in the pools. They weren't dynamiting—we would have heard the detonation. Nor were they using lime. The contaminated water was analyzed in Dublin, but the chemists couldn't determine the poison.

With 13 men working under me, our stream patrol was rigid. Sometimes we encountered tenants along a stream late at night, when they had no proper business to be about. But invariably we found no incriminating evidence such as poison, lime or nets. After six months, I admitted defeat. When the water was low there would be a foray on the pools and the next morning we'd find hundreds of dead salmon afloat; but how the poachers got in their deadly work we couldn't discover.

I suppose you are beginning to wonder where that Irish setter bitch comes into my story, for I started to tell you about the greatest bird dog I ever saw, and here I am involved in a story about salmon poaching. But it all comes together eventually, as you will see.

At the far end of our valley, most remote from the manor house, was the moor holding the best grouse shooting on the property. This moor was between two glens. In one glen lived a family named O'Sullivan; in the other, a family named O'Shea. There were 27 small farms in the two glens; the O'Sheas accounted for 14, the O'Sullivans for 13. They were fine folk; tall, good-looking, courteous. Both the O'Sheas and O'Sullivans fancied dogs and they raised some fine Irish setters.

My first summer on the estate, I went up into this part of the property to survey grouse prospects. I was attempting to gain the confidence of the tenants, too, for I'd found when working as a game keeper in Scotland that it was far easier to minimize poaching if one treated the tenantry with consideration. I invariably stopped in to "hello" each family, inquire for their health, in the hope that they would come to consider me a friend rather than a private "peeler" for the Marquis.

One July afternoon I stopped in the glen to talk with several O'Sullivan families. One young lad, perhaps emboldened by the poteen of which we'd partaken, suddenly asked: "We've heard tell that you've judged the big field trials they do be having in Scotland and England 'beyond, and would it be too much to be asking for you to do the same here and judge our dogs in the week that's coming, when the O'Sullivans and O'Sheas will be holding our yearly trial?"

Here was strange news, indeed! Now, the tenants had the right to keep as many dogs as they liked, but had no right to run them on the grouse moors. And here was a field trial scheduled shortly before the Marquis would arrive from London with a party of friends for the shooting. And on our best moor, too!

"You're not supposed to work dogs on those moors," I replied. "If the Marquis knew this, he'd put a stop to it in a hurry."

"Oh, but Mr. Hogan, sure you nor any of your men leave the Big House but we here in the glen know it before you could say 'spalpeen,' and when you or the Marquis got here there wouldn't be a dog itself to be seen."

I realized the young fellow was correct. There was a grapevine method of communication throughout the estate and, should we try to stop their trial, they'd have plenty of warning to get the dogs off the moor. Suddenly it occurred to me to try to strike a bargain. I was anxious to get the salmon poisoning stopped, and just a day or two previously the Marquis had suggested a willingness to grant angling privileges—that is, the right to fish with hook and line for what salmon the tenants wanted to eat—in return for a promise to quit the fish poisoning.

I said: "Terrence, I might make a deal with you. If I consent to judge your field trial, and secure the Marquis' full consent for you to have trials, and with the additional right for all of you to fish with hook and line when you want salmon for the table, will you people, in turn, promise to cease forever your poisoning of fish?" And I added: "And in addition, you'll tell me how you've been able to keep poisoning these pools, and what you've been putting into the water?"

"Mr. Hogan," he replied, "I can't speak for all of us here in the glen, nor the O'Sheas beyond the mountain, but before today is a week you'll have our answer."

Upon my return I told the Marquis about my offer to the O'Sullivans. The Marquis was as astonished as I was that field trials were held on the estate. "I've been here for 30 years and I didn't know until now the tenants held field trials. They're a sly lot. But go ahead! Give them the right to fish with hook and line in return for their promise not to poison further, and judge their field trial, too. You might keep your eyes open for a good dog, too!" The Marquis had long wanted to acquire some top flight Irish setters.

In a few days, a delegation of the O'Sullivans and the O'Sheas came to my office. "We've decided to accept your offer."

First, I made them reveal their method of poisoning salmon. I had been a game keeper for a good many years; but these people had a way of poisoning that was unknown to me, and one probably used only in this particular valley. In that part of Ireland grows a weed called "bonikeen." I believe the botanical name is *spurge*. The weed is similar to the milkweed in this country, containing a milky sap.

The peasants would cut this weed into small pieces and put them in a gunny sack. At night, they would take these bags to the head of a pool, immerse them and, barefooted, jump up and down on the sacks and squeeze the milk out of the bonikeen. The milk had a paralyzing effect on the gills of the fish. When the substance had circulated through a pool, the salmon would jump for air, making tremendous leaps out of the water. Many would land on the shore, and the peasant women and children would seize and sack them. In a few moments, 15 or 20 people could have a big mess of fish.

The unfortunate part of it was that the milk remained in the water, penetrated down stream and gradually killed other fish over a period of hours. For every fish the peasants took home, 50 or 60 additional fish would eventually die. It was an insidious form of poisoning and when stamped out by my arrangement to permit the tenants to fish with hook and line, the streams improved immeasurably.

The field trial was to be held the first Sunday in August. I was asked to be on the moor by four o'clock in the morning, an early hour, indeed. But I was on hand, bursting with curiosity. What kind of a trial would these simple people have and how would the dogs perform? I can honestly say I have never gone to a field trial with more eagerness. Nor have I ever attended a more unusual one.

The O'Sullivans were noted for their hams—each family raised pigs and they were experts at curing and smoking meat. At 4 o'clock in the morning, the sun still hidden behind the heather rimmed mountain ridges, with peat smoke from the farm houses hanging low in the glen, we sat down to an open air breakfast of ham and eggs, the like of which I've never tasted before or since.

There were 27 entries in the trial, one from each family; 14 dogs from the O'Sheas, 13 from the O'Sullivans. As we sat about three long tables in the open—perhaps 100 souls, including the women and children—many wagers were offered and taken. The two clans, living amicably throughout the year, became determined opponents once each year, when the O'Shea dogs competed with the O'Sullivan dogs.

The first brace was cut loose about 5:30 or 6. In each brace an O'Sullivan entry was matched against an O'Shea entry. Both clans followed the running with intense interest. Never have I seen a gallery so absorbed in the running. When an O'Shea dog would make a sensational find, the cheers and cries from the O'Sheas would echo throughout the glen. Muttered ridicule from the O'Sullivans might provoke curses and high shouting in return. Twice during the running, fist fights were averted only when I threatened to withdraw unless the altercations ceased.

At 11 in the morning, we paused for the heat of the day to pass. We resumed the running about 3 in the afternoon, and by 5 o'clock, 13 braces had run, leaving only one entry, a bye, to complete the stake. When I called for the bye dog to come forward, Terrence O'Sullivan, the lad who had asked me to judge the trial, stepped proudly forth with a diminutive, trembling bitch.

"Here she is, Kathleen Ni Houlihan, the finest setter of all Ireland," he announced, with a firm look at one of the O'Sheas, the owner of the dog which up to that time was high dog in the stake. Everyone knew that on this little bitch the hopes of the O'Sullivans rested. Kathleen Ni Houlihan must win—or the O'Sullivans were defeated.

Kathleen was the smallest Irish setter I've ever seen. She couldn't have weighed more than 30 pounds—about the size of a miniature poodle. I looked down at her and thought, "Poor little bitch, you've a big job on your hands today." She wagged her tail; her dark, tar-brown eyes snapped in seeming defiance. "Cut her loose," I cried.

The little bitch flew off. In two minutes I knew I was looking at one of the greatest dogs I'd ever seen. Never have I seen a dog—no matter the breed—move with the grace and style of that little Irish setter. Her tail action was most thrilling—a russet plume dancing merrily through the purple heather.

Speed! You remember some fast ground races by English pointers? Well, I do, too; but I've never seen a dog equal to Kathleen. And on point—Michael Angelo himself would have been hard pressed to delineate the grace and symmetry of that little bitch as she stood, transfixed, on her first find—a single grouse.

She held her head imperiously high; her tail stood straight out of the heather. Her manners were perfect. She was as steady as a rock to the flush. We didn't shoot, not even blanks, but I could tell by every movement she made—or rather failed to make—that had an old eight-gauge been fired over her head, she'd have stood as steady as the Blarney stone.

For 30 minutes she held me enthralled. She is the one dog of which

I can say, after 50 years of handling dogs: "This was the one that had everything."

I don't need to tell you boys the beauty of a top flight running dog. It's the poetry of motion, of rhythm, in its highest form, as aesthetic as dancing or sculpture.

And Kathleen had it all. She was the greatest class dog I've ever seen in the field.

At the conclusion of her heat, there was no question in my mind about the winner—Kathleen was the one. But my book showed that the O'Shea dog had had more finds. The ground race of the O'Shea entry, the style, the class, couldn't compare with Kathleen's, but the record of finds was hard to rule out. True, the O'Shea dog had run over a better course, and before the birds had been widely scattered—but in a trial finds are hard to laugh off.

I decided to call a second series. I looked forward to watching a great race, in which my favorite would so outclass the O'Shea dog that even the O'Sheas would admit defeat graciously.

When I announced a second series, the crowd went wild. The poteen bottles had been freely circulating all afternoon and many of the men were in high and boisterous spirits. Once again, wagers flew about—wagers, not of money, as these simple people had little of that, but of bacon, hams, eggs, and some of the women wagered butter!

The two dogs bounded forth, with undiminished eagerness. Although Kathleen had just completed a 30-minute heat, and the O'Shea dog had had several hours rest, Kathleen immediately took the lead and made a tremendous cast over a slope. Just as Kathleen came back from over the ridge, head high into the wind, she swung into a point with that style I can never forget. Silhouetted against the saphhire, cloud-flecked sky, she was a bronze statue emerging from the heather about her feet! As long as I live, I'll remember that point.

The O'Shea dog, seeing her point, came in closely, and backed with perfect manners. We hurried up. Twice I saw Kathleen half turn her head, bare her teeth and snarl at the backing dog. Suddenly, like a fury, Kathleen wheeled and nailed the O'Shea dog on the muzzle!

In 30 seconds the greatest performing Irish setter I've ever seen killed her chance for first place. When the owners had parted the dogs, Kathleen, heretofore handling like a glove, disobeyed all her master's shouted commands, and streaked across the moor, down into the glen, and back to her home.

Her young master finally abandoned trying to stop her and, turning to me, disconsolately said: "Poor Kathleen—she just can't bear to have an O'Shea dog back her."

Then, defiantly, as shouts of victory were arising from the O'Shea contingent: "But she'll find more birds, day in, day out, than any dog in Ireland."

"I don't doubt that, my lad," I said, "and I think I might be able to break her to accept a back. I'd like to own Kathleen. Right now, I'd offer 25 pounds for her."

"Oh, no, Mr. Hogan, Kathleen is not for sale."

I offered 50 pounds. Seventy-five. I stretched myself to 100 pounds. Terrence O'Sullivan, who probably to his dying day never had so much as a five-pound note in his pocket at one time, declined all offers. Finally, to brush aside by persistence, or perhaps not to appear rude, young Terrence laughingly said:

"Sure, Mr. Hogan, the O'Sullivans never sell a good dog. If it's a good one, we keep it ourselves. If it's a poor one, we give it to the O'Sheas beyond the glen."

Darkness closed in. The snowfall thickened. There was a long pause when Martin ceased speaking.

Finally he continued: "Whenever I hear people in this country ridicule the Irish setter, I smile and say to myself: 'Had I been able to lay hands upon her, Kathleen Ni Houlihan would be known today far, far beyond the hills and glens of the County Kerry—she'd be known everywhere that great dogs are known.'"

Bear Valley Pay Day

By TED TRUEBLOOD

THEY SAY THERE ARE MORE WAYS THAN ONE TO SKIN A CAT. I wouldn't know. For my money, any dead cat is a good cat, and I don't care whether he is skinned or not.

There also is more than one way to catch a salmon. I found that out for myself. My brother Burtt is a strong advocate of the whoop, holler and cuss method, while I place my faith in a tight line and silent prayer. I have prayed in some pretty fair fish.

I think maybe his method is better. I always can tell when he hooks one, and I start running with the camera. Once I met a bull elk running hell-bent my way when I was sprinting through a patch of jackpines to cut across a bend in the creek. I think it scared me worse than the elk.

Burtt caught that particular salmon. It was a six-jump, six-whoop and two-holler fish—a good one. I got there just in time to watch him turn it loose and congratulate him on a salmon-strike bellow that put the fear of disaster in a bull elk. I'd have made it sooner, but my legs seemed a little rubbery.

Because things like that always are coming up when you are salmon fishing, it is no sport for anybody with a weak heart. The tension it builds up is terrific. From the time the duffel is loaded into the car until the first fish is landed there is a constantly increasing pressure. Last time we had it bad.

My wife, my brother and I arrived in Bear Valley after sunset. By the time we found a place to camp it was too dark to see whether there were any salmon in the big pool near by—and that wasn't even decent. Camping within casting distance of a good salmon pool and not being able to see whether there are fish in it is worse than living across the alley from a girls' dormitory with frosted glass in all the windows.

Burtt and I hurriedly built a fire, cut a big armload of wood and then finished making camp while Ellen was getting supper. After we had eaten we sat around the fire a long time, speculating on the fishing we might have during the two days we had to stay. Finally we went to bed.

When I woke up, the cold light of dawn was seeping in through the tent and I could hear a fire crackling and bacon sizzling. Burtt was up, and breakfast was nearly ready. With the aroma of coffee and bacon drifting into the tent, it didn't take Ellen and me long to tumble out of bed and dress. When we stepped outside, we discovered that, even though it was August 12, it was cold. Everything was covered with heavy white frost, and there was ice in the wash-pan. Bear Valley is 6,500 feet above sea-level.

We finished breakfast, set up our tackle and were ready to go fishing before sunup. Walking down to the pool, I felt like a shop-girl getting ready for a date with Frank Sinatra. Something wonderful might happen. I was afraid it wouldn't, but maybe it would!

At the lower end of the pool we cautiously peered through the willows. Man alive! There were half a dozen salmon in about two feet of moderately swift water a few yards above the riffle.

We eased back and held a parley. A little strip of gravel behind a fringe of willows twenty feet downstream from the fish was decided upon as the best spot from which to operate, and when we matched for first cast I won. I moved into position and snapped the rod back and forth a couple of times to get the feel of it. Everything in the world depended on that cast.

I flipped the lure out, and luckily it landed just right. I started reeling, and the wabbler began to move toward the fish, fluttering and darting as I manipulated the rod. When it was a yard away, they hadn't moved. Two feet, one foot; they seemed to ignore it. The lure was even with their noses. They lay there like logs. I began to hate them. Just as it passed, one of the smaller fish turned and followed it leisurely. I kept the wabbler coming. He kept coming. I reeled a trifle faster. He swam a trifle faster.

Finally the lure was nearly in. It was starting down over the riffle, ten feet away, with the salmon just behind. You couldn't have slipped your hand between the wabbler and his nose. Closer and closer. A few more turns of the reel handle, and I'd have the lure right up on the bank. I looked down on the salmon over the low willows and could count his spots.

The wabbler was within inches of the beach when it happened. The salmon opened his mouth, slipped up on the wabbler and snapped his jaws shut like a rat trap. I socked him as he whirled around with his tail half out of the shallow water.

The dynamite exploded, and away he went. The salmon streaked down the creek, I shot out of the willows, the line poured out of the guides, and a thousand acres of Bear Valley silence went wherever silence goes. Burtt whooped, hollered and cussed. Ellen screamed. I prayed, reeled and ran—down the creek and around the bend. The reel hummed. The salmon jumped, and jumped again. If every chinook I caught meant a year off my life I'd fish for them until I died.

Down the creek a hundred yards I finally led him in, and Burtt slipped the home-made gaff into his gills. He was a prime fish, a small male, probably 6 or 8 pounds. I don't know what he weighed, and I don't care. Right then I wouldn't have traded him for a box-car full of Powers models. Burtt held him while I snapped a picture.

Then we all sat down on a log to relax, and Burtt said, "Brother, this is the day they give babies away!"

He was right.

After we took a smoke, I dressed my fish and carried him to camp. We tried another cast or two for the salmon in the pool beside the camp, but they were nervous and suspicious and would not strike; so we started down the creek.

For a quarter of a mile the stream flowed swiftly over an even bed with no holes likely to harbor a salmon. We hiked briskly along until we reached a spot where it glided over a riffle and flattened out into a pool possibly fifty yards across and two hundred long. In such water salmon normally lie either in the current just below the riffle or near the tail of the pool where the water quickens to drop over the next bar.

We were unable to see any fish at the head of the pool, and a half a dozen inquiring casts failed to bring any action; so we walked slowly on toward the tail, watching the water carefully for fish that might be cruising between the two favored spots. About halfway down the pool Ellen spotted a pair of fish swimming slowly upstream about two-thirds of the way to the other bank.

Her first cast fell a little short, but her second was just right, about fifteen feet ahead of the fish and a little beyond. She began to reel slowly, bringing the lure across just in front of them. The smaller of the two swung after the little red-and-white plug and followed it for twenty feet, but then turned back and continued upstream with his companion. Although we made several more casts, we failed to interest them further.

Just above the riffle we saw four salmon in water not more than eighteen inches deep. One was fairly large, two were about the size of the one I caught in the pool beside camp, and the fourth was a jack. It didn't take us ten seconds to decide we wanted that jack salmon.

Now, according to some of the experts, a jack salmon is a male chinook that develops sexually before he gets his growth. Consequently he gets the urge to run with the big salmon when he is only about the size of a good trout, sixteen inches to two feet long.

From the scientific standpoint, that may be correct. From the angler's side of the fence, the description is as inadequate as saying a ruffed grouse is a gallinaceous bird resembling the barnyard chicken. A jack salmon is the most amazing combination of coil springs, dynamite and live rubber ever put together in the form of a fish. I've caught some that went into the air ten times during the first ten seconds, bouncing off the water between jumps like a racing outboard on a windy day.

Burtt made a cast well beyond the four salmon and let it drift until his lure was just right to reel in front of the jack, which was the farthest downstream. As he began to reel, one of the medium-size salmon started drifting backward. By the time the lure was in front of the jack the larger fish was beside him. Any pessimist could guess what happened. The jack gave the lure a disdainful look and sidled away, but the larger salmon went for it like a government man for a sixteen-page questionnaire.

It was fun, even if it wasn't the fish we wanted. The salmon chased all over the pool and finally sliced down through the riffle, jumping half a dozen times in the process. Burtt whooped, hollered and cussed plenty before he finally worked it in and gaffed it. It was another male about the size of mine.

Continuing downstream, we skirted the edge of a bluff and found the next fish in a deep, moderately swift run which swung in a curve toward our bank. We worked our lures down toward them from above.

The fish that struck was a wild, crazy salmon that acted like a 12-inch rainbow. He wasn't as fast as a jack, but there certainly weren't any barnacles on his hull. He saw the wabbler coming when it was six feet away and charged it like a scared rabbit bursting out of a brush pile. I struck, but he was coming straight toward me, so that I couldn't set the hooks too well. When he felt them, he sailed high out of the water in a magnificent leap—and that was all. One split fraction of a second I could see the wabbler in his mouth, and the next it was sailing through the air and he was free.

We approached the next pool more carefully, and there Ellen raised, hooked and landed her first fish. It was a beautiful male in prime condition, but was not spectacular. He broke water only once, although he put up a strong, determined fight.

I'm afraid we'll never see a day like that again. A lazy breeze was herding a few fluffy clouds around the sky, and the temperature was delightful. Bear Valley's miles of knee-high grass were sprinkled with wildflowers. The water was clear as quartz crystal, and neither too high nor too low.

But best of all, the salmon, fresh-run and present in uncountable numbers, were in just the right mood. Some struck like native trout. Others had to be coaxed. In fact, the lure usually had to be presented exactly right, and sometimes several changes were necessary to find a plug that would interest a fish. Once in a while we could not get a strike out of a pool at all. It was fishing that kept us on our toes.

One of the prime blessings was that the salmon ran small. Most of them would weigh between 8 and 12 pounds, which was just right for our light tackle. On fish that size we could reasonably expect to land about 80 per cent of those we hooked. We saw a few big ones, salmon that would weigh in the neighborhood of 20 pounds, but we didn't cast to them. We were fishing for fun, not records, and playing a fish for two or three hours or longer gets tiresome.

After killing a fish apiece we left the gaff stuck up beside the creek and started turning them back. It was a grand day to experiment. We had started fishing with our hottest lures, naturally, but after playing a few fish we began to try new plugs and wabblers. After running through his entire assortment of lures, Burtt settled on an old-fashioned, minnow-shaped plug with a small spinner blade fore and aft. It was colored like a little Dolly Varden, had a slow motion and sank fast. It was deadly!

I experimented with various spinner combinations, getting one fellow on a hammered brass Bear Valley spinner with a red-and-white bucktail, but that was all. My experience checked with that of previous trips when spinners always came out at the bottom of the list as salmon lures. Except for Burtt's yellow-green plug, small red-and-white sinking lures, either plugs or metal wabblers, were best. After a while, away downstream, we noticed that the sun was getting close to the western mountains.

We had left camp that morning without a lunch, but with the firm intention of returning along in the middle of the day, grabbing a bite to eat, resting a while and getting in on the evening fishing. We got in on the evening fishing, all right, but it was darker than the back door of a coal mine when we finally stumbled into camp, and long before we arrived I was so hungry that I found myself envying the beavers because they could strip a meal off the most convenient willow.

Once we got in, however, it didn't take long to get a meal on the fire, and in less than an hour we were eating salmon steaks and corn on the cob. Right after dinner we did the dishes and tumbled into bed. And we were asleep almost before we could pull up the covers.

Next day we were honest enough to admit that we'd never get back to camp before dark; so we packed a good lunch to take along. We ate about noon under a solitary pine beside Bear Valley Creek, where the breeze fanned through just strong enough to make the asters nod and discourage the occasional mosquito that had survived the freeze the night we arrived. It was the most pleasant noon hour I've ever enjoyed.

We had two or three salmon apiece to our credit—all of which had been released—and we had been fishing long enough so that we could relax and enjoy ourselves. The air was just halfway between too cool and too warm. You get a lot of summer days like that at high altitudes, and they have the same grand-to-be-alive quality that October days often have at lower elevations. One of the best ways to enjoy them is to lie down in the sun with your hat over your face and go to sleep. Which we did.

While I was asleep I dreamed I was rich, and when we woke up I told Ellen and Burtt about it.

"What would you do if you had a million dollars?" Ellen asked me.

Her question set off a discussion that lasted for some time, but Burtt terminated it with this remark: "If I had all the money I wanted and could go any place I wanted to go and do anything I wanted to do, I'd be sitting right here in Bear Valley under this pine tree, getting ready to go salmon fishing in about five minutes!"

A Shift in the Wind

By SIGURD OLSON

MY MIND WAS MADE UP. I WOULD WORK ALL DAY SATURDAY and might even go to church on Sunday morning. The more I thought about it, the more decisive and masterful I became. My old gypsy ways were over. I was beginning to see that there was infinitely more satisfaction in getting a host of long-neglected jobs out of the way than in heading for the rice beds to what I knew would be just another fiasco as far as ducks were concerned. I felt virtuous and substantial. This weekend I'd stay home.

But as the days passed and Friday night was only a matter of hours away, a strange excitement filled my being. I had a feeling that something unusual was going to happen and I was never one to take my hunches lightly. There was, I began to sense, just the barest ghost of a chance that the wind might shift for perhaps an hour, just long enough to make them uneasy. One shot would be enough, one last flock careening over the decoys.

Another thing, it was getting late. October was getting well along and though the weather wasn't ripe, it was the time of year when anything might happen and wouldn't it be criminal to be caught with a shovel in one's hand or pushing a wheelbarrow with the flight coming down? And this I knew, too, that when the ducks did come, they would come with a rush. All they needed was a jittery temperature and a shift of the breeze to send them hurtling down out of the north.

And though the days for a month had been warm, I knew the snow soon would be flying and then it would be all over, portages covered with yellowing leaves, the rice beds blue and gold. There was just a chance something might happen and it wouldn't hurt to take a little swing around to look things over. If there was nothing doing, I would turn right around and come back, finish that perennial bed, the storm windows and the other things that had been waiting all fall.

"Thought you were staying home this weekend," queried Elizabeth, as she watched me stack the tools. "You know there isn't a chance of a flight this weekend any more than last. The weather report says there will be no change and you know yourself the barometer is steady."

I tried to explain that I had been having a feeling that most barometers couldn't register, a sort of a hunch that something might happen which would redeem the past barren month, that to play safe I'd decided to look things over once more, a sort of final reconnaissance, so to speak.

Two hours later, I was in my old blind looking at the same old duckless skyline, watching the slowly drifting haze of forest smoke and a coppery sun working its way over the northern Minnesota wild rice beds. A lone mallard took to the air far down shore, winged its way leisurely toward the horizon. I followed its slow, almost tired flight until it was a mere speck drifting over the trees. For a moment it disappeared and then I saw it again, now steadily holding one position. Suddenly, I realized that it was larger, that it had changed the direction of flight and was coming toward me.

The bird was dropping fast toward the rice bed it had left, then rose once more high above the trees; another low flying circle close to the water and then to my delighted eyes there were two heading swiftly toward my blind. No chance of that pair decoying to a bunch of bluebills off a point. They were looking for some quiet, shallow bay down the lake. There was just a chance, however, that they might come within range.

I slipped off my safety, got set—no use even trying to call that pair—a chance for a double if they were close—hold dead on and pull ahead. Another few seconds and they would be in range. Big birds they were and slow, heavy with the rice they'd been feeding on all fall; not too much of a lead. One was slightly ahead. I held to the point of its bill, followed through and fired, turned quickly and caught the second as it was climbing for the clouds. Both birds were falling now, fell almost together in twin water spouts in the midst of the decoys.

In a moment I had them back in the blind, a greenhead and his mate, laid them close beside me where I could watch the changing colors of their plumage and where I could feel them once in a while just to know my luck had changed. We would have them for Sunday dinner stuffed with wild rice, some cranberries and all the trimmings, concrete evidence of my excellent judgment. I was almost happy as I stood there congratulating myself, almost forgot that my good fortune wasn't due to a shifting of the wind or a change of weather; almost forgot that what I really hoped would happen, that the flight of northern bluebills would somehow get under way, seemed no nearer to materialization.

A raven wheeled high in the still smoky blue, circling, floating on the light breeze. One wing, I noticed, had lost a feather. It was a rather ragged looking pinion and the bird seemed to favor that side more than the other.

The great bird swung toward me, spiraled sharply downward and lit in a pine tree back of the blind. Then and there it proceeded to tell the world what it thought and watched me with a mind, I was sure, to the potential carrion it hoped I might become. While watching the raven and marveling at the superb scratchiness of its voice, I suddenly became conscious of a difference in the behavior of the blocks. For hours they had bobbed steadily, sedately, never changing position; but now they were bouncing around frantically, pulling their anchor strings, getting together in peculiar and undignified formations; all that, in spite of the fact that there had been no apparent change of wind. I had been so busy visiting with the raven that I had failed to notice what was going on, but now I watched the sky, the decoys and the water with new excitement.

Long experience had taught me that decoys can be as good barometers of weather change as the waves themselves. Now they were riding quietly for the first time since I came and the water was dead calm. Then a long series of riffles started out from shore and the rice bent and swayed beyond the decoys, swayed toward the south in a distinct breeze from the hills behind me. In half an hour the air began to clear as the wind out of the north steadied and I knew my hunch had been correct. At least for the moment, things were different.

If it would only hold, the ducks back in the innumerable pot holes and beaver flowages would get restless and begin to move. I watched those new riffles and prayed. If they stayed, my weekends of waiting would not have been in vain, my sacrifice of the perennials would be more than justified and everything else answered for.

The sky began to darken with real clouds, not smoke this time, and the shores changed from their old sunny gray and red to a somber dullness. The coppery sun disappeared entirely and the air grew appreciably colder. If I were a mallard or even a bluebill, I thought excitedly, and saw what was in the wind, I would pick right up, no matter where I happened to be, and streak straight for the south.

But the mallards did not share my excitement, or the bluebills, and two long hours went by before anything happened. Then came a swift hurricane of wings that almost took my breath away, one closely packed, lonesome bunch of bluebills streaking it down the channel with the speed that only miles of flying can give. Far out of range, the flock bore steadily for the west end of the rice bed with a surety of purpose that bespoke no interest in me, the decoys, or the wonderful stand of rice along my side of the shore. I watched desperately as they grew smaller and smaller, faded at last against the rocks and trees of the far end of the lake. Then, for a panicky moment, I thought I had lost them entirely, that drifting patch of black dots soaring for a moment into the blue only to fuse an instant later with the haze. Then, miracle of miracles, the dots suddenly grew more distinct again, swung swiftly into the wind and came once more down the center of the channel, this time directly toward my point. I crouched, got under cover, prayed with all my soul once more. This was the moment, this the realization of the hunch I had had all week. All I asked was one short chance.

They were getting larger, swinging toward shore, would surely be in range if they held their present course. Still too high, but as they went over I called steadily, seductively, saw them hesitate, then veer. They had heard and were coming over. This time it would be different.

I shifted my stance, parted the brush in front of me, braced myself in good shooting position, got set.

They were swinging in now, a matter of seconds and they would be in range. Perennials, storm windows, fertilizer and shrubbery, what piddling, mediocre stuff. This was worth dying for.

My safety was off, a new shell in the chamber. A split second and they were in—over the decoys—pandemonium—whistling wings—outstretched necks—tails and feet braced for the landing—consternation as I rose.

"Pick your bird and hold dead on; don't shoot at the bunch; always pick a single." The old admonitions flashed into mind. I drew hastily on a big black and white drake, fired and watched with joy as he crumpled neatly and lit. Turning, I drew speedily on another quartering away, saw him skate on the water, bounce with his momentum. And they were gone as swiftly as they had come.

But what was that? A lone single had separated himself from the flock and was tearing back along the shoreline as though possessed. He was coming high, just at the limit of range, would pass right over my point, a perfect overhead shot. Once again I held at the end of a bill boring into space, this time with a feeling that I could not miss, followed an instant as the extremity of the angle swept just ahead and fired. At the report, he folded his wings, did a somersault, dive for the rice bed, struck in a funnel of spray. It was the sort of shot one remembers all winter long and I yelled for the sheer joy that was mine. That alone was worth the whole season of waiting, days of standing around with nothing to while away the hours but the chickadees and whiskey jacks, the long empty days with not a wing moving. This was more than compensation, it was double proof that my judgment was infallible.

Pushing the canoe out into the rice, I picked up my ducks almost reverently, two drakes and a hen, all well feathered and plump, the first of the northerns. Back on shore, I hung them carefully in the crotch of an aspen, hung my two mallards just below, admired them to my heart's content. No ordinary birds those, each one a thrilling shot, a story in itself.

I watched the horizon an hour longer, but not another duck swung into view. The shifting of the wind had unsettled one lone flock or perhaps it was just my luck. In any case, the rest of the bluebills knew and to prove that contention, the sun came out once more and the clouds evaporated into the same old hazy sky I had known for a month. Gradually, the wind shifted back to its accustomed corner in the southwest and the flight was over.

Tomorrow, I reflected, was Sunday. Chances were that after this lone heaven-sent flurry, nothing would stir for another week. I decided to pick up my outfit, my five beautiful ducks, and go home. In the morning, I thought righteously, I would go to church as a substantial citizen should. I might even get up early and attack that perennial bed or take off the screens. Here was a chance to redeem myself in the eyes of the world.

As I paddled down the lake that afternoon, my mind was at peace and I was happy, happy with the knowledge that I was doing right and that all was well. But at the portage I did an unforgivable thing for a man who has made up his mind. I turned to have one last look at the rice beds against the sunset, stood there athrill with their beauty, watching and wondering. Suddenly against the rosy sky was a long V of black dots and the peace that was mine a moment before vanished swiftly. There must have been a hundred and they were settling into the rice near the blind I had left. And there were more, flock after flock in silhouette against the sky. The rice was alive with wings. These ducks, I knew, were riding in ahead of a storm. The flight was on.

For a long time I stood without moving, watched the incoming flocks until it grew too dark to see, wondering what to do. And then I knew, for after all I had promised no one but myself. Almost stealthily, I cached the decoys where I could find them easily in the dark of the morning, threw on the canoe, plodded up the portage toward home.

The Tail-Ender

By HENRY P. DAVIS

THERE ARE TWO KINDS OF PEOPLE IN MY HOME TOWN: THOSE WHO foxhunt—and those who don't. The latter class is not very popular.

Newcomers receive a cordial welcome, for we are hospitable folks. But the news that they have moved into a foxhunting community is imparted in a polite, roundabout, but quite definite way.

Cap'n Jeff, the official greeter, will say, "We're glad to have you folks among us. We'll try to make you feel at home and we hope you'll be happy here. If you happen to hear, and I reckon you will, a pack of hounds running sometimes late at night, don't let it bother you. It's just us foxhunters having some fun. And we'd be mighty glad to have you join us." That's the official invitation—and the only one ever extended.

Take it or leave it. If the invitation is accepted, all well and good.

All courtesies possible are extended. If no interest is shown or weak excuses made, there is no lessening of hospitality, but the head of the house finds himself outside the "inner circle" until, as many do, he "tries out" foxhunting. Once inoculated, he generally becomes one of the regulars.

There are three kinds of foxhunters in my Home Town: fox-hunters who are everything the name implies, owning their own hounds and hunting them; foxhunters who sit on their front porches and listen to the hound chorus as it ebbs and flows across the rolling countryside—and "joiners."

Which brings us around to Tal Murray. Old Tal Murray, a self-effacing landmark in our community, who did much for many without thought of credit to himself. No one knows how much. Nobody even gives it a thought. But just bring up his name in the nightly drug store conversation and there comes to every old-timer present a smile, a skipped heart beat, the memory of "Tail-ender." For Tal Murray owned Tail-ender, a hound well remembered in our community. Some called him great. Well-remembered in our community means the same thing.

Tal and Tail-ender embodied the spirit of the chase—and a man's love for, and pride in, his dog. For a good many reasons, Tal had been a "joiner." He had no hounds of his own, but no matter in what section we hunted he would generally turn up. We got so we sort of listened for the "clopaclopclop" of the little bay mare he called his "noddin' hoss" when the hunt was up and the going good. He always timed his arrival properly. When the race was on and everyone was in high fettle and "joiners" were welcome, someone would say, "Well, I reckon old Tal'll be along d'rectly." Sure enough, presently around the bend would come the nodding head of bay Ella, with Tal sitting straight as an Indian in the saddle. As he eased alongside he'd invariably say, "Jumped him, ain't yuh?"

Yes, Tal was always welcome. Quiet, unobtrusive and under-standing, he said little and what he did say was kindly, considerate and encouraging. No matter whose dog was leading, to Tal the pack was always "right." No man loved foxhunting more and he knew every foot of the country for miles around. So we often wondered why he didn't have a hound or two of his own. Why his abundant praise was lavished on our hounds instead of some who ate his own pot-licker. No one chided him about it, for, as I say, Tal was always welcome.

One night Tal was late. Old Red had been giving our hounds merry hell, and vice versa, for more than an hour when we came upon him. As we topped the highest point on Devil's Backbone, Tal was standing by a rock in the moonlight, Ella tethered placidly, but attentively, nearby.

Sharply silhouetted against a background of moonlight, Tal was listening to mellow music made by the four-footed chorus which swung up and over and through the rough country below. Mumbling to himself, we thought. Then we saw that at his side crouched a dog, eager of ears and tail a-wag.

"By Joe," said one. "Old Tal's got hisse'f a houn'."

And sure enough he had. Tal was immediately overwhelmed with banter of one sort or another—congratulatory and otherwise. But with all our rough talk we were genuinely interested, and he knew it. So he let us have our fling. And what a fling we had! No one listened to the race that was going on, hammer and tongs, in the valley below us. Forgotten was the argument about whether Jimminy Cricket or Martha was leading the pack. Forgotten was everything except *Old Tal has a hound!*

The Colonel took no part in our chatter. Just sat on his horse and looked at Tal's hound. For, time after time, he had offered old Tal his pick of a litter and I guess he was just about as curious as we were. With a nod of his head he called me to him and whispered, "Kick up a fire and we'll look at Mr. Murray's hound. I think he'd like to tell us about him."

We didn't need a fire for warmth, although the night was cool. But there is something about a fire in the open, daytime or night, that draws folks, makes them sort of thaw out, physically, mentally and conversationally.

As the flickering flame mingled with moonbeams melting through the scrub oak everybody, including Tal, gathered 'round.

He came in and stood—with a raw-boned young hound at his side. I won't forget the sight, for moonlight threw the shadows of both across us all. Even across my puny little fire, Tal had the spotlight tonight. The dog seemed to sense, too, that he was the focus point of all eyes. He shrank against Tal's booted leg and stood with lowered flag and quivering muscles.

There was both apology and pride in Tal's voice as he spoke his piece. "Wal, y'all seem to wonder 'bout this here pup," he said, "so I reck'n I'd better tell you 'bout him. I've wanted a real fox dog fur a long time so I could reely feel like I was *one* of you fellers when I joined up with you these nights. Wanted to git my dog in my own way. Never seemed to find one to suit. Till t'other day that hoss trader feller, that comes through here twicet a year and camps in my pasture, turned into my road lookin' like a cucus peerade.

"Had a span of spangled calicos pullin' his waggin and strung out behind it was fo'teen head of the dangest lookin' hoss-flesh y'ever seen. All but two or three were jus' plain snides.

"At the tail end of the procession, this here young houn' come a trottin' along, proud as Piety and purty as a prize punkin. An' I said right there 'That's the houn' I'm a-lookin' fur.'

"So the fust thing I know that hoss trader feller had that old heavey mare of mine—an' I had fo' dollars an' this here houn'. Got papers on him, too, long as a black snake. He come from down in Jefferson county and I figured he'd fit in right well with y'all's pack."

Tal leaned down and stroked the velvet ear of his new possession and waited for our approval—which he promptly got. Our enthusiasm pleased the old fellow mightily and he led his dog out for closer inspection. He was a good looking black and tan, with white points and a white shirt front.

"Tried him out yet?" asked someone.

"Nope," answered Tal. "Thought I'd wait and see how you fellers cottoned to him. Thought mebbe y'all might not like my havin' a houn' that come from aways off."

He was reassured on that point and we were all for putting him in the race that night but Tal begged off. "Ef y'all don't mind," he said, "I'd like to let him just go 'long an' lissen. Sorter git the lay of things, and used to us. That hoss trader feller g'arnteed him as a real fox dog and I shore hope he is. . . . Anyhow, that old heavey mare wa'nt wuth much more'n fo' dollars."

Business called me away for a while and when I returned the season was on the wane. My first question to the Colonel was, "How's Tal's hound?"

"He'll run, but he won't pack," he said. "Good mouth—and stays. But always behind. As if he is a little bit afraid to fight for the lead. Grand nose. Runs like a streak by himself. Can unravel any check. But he must have been mauled, for he's pack-shy. Always behind—but not far. Remember the night we came across the two of 'em? And Tal said he first saw the dog at the tail-end of the horse trader's troop? Well, he's still in that position in our pack. And the boys have named him—Tail-ender!"

"How does Tal take that?" I asked.

"Oh, you know Tal. He doesn't seem to mind. Thinks that hound is the greatest dog that ever happened. Says he'll show us all some day. And I wouldn't be surprised if he does. Hope so, anyway."

The Colonel was very fond of old Tal Murray. Liked his young hound, too. He never engaged in the raillery which always followed Tail-ender as he swung by some hundred yards in the rear of the pack. Along toward the end of the season, and even after, for that matter, we noticed that several times a week he'd saddle Fairy in mid-afternoon and jog away, with one or two couples of old and pensioned hounds at heel. "Just going to give the 'old folks' a little exercise," he'd tell Mother. "But dont wait supper on me." And he always took the lower road which led to Tal Murray's.

I suspected that he and Tal had something on the fire and ventured so far one day as to ask him, "How's Tail-ender coming along? You and Tal must..."

He silenced me with a look and said, "Tal may have a surprise for the boys next season."

Four of our bitches spent that summer out at Tal's.

"Thought they might like a change of scenery," the Colonel said by way of explanation. A harem for Tail-ender, I thought. But not out loud.

We gathered in the Sundown Hills for the first meet of the season. Always a gala occasion, the Hell-or-High-Water foxhunting clan *really* turned out this time. Horseback, muleback, in buggies and afoot, the countryside congregated to partake of the bounty provided by the Colonel and Cap'n Zack and listen to music mankind cannot make.

Black Newby and his helpers, Tobe and Kip, were busy at the barbecue pit, "mopping" the meat of a good sized yearling bull, two goats and a pair of sheep, with juice from the sauce pail, when the Colonel and Cap'n Zack rode up in late afternoon. Esau, the "hound boy," staked his charges out under the hill, away from cantankerous horses and curious kids. The barrel of persimmon beer was tapped and tasted, saddle cinches loosened and all was ready for the frolic. And, in less time than it takes to tell, it began. There was the usual round of greetings as each "joiner" arrived but soon there was a general settling down to plain and fancy eating of the barbecue and trimmin's.

All the regulars were there—all but Tal. I wondered about that. But soon the moon peeped up over the ridge and gave us a knowing nod, and *here came Tal.* Astride Ella as usual, with Tail-ender proudly trotting along close by. And at his side was our old limping Fly, who had run the pads off her left hind foot years ago and about whom I'd almost forgotten. The Colonel had given her to Tal one day saying, "She'll be company for Tail—er, your dog."

When Tal rode into the grove someone chuckled and said, "Just look at that combination! Old Tal, a stumblin' mare, a crippled bitch and a shy dog. Ain't we got fun!" The Colonel smiled, but said nothing.

As Tal dismounted, old Fly caught a glimpse of the picket line below and hobbled down the hill to renew acquaintance with her former kennel mates. Tail-ender trotted along, too. Presently a yell from Esau and a roar from a score or more hounds' throats brought us all to our feet and up running. Tail-ender had our Tattler down. And was giving him—the big boisterous, blustering bully of the pack— the licking of his life! Tail-ender, the shy, was a ball of fire and fury and it took the combined efforts of Esau and Tal to pull him off the chastised Tattler.

"Well, can you beat that?" one said. "The worm has turned! Whatch' been feedin' him, Tal? Gunpowder?" Tal merely smiled.

"Seem lak he makin' up fuh los' time," chuckled Esau. " 'At Tat-tluh dawg needed jes' whut he got."

We lingered over the board as the moon came up. Tal and the Colonel were talking together as Tal nibbled on a meaty rib. I eased over and heard the Colonel say in low tones, "We could cast him away first, let him strike and then put the pack in if you'd like, Tal."

The old man smiled and replied, "Thanky, Colonel. But I'd ruther he took his chances with t'others. From the way he jumped Tattler hit looks like our experiment is gonna work."

The Colonel rose. "Let's mount, gentlemen, and see what the night will offer." A short blast on the horn and the pack was straining at the picket line, flags up, eyes eager and mouths a-whine.

They were cast in the valley below us and faded away like silent skirmishers. None was left except old Fly who plodded along by Tal. Presently a roll of music rang from the ridge on the far side of the valley, rippling its liquid note over the open spaces and into the scrub oak hills. "What hound?" asked one. And ten voices cried, *"Tail-ender, by gad!"*

Tal looked at the Colonel and fairly beamed. "Now we'll see," he said as the pack harked in.

It is only natural for a pack-mauled hound, or one otherwise made shy, to relinquish the lead quickly and willingly, drop back to the rear or even quit entirely when the pack harks in to his strike. We all knew that Tail-ender could run like a tornado when he wanted to. And we all knew that he was, or had been, pack-shy. So we held our breaths as we rode to the crossing and waited for the rolling cascade of music to come back over the hills. We loved and respected old Tal more than he knew and we, to a man, wanted this drama to end happily. Our worries were wasted.

For true to his usual custom, Master Greycoat looped and came straight through "carryin' the mail." Behind him, head up and tail high, reached Tail-ender, in that swinging frictionless gallop which does not recognize fatigue. And behind Tail-ender—*behind* him, mind you—came the pack, its mixed chorus playing the accompaniment for Tail-ender's solo! *Behind* him then and behind him all through that race—for Tail-ender, the shy, had come into his own.

And why not, please? Hadn't he been the boss of his own kennel all summer? Hadn't he licked the bully of the pack? Hadn't he struck and jumped that fox? Wasn't he as good as any hound in that pack— or any other pack? You bet—and now he was out to show 'em! And show 'em he did. No dog had his nose in front of Tail-ender that night.

He holed the first fox in an hour and a half. Then jumped another and repeated the performance. In working out checks, in just plain slam-bang-slashing driving there was only one dog in those races that night. Tail-ender. We whooped and yelled and pounded old Tal on the back until he was black and blue. He'd only grin, look at the Colonel and say, "Sorter come inter his own, ain't he?"

It was a grand opening of a grand season, staged and timed perfectly. And it developed that the Colonel was the director of the play.

Wise in the ways of men and animals, he knew that the shyness of Tail-ender and his master, too, was born of a complex termed inferiority. So he set about to correct it, knowing the hidden worth of both. He'd slip out to Tal's with one or two couples of our oldest hounds and run them with the young dog, first allowing Tail-ender to get a fox up and going before he uncoupled the oldsters. Thus the shy one began to gain confidence in his own ability. The trump card in the Colonel's strategy, however, was played when he boarded some of our bitches out at Tal's that summer. This gave Tail-ender a court, made him the cock-of-the-walk and he reacted to this new feeling of importance just as the Colonel expected.

The metamorphosis of Tail-ender became a legend in our country. And brought laurels to Tal the like of which he had never dreamed. He was elected, without opposition, Justice of the Peace in his township and for years meted out justice with Solomon-like wisdom. And Tail-ender was always in the front rank of our pack until old age retired him.

"Jedge" Talbott Hemingway Murray and his dog, Tail-ender, are gone now, long ago. But their story lives and serves to illustrate the kindly feeling all foxhunters bear for each other. Love of the chase, of fair play, respect and affection for hounds and hills and woods and swamps make kin folks of the foxhunting clan the world over.

Pop Goes the Beagle

By SGT. TOM BURRIER

TROUBLE IS," POP WAS SAYING, "YOU DON'T WANT TO DO ANY MORE walking than you have to. You're getting soft from that desk job—not enough exercise. Why, when I was your age I thought nothing of a three-day hunting trip through the Big Smokies from Knoxville, with only my rifle, a bag of flour, and a little salt."

I was about to observe that I didn't think much of it, either, but I held my tongue. It was no time for levity. I waited for Dad to finish his trip through the Big Smokies.

"... And then we'd go fishing for a week just to top it off," he said, eyeing me reproachfully.

"It isn't the walking that bothers me," I said. "I thought it might be better to wait a couple of days, until we could borrow a beagle. It's hard work, hunting cottontail without a dog."

"That's true," he admitted. "But I figure I'd play dog, and we'll do better than we would with the beagle."

I tried to picture Pop chasing rabbits in the manner of a beagle, and gave up. "We could take Nicky," I suggested. Nicky was a six-month-old pointer pup as yet untried in the field.

"And make a *rabbit* dog out of a prize pointer?" he shouted.

"I was only kidding," I said hastily. "I know you don't like to have but one breed of dog at a time. It's too bad we don't buy a beagle pup, though, and raise him with Nicky. Then we could hunt rabbits when we wanted and not have to wear our legs off."

Thus, the next day's shoot was arranged—without the beagle.

We were home at Oak Harbor, on Whidby Island. Dad had been waiting all summer for the first cottontail hunt. In seasons past we had used dogs borrowed from a friend who owned a kennel. But now he was away on a trip, and not expected back for three or four days.

The origin of Whidby cottontails is worth a story in itself—

Whidby is an island in Washington's Puget Sound, the second largest island in continental United States. Its twisting, 60-mile length was entirely isolated from the mainland except by ferry before the building of the Deception Pass Bridge in 1934. For the sportsmen it was a paradise: deer in the thick evergreen forests, grouse and timberdoodles waiting in the marshy willow stands, pheasants in the cornfields, ducks along the salt shores and inland lakes. All these in abundance—but no rabbits.

Sporting residents discussed rounding out the year's shooting opportunities and finally did something about it. In neighboring Skagit County they trapped a dozen pair of wild cottontails and "planted" them on south Whidby, then sat back to watch results.

The first year there was no sign of the original twenty-four rabbits, but the second year farmers complained of raids on their gardens. By the third fall, cottontails had spread over most of the island. The rabbits increased far past the vision of their sponsors.

The cottontails prospered until the state game department was forced to declare a year-round open season. They were eating the farmers literally out of house and home. Night shooting became popular and an influx of mainland hunters soon reduced the cottontails to a more relative position in the game picture. A fixed rabbit season returned to the game laws.

But the surviving rabbits had changed.

Where they had been easily potted in open fields while they munched carrots or kale tops, they now became cautious and more alert. They skulked in fence rows and brush patches during the day and emerged in the early morning or late afternoon for a meal in the alfalfa. They would lie close to cover, like an old cock pheasant. The only certain way of getting a shot was by using a rabbit hound.

I had that in mind when Dad proposed the dogless hunt. However, if he wanted to take over the canine assignment I was willing. The walking would be a good setting-up exercise for the upland bird season. ...

There's a feeling of excitement the night before a season opens, even to an old-timer like Dad. We sat up before the fireplace, the crackling beach wood sending transparent blue flames up the chimney. It was early dark outside, and we'd finished a comfortable supper. Mom had spread newspapers on the floor when we started to clean the guns; it would save scraping away the oil spots later, she said.

Both guns were .410's. Dad's was a double which he'd bored to take three-inch shells. Mine was a single that Grandfather had presented to me on my seventh birthday. It was scratched and nicked with the marks of a thousand hunting trips, but it wasn't because of sentiment that I used it. It was a perfect rabbit gun: full choke, light weight, easy to swing through on a bounding brush-hugging target. The lack of a second shot didn't bother me—the close-shooting little pop-gun usually gave me a clean kill or a complete miss.

Knowing we had a hard day ahead of us, we turned in early. ...

The ground mists had drifted off, and the tiny glistening dewdrops were fast disappearing from the fields when we parked the car next morning. The farm presented a wide variety of cover: wheat stubble, fern-choked wood lots, alfalfa patches—about anything a rabbit might desire in the way of a home.

"There's something bothering me, Pop," I said seriously, lifting the little gun from the back seat.

Dad was loading the double. "Yeah? What's that?"

"If you're going to play dog, shouldn't you be on all fours?"

He snorted. "Just see you don't waste any shells when I kick 'em out. And don't worry about my two legs."

We started through a wood lot, the tall ferns flicking beads of water as we pressed forward. An old rail fence zigzagged among blackened tree stumps, and shaped our course. Dad was wetly intent on his role of dog, and thrashed into the wild rose and willow seedlings that lined the fence. I brushed the cobwebs from my face and trailed behind.

The first I knew of game was Dad's shout. Then a white and brown streak flashed across an opening in the ferns. I didn't even get the gun up.

"Do you want 'em closer than that; or are you trying to keep a 100 per cent average?"

"Didn't have time," I confessed. "I really didn't think there'd be anything in there."

We continued down the fence line, Dad pushing through the close-grown bushes. I moved out about fifty yards, paralleling his course.

"Watch it when we hit the corner," Dad called. "There might be a rabbit or two in here that'll come out this side."

I walked cautiously, trying to keep an open space ahead for a possible shot. We were almost to the fence junction and I halted on a little rise.

Dad crashed into the fence corner. There was a blur of movement almost under his feet. A cottontail was streaking away from the fence, bounding toward the trees and safety. I swung the .410 and fired through the opening. The rabbit tumbled end-over-end and lay still. I reloaded and walked down to pick him up. Dad emerged from the brush, wet and panting.

"Nice shot," he said. "Let's try the alfalfa field. There should be a few lying close this early in the morning."

We climbed the fence and jumped down on the green surface. Early fall rains had helped the alfalfa. Clumps stood six to eight inches above ground, and budded as if spring were just around the corner. Scattered about the big field were several rockpiles looking like the shattered battlements of some medieval castle.

We had taken only a dozen steps into the field when Dad raised the double and fired—and fired again! The cottontail had jumped twenty yards to his right. The second barrel nailed the rabbit close to the fence line.

"That cuts your average to fifty per cent right off!" I called across to him.

He didn't answer as he put the rabbit carefully into his game pocket. However, there was a "wait and see" look on his face as we resumed our trip across the field.

I thought of that when I exploded a shovelful of dirt behind the next bunny that jumped from cover and Dad scored with his left barrel.

"Shall we talk about averages again, or wait until I dog out these rockpiles?" Dad called. This time I had nothing to say.

A tangled mass of wild rose and willow shrubs crested the gray rockpiles. Field grasses had added their roots and stalks to the bulky tangle.

Dad hesitated. "Better get over on the other side and I'll see if I can get into this stuff."

I walked carefully around the fringe. Dad plunged in, hip deep in brush. The rocks rolled and rattled underfoot.

There was a sudden flurry of movement. A cottontail flashed from cover and bounded in long leaps over the alfalfa. He crumpled when I pulled the trigger.

Two echoing shots rang out behind me.

"Pick up that pair to your left when you get time," Dad called.

"Two! You took a double?"

"It isn't so hard when you learn. That single barrel has been a good alibi until now when we can scare out more than one rabbit at a time." He emerged, puffing, near where I stood.

I had the rabbits and stuffed them in Dad's hunting coat. He always wore one with large game pockets—"Just in case I get lucky," as he put it.

We worked the surrounding stubble fields without much success. Once a cottontail bounced from under my feet. I lowered my average further with a shot that only hastened him on his way.

We paused for breath and a smoke. "Do you think we can get into the stump pile behind the barn?"

"Might be worth a try," Dad agreed. "At least there are no rose bushes growing there. Let's go."

I snubbed my cigarette and we crossed toward the big brush pile. A bulldozer had tossed this crazy tangle of snags together years before. It was hard to get through with the logs criss-crossed in every direction like a pioneer blockhouse, and ferns and small fir trees sprouting up through the openings.

"Want me to play Rover this time?" I asked.

"No, I started this dogging—might as well finish it. Besides, I'll have a good spot to shoot from on top of that pile."

I walked out into the field opposite where Dad was heading in. He jumped from a log and the brush pile exploded rabbits! I swung desperately on the nearest brown-gray streak of fur; my average picked up. I pulled on another bounding form before I remembered I hadn't reloaded!

Dad was standing on a log watching one edge of the pile intently. I walked carefully to the brushy tuft he indicated and kicked it.

Out leaped a rabbit in high gear. On Dad's second shot he stopped abruptly in mid-air and came down without a quiver.

"How about calling it a day?"

The sun was high as we made our way back to the car with game pockets heavy. Dad was lagging so I slowed my pace.

"You know, I've been thinking," he said slowly, "Nicky may need a playmate at that. Suppose we run out to the kennels next week; just to look at the pups?

The pointer and the beagle get along swell.

Wicomico Salmon

By F. WALLACE TABER

ARRY-THE-HORSE DID NOT PURCHASE MERELY HIS SHARE OF fishing equipment. He purchased more than his share. He didn't do it to hoard, he just naturally enjoyed buying. He enjoyed equally well giving his equipment away to his following of young anglers. "Gettin' votes," he'd say. "Anyway, I got another one." And he was telling the truth. Chances are he had two or three more, possibly another whole gross. He enjoyed buying, and he did a lot of it. In fact Ollie Atlas used to say that Harry kept him in business. "If the wholesale houses run out of stocks completely, I'll call Harry-the-Horse in and buy back some of his supplies," Ollie would say. "It'll keep me in business for the duration."

How else explain the sudden appearance of a shoe box full of gang hooks that saved the day that time down on the Wicomico when the "ring" perch decided to obey the solunar tables and failed to bite? You see, we thought all the time that Harry-the-Horse had the lunch in the shoe box. He always insisted on fixing up the lunch, for he ate like a horse and no one else could properly provide for his ravenous appetite—he was always grousing about being starved and undernourished.

Harry had carefully placed the shoe box, along with three oversized tackle boxes, under the stern seat in the row boat. And, with four rods neatly cluttering up the bottom of the boat, using a fly rod for fishing, Harry-the-Horse looked like an animated version of a VL&A catalogue.

"Forgawdsakes, Harry," blurted Jack, "why don't you leave that warehouse under the bed when you go fishin'? Good thing George isn't along or he'd throw you and your hardware store into the drink."

"Why," I added fuel to the fire, "don't you charter a barge? Two fly rods, a casting rod and—what are you going to do with those two boat rods? The stripers aren't due until June and the blues aren't scheduled until August."

"Never mind those rods, just watch where you're oaring this clink," Harry responded, shifting his weight in time to prevent a collision with a submerged stump. And, when I say weight, I'm not just talking. Even without his appetite, Harry-the-Horse, by dint of his heft, could still well merit this moniker.

And so we rowed down the stream, we rode Harry who, good-naturedly, gave rebuttal to every jibe, parrying each blow directed at his overly numerous paraphernalia.

"Boat rods for ring perch," Jack offered contemptuously when the ribbing seemed momentarily to have subsided. "Why, we used those for salmon in the Rogue out Oregon way. This is Maryland and we're on the Wicomico. Yellow perch, not salmon."

Yes, it was the Wicomico, a beautiful broad river feeding into the lower Potomac 30 miles south of the Nation's capital. Its meandering course through cypress-studded flats and hardwood forest painted as pretty a picture as an outdoorsman could ask for. And, as we wound our way down its course to our favorite perch hole that March morning, it was difficult to realize that there was anything but peace everywhere. When Jack and I tired of talking, only the splashing of the oars and the creaking of the locks broke the silent tranquillity of our haunt.

"Ring" perch, or yellow perch as they are more widely called, offer the earliest fishing in this part of the country. While other game fish are still dormantly awaiting the coming of summer, the ring perch are headed well on their way to the spawning grounds. They come in such numbers as to darken the sparkling-white, quartz sands over which they swim. Up out of the Chesapeake, slowly at first, and then en masse, they fin their matrimonial way to the spawning grounds of their parents, their grandparents and probably their entire lineage. The early arrivals seek the deep pools in the rivers and there await the main contingent before moving out onto the favorite spawning grounds.

It is in these holes that fishermen dwelling in the capital city find their March fishing. And temperamental fishing it is, too. If everything is right, the home bathtub couldn't begin to hold all the perch that even a mediocre fisherman can catch in the course of a day. If everything isn't right . . .

Yes, not only was everything not right, but we had decided that everything was definitely all wrong. The tide, always difficult to predict because of the distance from the Chesapeake and the effects of local prevailing winds, was racing out with reckless abandon. The weather wasn't exactly what one would write home about. In fact, the wool-lined windbreaker that Harry wore was the envy of my eye, and twice I heard Jack attempting to perfect a barter. Yes, from all appearances we had just hit *one of those days*, a day when crow shooting would in all likelihood produce a peck more fun.

"How about a spinner with blood worms trailing?" I hopefully asked Jack, who was the acknowledged piscatorial champion of the section.

"I've tried them, Wally. Fact is, I've tried everything from double-o drones to dry flies. We've just hit it wrong," shrugged Jack, eyeing Harry, who was wrapped around an over-hanging tree on the far side of the bank completely oblivious to the no-bite attitude of the perch. "By golly, Harry, you're a jinx," shouted Jack. "Another time and we'll leave you at home. If you hadn't showed up with all that tackle and those five *keep-a-live* stringers, we'd have fish aplenty. It's bad enough to bring one stringer, but to bring five of the damned things is sacrilege."

"Now, wait a minute," smiled Harry-the-Horse, "wait a minute. If the perch were biting, you know that I'd fill 'em up by myself."

"With five rods, I don't see how even you could fail."

With the persistence of Job we switched baits, changed rigs, tried new holes, fished from the bank and boat alternately ... in fact, did everything that the books call for. Still no perch. The tide had even changed and was starting in, but the temperamental perch were from all appearances on the prod, without the slightest interest in what we had to offer. By the time noon had rolled around, with appetites that would have done justice to a growing lion, we were sitting astride a half submerged log miles down the river from the shack.

"Break out the lunch, Jack." It was Harry-the-Horse who had finally succumbed to the pangs of hunger. "I'm starved. I could eat a horse 'n buggy and chase the driver."

"You're always grousing about being hungry," taunted Jack. "I hope you've got enough lunch for a change."

"*I've* got enough lunch?" questioned Harry. "You mean I'm supposed to have the lunch? I thought you had it!"

"Me?" yowled Jack. "What in the name of the great horned spoon do you think I am, a pack mule? Don't answer that! I just toted your sporting goods store down to the boat, that's all. But quit the bickering. Let's get down to eating. Break out that shoe box."

"That shoe box?" bellowed Harry. "That shoe box? That's tackle, not lunch. Don't tell me you've forgotten the lunch ... the food ... the staff of life! I set it right on the running board where you'd be sure to see it. Oh, Jack, you couldn't do this to me," Harry-the-Horse wailed in bitter anguish.

"By golly," I contributed after rushing to the boat and making a thorough search, "we've left the lunch behind. That is, unless Harry-the-Horse ate it up when we weren't looking."

"Well, I did stick a couple of sandwiches into my pocket just to sort of tide me over till lunch," Harry sheepishly admitted, "but they were gone hours ago."

"What sort of tackle you got in that durned shoe box?" Jack snarled in utter disgust.

"Gang-hooks," Harry-the-Horse said meekly.

"Gang-hooks," exploded Jack. "A whole shoe box full of gang-hooks, two tackle boxes, five rods, five stringers and NO LUNCH. Gaddie, I'm going mad!" And he pulled his hat off, jumped on it and in mockery pulled his hair.

"What in the world are you planning on hooking with these anchors?" I asked Harry as I removed one of the 3-o gang-hooks from the shoe box wherein lay tangled fully five dozen of the treacherous trebles. "Planning on dragging for a body?"

"By golly, I forgot all about those 3-way silver bucktails," exclaimed Harry, disregarding my query. "Here, I'll show you." And with that Harry leaned his fly rod against a cypress butt and reached for a boat rod. Quickly he seated the deep-sea reel into its seat, strung the rod, affixed a set of gang-hooks to the end of the line and finished by tying on a 2-ounce sinker about a foot up the line from the set of gangs.

"There," said Harry with obvious satisfaction. "Let's see. Yep, this is the exact hole," he continued as though answering his own unspoken question.

With that bit of to-do and distinctly to our utter amazement, Harry-the-Horse slung a shoulder of beef behind the boat rod and sent the line sailing across the drink to go plunking in near the opposite bank. Three seconds he waited and then gave such a jerk as I've never before seen. Then he quickly but somewhat clumsily wound in the slack. Another jerk and again he wound in the slack. Another jerk ... wind ... jerk ... wind. I stood there in amazement; Jack stood there in amazement.

"That's funny," mumbled Harry as the sinker and hooks lurched out of the water with the final jerk and sailed dangerously close to his head. "Must have been the wrong spot ... he said you'd get one every cast." And with that Harry-the-Horse lambasted the sinker and gang-hooks into another sector of the river, starting once again the jerk-wind pantomime.

Harry's rod suddenly bent and he straightened up as though on the receiving end of a haymaker. Then the rod straightened out again and Harry continued his jerk-wind program until the sinker and hook came flying out of the water again.

"Must have touched him," suggested Harry-the-Horse as he prepared to have at it again. "Ye gods, look at this scale," exclaimed Harry removing a young saucer from the point of one of the gang-hooks. "Must have come off a whale." Harry actually displayed a scale that was nearly an inch in diameter and as thick as cat hide.

Harry-the-Horse was already out in the river again, this time jerking with enough fervor to unseat Lancelot and drop his charger to boot. At about the same point the rod again suddenly bent and creaked under the strain of Harry's hefting against something equally unmovable. This time, however, the rod stayed bent, and the line began to race up the river with Harry pumping on the rod end for dear life. In spite of his heft, the line was gaining on him. Five turns of the reel in and seven out. The drag was too loose. Harry put the butt between his legs and pumped some more. Then he ran up the shore a way and repeated the performance. By then the line was heading down stream and Harry was following suit along the bank.

"Tighten the star drag," Jack finally found his tongue and rushed forward to lend a hand. "Let me have it," Jack offered his help by sticking his hands in and giving the drag another twist.

Snap went the line and Harry-the-Horse picked himself up out of a heap where the sudden break in combat had landed him with no little force.

"Now, see what you've done," sighed Harry in disgust, "always doggin' a fellow. You just couldn't stand to watch for a while and let someone else catch a fish."

"A fish," Jack said, somewhat apologetic for having set the drag too tightly, causing the line to break. "A fish, Man, you had an alligator for certain."

With that there was a mad scramble to repair Harry's line and to set up the other boat rod. I, being slightly closer to the boat than Jack, gained possession of the second rod, which is 10 points of the law. Jack, nevertheless, helped Harry string his rod anew and even offered to do the casting and retrieving for him, a suggestion which Harry politely declined.

In jig time the rod was bending under the weighty jerks of Harry-the-Horse, and I hesitated in stringing up the spare rod to watch the first retrieve.

About the same spot, the rod failed to come out of the bend as Harry applied the jerk-wind succession and Harry let out a yowl. "I've got him again," he yelled as though attempting to scare whatever it was into submission. "He's a little one, but I've got him anyway. He's coming in easy. No, he's not so little." Harry carried on a one-man conversation as the rod bent under a delayed run. Then Harry pumped and pumped and the line approached shore. Meanwhile I had dropped my rod into the boat and ran up the bank to lend Harry a hand if it were needed.

About the time I got to his side, Harry swung a shining, flopping fish of about five pounds onto the bank.

"A carp," gasped Jack, grasping the floundering fish by the Strangler Lewis method. "A carp, a leather-backed carp... mirror carp. How did you happen to try this?" he asked, looking up from his kneeling position at Harry-the-Horse, who nonchalantly smiled down at him.

"Oh," responded Harry, apparently much amused and somewhat self-satisfied, "just intuition, I guess you'd call it."

"Cut the funny-man stuff," Jack argued.

"Well," drawled Harry although his Florida accent was long ago covered up by Washington, D.C., hodge-podge. "You remember that lad, the one I gave the old bass pluggin' rod and reel? Well, he told me the last time we were perch fishing that I should try snaggin' carp in this hole. He said that there were a few mirror carp, but most were German ones. He does it all the time . . . says that they hole up here during the winter . . . there's some that'll go 40 pounds."

"Carp!" Jack was flabbergasted. "Who'd have thunk it. *Wicomico Salmon.* I'll never ride you again as long as I live about bringing too much tackle along, and I'll row every ounce of the way home," which was rather more than somewhat of a promise for Jack, especially with no lunch under his belt. "Now, can I have at it once?"

Within an hour we had all tasted pay dirt. Jack had managed to break his casting rod on a twelve pounder which he finally landed by hand, but we had traded off on the two boat rods until all of us were ready to call it a day. All five stringers were full to the breaking point and the boat was full to the gunnels with flipping carp ranging from four to twenty-four pounds. Between the jerkin' and windin' and the fightin', catching *Wicomico Salmon* is really work, but most enjoyable work when the ring perch aren't bitin'.

P.S. Halfway home, with the tide racing against us, Jack began bellyachin' about Harry-the-Horse's heft, his tackle store and why didn't he do his share of rowin' instead of sitting a-stern there like a stuffed hop toad. All was a way off and forgiven, however, when the butcher handed us $12.40 for the 124 pounds of carp. And, better yet, we got orders for all we could catch at 10 cents a pound providing we brought them in alive. This, of course, was no trick since carp live for hours in a damp gunny sack.

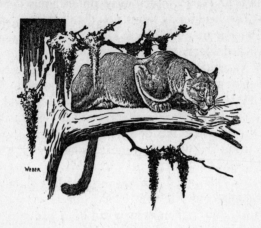

Scairty Cat

By DAVID M. NEWELL

I KICKED INTO THE PILE OF GRASS, LEAVES AND PINE NEEDLES UNTIL a patch of coarse gray bristles was exposed. I had expected to find a deer, and this was a surprise. Here was a wild boar—one of the biggest ones I had ever seen. He must have weighed close to three hundred pounds, and his tusks were at least five inches long. A dangerous critter to fool with, but there he lay, dead as a hammer. I looked around. The whole story was written in the mud, there at the edge of the swamp.

The big boar had been feeding, rooting around under the pines and cabbage palms. Suddenly he had started to run. There were great, long gashes in the mud, where his sharp hoofs had dug in. But he had not gone thirty yards before he was down. There was some sign of a struggle, but not a great deal. Whatever varmint had jumped on that hog had been much of a man. I knew, of course, what had killed him, for the tracks were there, but it was still hard to believe. A wild razorback hog is a tough customer.

An hour later we looked up at a big tawny cat, crouched high in a giant cypress. At the foot of the tree sat a little fox-terrier, wagging her tail triumphantly and showing no fear whatever of the killer of the Everglades. She'd had a few hounds to help her during the chase, it is true, but that wouldn't have made any difference to her or to the cat, either. He'd have run and she'd have chased him. All of which doesn't make much sense.

Here was a cat weighing about 150 pounds, which had just killed a boar weighing twice as much—a fierce, savage cat, quick as lightning, against which no dog or man would have a chance. And yet this big, powerful brute was high up in a tree, apparently scared to death. He wasn't even growling.

All of which goes to show that the panther, puma, cougar, mountain lion, or whatever you choose to call him, is one of the most puzzling creatures on earth. Naturally, then, he will be misunderstood. Wild tales have been told—and will be told—about him.

I remember a book I read when I was a boy. It was a very exciting book, and it had to do with Indians, cowpunchers, gun-fighters and pumas. There was one whole chapter devoted to a pitched battle between a band of Indians and a pack of panthers. I remember, also, other stories of panthers which stalked and screamed and leaped on people from the limbs of trees. I grew up with the idea that panthers were plenty bad medicine, and I have no doubt but that there are a good many million other boys who are growing up with the same impression. It's too bad, but this really won't ever make much difference to many of them. The poor panther is rapidly going the way of the dodo.

What I have to say about these big cats is based on my own experience with them over twenty years' hunting in widely removed localities, and when I say "widely" I mean about six thousand miles—from southern Brazil to British Columbia. I have hunted them and studied them in the South American jungles, the Sierra Madres of old Mexico, the Florida Everglades and the Pacific Northwest, and their habits are much the same, wherever they are found. I do not believe any other animal has such wide distribution or adapts itself to such extremes of climate and topography, unless it be the tiger, which ranges from Siberia across China and down through India.

A big male panther will weigh up to 200 pounds, but 150 is nearer the average. Females are considerably smaller. Of nine which I have examined in Florida, none weighed over 150, and one of the grown females—an old animal—weighed only 87 pounds, although their over-all measurements compared favorably with much heavier specimens from the Rockies. This same was true of the ones killed in South America. The southern specimens seemed to be slimmer in build than those from cold, rugged, mountain country.

Assuming an average weight for males of 150 pounds, it is almost unbelievable to find that such an animal can pull down creatures four and five times his own weight! It is not at all uncommon for a "lion" to kill a grown saddle pony or a good-sized steer. My partner and I got one in Arizona which had just killed a favorite cow horse, and had not only killed it, but had dragged it some distance to get it into a brushy ravine. Did you ever try to drag a dead horse? This lion weighed around 200, but what 200-pound man could drag a dead horse?

On many occasions I have found where a panther had killed an alligator or a crocodile and eaten the tail. True, most of these kills were small reptiles, usually less than nine feet in length, but a nine-foot crocodile is quite an armful.

Venison is the main diet of these big cats, unless they happen to live in a ranching country and have acquired a taste for colts and horses. One of the strangest observations I have been able to make is that eight out of ten times a panther will kill a big buck with horns. A doe would be easier to stalk and far easier to kill, but he chooses the buck. I do not pretend to know the answer to this, but I have a feeling that it is an instinct within the beast which causes him to conserve, unknowingly, his source of supply.

I hope that you will read this statement again. I did *not* say that a panther *always* kills a buck, and I certainly did not say that he is de-liberately a conservationist. I am merely giving you my own experi-ences for what they are worth. While I'm sticking my neck out I might as well add that I have never heard a panther scream. If you have, please don't write me about it. I believe you.

Having established the fact that the panther is a big, powerful cat, larger and stronger than a leopard, let's try to figure out why he is such a coward when it comes to man. I have been told that a leopard is one of the most savage and dangerous animals alive, and it is well known that leopards kill many people annually in both Africa and Asia, deliberately preying on them. The jaguar, while not in the habit of preying on man, is a dangerous customer when wounded or brought to bay. The panther, however, is the world's greatest four-flusher when it comes to contact with man. He will growl and flatten his ears. His tail will twitch and his eyes will turn green. He will go through all the motions, but he won't attack. As the old darky said, "He kin cloud up, but he can't rain!"

Why is this? I don't know. I do know from personal experience that it is true. I'll cite a few examples, and you can be the judge as to whether or not the panther in the case had a chance to fight.

My dogs treed a panther in Arizona, down near the mouth of Cave Creek, and I decided that I wanted to take him alive. There were four dogs raving around the bottom of the gnarled cedar, and I tied them all under another tree, perhaps twenty yards away. Then I took my rope and went up after the panther. I never was a fancy roper, and there were a lot of little dead limbs in the way, so that I had to make at least six throws before my loop settled where I wanted it. During this time the panther growled and spat and slapped at the rope—but he didn't leap down at me.

When the rope tightened on his neck, he leaped, just as far in the other direction as he could go. The dogs were enjoying the show, and when the big cat hit the ground and began to do a dance on the end of the rope they went crazy. That hubbub was too much for the cat. He came right back up the tree! There wasn't time for me to do anything. I hadn't figured on this. I was too high to jump out without breaking a leg, but here came a wild-eyed panther clawing up the tree!

Luckily I hung on to the rope, for the panther had jumped out on one side of a limb below me and was coming up the other side. I could snub him, and did I snub him! He gagged and choked and finally jumped down again. This time I lost no time in following him to the ground, and after a great deal of grief I managed to tie him up. During the shuffle he had a dozen chances to jump me, but he fought purely a defensive fight all the way through.

Another time, in the Everglades, I had a wounded panther run right into me. He didn't even slap at me as he went by. I slapped at him with an eighty-dollar camera, but fortunately missed!

A short time before this, Uncle George Rawls was looking up some lost hogs and his dogs got after a panther, baying it finally in a cave on the bank of the river. George didn't have a gun, but he had a pocket-knife. He cut a long pole, lashed his knife to the end of the pole with a boot-lace, and speared that cat to death. It bit and fought at his improvised spear, but it didn't come out fighting.

I'll tell you one more. This time I was scared. I got closer to the big cat than I intended to, about three feet, as a matter of fact. We had started out from our camp in Brazil to look for some jaguar cubs. The day before we had killed an old female *tigre*, and because there was milk in her udders we knew the cubs were near by somewhere. It was late in the day, very hot, and the dogs were tired; so we decided to hunt the cubs next morning.

Right off the bat we jumped this panther. He was lying in a little patch of jungle, and a young spotted hound named Bill winded him. There was no trailing to it, just sudden pandemonium. Out came the panther, with his tail straight in the air and Bill grabbing at his flanks. The other dogs took to him, and we spurred our horses. It was just like an old-fashioned wild west show—Indians whooping, horses galloping, rifles cracking.

I'll never forget Uncle George. He was shooting a little .44 carbine, and he was holding it out like a pistol, building a fog around that cat! I have seen a lot of scared critters, but I know that panther was the scaredest thing I ever saw in my life. He really stretched out. He looked nine feet long.

It was about half a mile to the next jungle, and I was on a darned good horse. I knew I could catch that cat out across the open prairie, and I did a piece of riding. Shucks! I didn't even start to close the gap. When we got to the jungle, the dogs were raising Cain at the foot of a big hardwood and the panther was up in a fork. His tongue was out, and you could see his heart-beat a hundred yards. We took some pictures of him, and then one of the Indians swung his rope.

Those South American Indians use rawhide ropes sixty feet long, and they're plenty good! The loop, however, struck the trunk of the tree, glancing off the big cat's back. When it did, he sailed out of there like a gigantic flying squirrel and hit the ground running. I was near my horse, and I didn't lose any time. The chase led straight down the edge of the thick stuff, and I spurred along the edge, whooping and hollering just for the fun of it.

The panther came out at the end of the jungle and headed across an open streak toward another clump. I shot at him twice with my six-shooter and didn't miss him over fifty feet either time. Then he took another tree—or tried to take another tree. He hit away up on the side of the trunk, hung on for a minute, and then literally fell off. He was plumb pooped. The dogs were right on him, and now they set up a terrific clamor there in the vines and thick undergrowth.

There wasn't a second to lose, for, while a panther won't charge a man, he'll kill a good dog so fast that it will make your eyes water.

I sailed off my horse and scrambled into the vines as best I could, hoping that Jake and Bill and the rest would stay back long enough for me to get there. The cover was so thick that I couldn't see anything but the tops of the bushes thrashing around, and I certainly couldn't hear anything. One of the dogs was right beside me. I could see the bushes shaking and I could see him moving around.

Then it dawned on me that none of my dogs was tawny-colored. I was standing almost over the panther! When I located his head, he was looking right at me, and his expression was far from friendly. I shot him just over the right eye, and that was that. That cat didn't have to charge. All he had to do was to reach out!

From all these and a few other experiences I can only decide that our big American cat, *Felis cougar*, is a coward. Why? He's big enough and strong enough, and certainly stealthy enough, to prey on man. Perhaps its some peculiar quirk in his make-up similar to the strange cowardice of the possum. A possum is so overcome by terror that he not only refuses to fight, but gives up completely. Whereas an old boar coon will put up a terrific scrap against a dog, or a man either, a possum will lie down and close his eyes and drool at the mouth. Yet put this possum and coon in a cage together, and the possum will usually whip the coon! How come? I don't know.

Fear must have something to do with it, for there are cases of a panther carrying off a dog from a ranch yard and eating it. Yet if this same dog had discovered the panther first, the chances are that he would have chased it up the nearest tree.

I have been told by one or two old-timers that if you ever run into a panther just after he has killed, while the blood is fresh in his nose, he will show fight. I can well believe this, for I have done exactly that. Of course, I would not want to generalize because of this one experience, for it would not be a fair example.

The panther in the case had been in captivity for almost two years and was accustomed to humans, so that his reactions could not be taken as typical of the wild animal. However, he had just killed a deer, and I walked up intending to take it away from him. He didn't snarl or growl or flatten his ears. There was no threat to be seen except in his eyes and a faint twitching of his tail. He looked me straight in the face, and I didn't have to be much of a mind-reader to realize what he meant to do. He meant to come at me if I took one more step. I knew that—and so did the guy who was with me.

We got out of there in a hurry. That panther would have charged in a split second. I'm convinced of it. He had lost his natural fear of man.

I have only given you my own experiences and observations. There are always exceptions to any rule, and the man who makes flat, final statements about animals and their habits is a fool. So if your great-aunt Minnie was eaten by a panther and if your Uncle Zeb didn't sleep for three nights because a panther screamed around his camp and if your grandfather's horse had scars on its rear end from the time the panther missed the buggy, more power to you! I believe you. I still insist, however, that they're scairty cats—the panthers, not your relatives.

"Come On... Three!"

By HANK BRUNS

ALL RIGHT, MAYBE I SHOULDN'T HAVE BEEN SO COCKSURE, BUT after all, I had caught a lot of weakfish in my time. School fish over the oyster beds in Atlantic Highlands, purple-spotted warriors in Raritan Bay, when Raritan Bay was good, big yellow-finned tide-runners off the islands below Beach Haven. I had caught weakfish with shrimp, alive and dead, with shedder crab, with blood and sand and tapeworms, with squid, alive and tinned. I had drifted for them, jigged for them, cast for them. I know that the weakfish is Cyonoscion regalis, and anybody knows that the variety name means regal, or kingly. An extremely tough customer with nothing weak about him but his mouth and his name.

So, when Slim Merritt asked me to come along for trout, I was pleased, but not excited. Why should I be? I was new to Florida, but not new to the weakfish family, and this southern cousin was certainly nothing to get excited about. It was a Cyonoscion something or other, but the variety name wasn't regal, so why get respectful about it?

Slim hunched his shoulders and looked up at me. His brown eyes made his long saturnine countenance come alive. "You think you're a fisherman? O.K., we'll see on Sunday."

"What time do you pick me up?" I asked innocently.

"Five a.m. sharp," was the reply.

I decided to go along anyway.

Ernie is Slim's regular fishing partner, and of course, he is quiet. He had to be. He ran the kicker, after we had gotten the boat into the water, while Slim sat in the middle seat, rigging up. I had the choice spot, the bow, they told me elaborately. We put-putted through Surprise Lake, which is not a lake, but a body of salt water, partially enclosed. Slim said suddenly, "Ernie, you put the cork in?"

Ernie looked down, gasped and grasped a big cork that was floating on the four or five inches of water already in the boat. "By golly, I always forget those corks," he said mildly.

The cork was to let out rainwater while the boat was ashore, but they always forgot to replace it, and consequently the boat always had half a ton or so of water to carry around.

Finally we cut over into Blackwater Sound, a great shallow bay with much turtle grass bottom. "That's where the trout lie, over the grass," whispered Slim.

"What are you whispering about?" I demanded.

Ernie had cut off the motor, it was very quiet. He leaned toward me and answered for Slim, "He's just respectful."

"Nuts," whispered Slim, then cleared his throat and repeated, "NUTS!"

We began to cast. Slim sighted another boat. "There's Cliff!" he explained to me. "Cliff is our other partner, but he went swell on us, and bought his own boat. He's coming this way."

Our boats came together, and Slim introduced me to Cliff. "This is Hank. He writes fishing stories for the magazines." We shook hands, and Cliff had that "look" in his eyes. Why do fishermen always think that a guy who writes a bit is always an expert?

We returned to our fishing. A mild breeze blew across the flat water, and the sun was red in the faint smoke from Everglades fires.

Lines of pelicans flapped precisely overhead, and on the water sudden scutters of spray meant mullet. I had my usual rod. Slim spotted it.

"What th' hell you doing with that fly rod?" he demanded.

"Fishing," I answered brilliantly.

"You'll never hook a fish with that wand," he said scornfully, screwing up his face so that the smoke from his cigarette wouldn't get into his eyes, and staring at my rod.

As a matter of fact, the rod is a steel-head spinning rod, about seven and a half feet long, with a long cork butt, very graceful, very delicate, and ideal for plugging where accuracy is not necessary. It is made of the first two sections of a cross salmon fly rod. I like it, but had sense enough not to defend it too strongly against unknown fishing.

"Why not?" I asked.

"Because you can't get a 'lick' into it. Too much bend. And you can't set the hooks solid."

"What, my friend, is a 'lick'?"

"Look at Ernie casting. See what he does with his rod? That's a lick."

Ernie was whipping his plug out from the stern of the boat. He would turn the reel fast a few times, then stop reeling and yank curiously at the rod. Out on the surface I could see the plug throw up water, hesitate, and throw up some more. Then he turned the reel again. The plug took its normal course. Sometimes he reeled fast, sometimes slow, but always he paused and gave the plug that lick.

"You can't put a lick into the plug with that flexible rod." Slim went on, "not enough backbone."

"Well," I temporized, "I like the rod, so I'm going to try it awhile."

"Okeh," shrugged Slim, "be a wise guy."

All of us were working hard over the grass beds below. Every so often gray fish darted at a plug, flashed silver as he turned, and disappeared. "Striking short," said Slim, "have to try my special short-strike lick." He hunched his shoulders and bent over his rod, putting every enticing move into the plug that he knew. Nothing happened.

I watched my plug and Ernie and Slim, trying to imitate that lick of theirs. I made one particularly long cast, the plug smacked hard on the water, then dove as I gave it the best lick I could. Something heavy and solid ran into it, then made a sweeping run to the south. I was into a trout! The fish fought hard, sometimes at the surface.

sometimes out of sight below. I whipped him quickly enough, and naturally enough, with that long rod, and Ernie netted him.

"Not as good as a weakfish," I decided, "but a lot of fun."

"Nice," orated Ernie.

The fish was much like the northern weakfish, with two exceptions that I could see. I missed the beautiful purple spots, this fish had only the black, and in addition two very nasty fangs in the upper jaw. The fish was about two feet long.

Slim yelled, "Got mine!" and began to pump his running fish, which fought almost entirely on the surface, throwing water and rainbows in the early sunshine. He landed it, a fish of about sixteen inches, and I sniffed scornfully. "Did I understand you to say that I couldn't get that lick into the plug?"

"All right, all right," acceded Slim, "maybe I was wrong." He cast again, shouting as he pumped at his stiff little rod. "Come on, two!"

Ernie got one then, and on his next cast said, "Come on, two!" I began to get the idea. I cast a long one, almost into the mangroves, and as I reeled, I called, "Come on, TWO!" That did it. I was fast to another, but a much stronger fish this time. It circled constantly and bowed my slender rod dangerously. I couldn't see the fish; it didn't surface, but Ernie said laconically, "Jack."

"How do you know?"

Ernie just smiled, and when the fish finally quit, it was a three-pound jack. I released it because jacks aren't as good eating as trout, and resumed my calling and casting. I was smug and satisfied as I called, "Come on, THREE."

"Wait a minute there," said Slim, "jacks don't count."

"Okeh," I agreed airily, thinking what a cinch this was, "Come on, TWO!"

Ernie caught another then, a nice fish, thick bodied and long, but not longer than mine. He threw it into the box, and called, "Come on, three!"

We reached the end of a drift and Cliff came close. "What you guys calling for?"

Slim said, "Two."

"Three," said Ernie.

"Two," said I comfortably, and showed the big fish. Cliff's eyes widened and again he looked that way at me.

We separated and Slim soon had another trout on, after that he was calling, "Come on, three!·

I still felt comfortable. I was working hard, at any moment I would get that second trout, and be right up with them.

I had a violent strike; Ernie had one at the same time. We were both into jacks. The two fish crossed, and there was excitement.

Slim got another trout, and then he was yelling, "Come on four!" Ernie landed his third, and Slim got one immediately, and Ernie hooked two on one plug, and Slim lost two in succession. My head began to spin a little from the—sun. Everybody had fish. The place was lousy with them. Everybody was landing trout, and unhooking trout respectfully, with the pliers, and then, casting, hooking another. Everybody but me.

Ernie was calling "Come on, seven!" and Slim wanted number five. Sturdily I continued to call, "Come on, TWO!" hoping by some magic of coaxing to get those trout hitting my plug. What did those trout have that weakfish didn't? I worked hard, too. I cast and licked as constantly as the others. I tried every trick they seemed to be using, and a couple of others I invented on the spot.

Cliff drifted close, Slim called, "I'm looking for nine," and Ernie said, "Thirteen, for me." I didn't say anything. I was very busy casting on the other side of the boat.

The sun was high and burning. We would drift over the grass beds, casting hard, and then when we had passed the best grounds, Ernie would start the outboard, and back we'd go. Each time Ernie caught fish, Slim did too. The boat came to assume that satisfying fishy odor that all fishermen come to love.

Then I hit another fish, and it was a trout! I knew by the way he thrashed the surface. The water flew as he fought along the top. When I got the fish close to the boat, I wanted to hide under the seat. It was a blowfish only Slim called it a rabbitfish. Slim guffawed, Ernie smiled, and I took it. I changed my emphasis, calling earnestly, "COME ON, TWO!" Two finally pitied me and struck hard. When I boated it, Ernie said gently, "We always release them under twelve inches," and the little fellow dropped back into the water without a splash.

"COME ON, TWO!" I implored, but Slim said, "You can call for three now, Hank."

"COME ON, THREE!" I bellowed, taking heart. But it didn't do a bit of good. Slim forced his spare rod on me. "Here, take it," he insisted. "You gotta get yourself some fish. What'll the folks say?"

Humbly I accepted the little rod, earnestly I cast. Slim was calling,

"Come on, sixteen!" Ernie was working on twenty-six. I was just working.

"Come on, THREE!" I called.

I was tired. My wrist ached. That lick business was hard work, I decided. The sun was lowering along with my spirits. The only satisfaction I had was that the little rod wasn't any good either. Every time Cliff joined us, I got busy somewhere else. By the time we were ready to leave, I was whispering, "Come on, three" and hoping they wouldn't notice.

Fish can't be that different, we all know that. A weakfish is a weakfish. A bass is a bass. What's the difference where they live? Oh—yeah?

Ernie was saying, "Come on, TWENTY-SEVEN!"

Slim hollered, "Come on, EIGHTEEN!"

And what did I say; what was I breathing when the sun went down and we left the keys? Don't ask me, I'm disgusted.

Cicero—The Bar Walker

By CHARLES E. GILLHAM

PROBABLY THE GREEKS HAD A NAME FOR HIM—AND, NO DOUBT, IT was a dilly! Central Louisiana calls him a "Cicero" hunter; up Memphis way, Nash Buckingham, refers to this pest as a "Bar Walker"; in Illinois we designate him as a "Moon Shooter," and in Arizona he has the moniker of "Bank Hunter." A New York friend probably has the most descriptive term for this bird that is always getting into your hair; he calls him "John Highshot." Anyway, he is the gink who gets down wind from your blind a few hundred feet, and standing out in the broad open-faced spaces, snipes at all your swinging birds.

There "ain't no law" against ruining the shooting for everyone in a given area, providing that there is no trespassing involved. You can burn up your gun barrels, throw shot all over the neighboring hunters, and be a downright mess, yet it's against the law to attempt to kill you and dispose of your body. The fact that legitimate sportsmen are being deprived of their hard-earned pleasure by a misinformed or thoughtless individual, has nothing to do with the case.

Cicero usually waits until the evening before legal season to procure his duck stamp and hunting license, his plans of where to go are quite vague. Often he is attracted by shooting and hurries to the spot on opening day where he hears the greatest bombardment. The fact that he has no blind does not deter him, a few blades of grass are enough to crouch behind. If he has a couple of wooden decoys and a tin "duck whistle," John Highshot is really ready for action. No wonder the ducks hold us in such high disdain, and fly equally high.

Seldom, however, does this nimrod arise early enough to get into his blind. Usually he drives up to the lake in a shiny new car and parks it directly out in the sun, just behind your hide-out. Then, putting together his weapon, he takes a trial shot at a blackbird the psychological moment that the only flock of ducks for the day sails down the lake.

If there are birds moving, Cicero is in his glory. Anything that falls on his side of the lake is eagerly claimed. You can gamble on him being out of his concealment fully eighty per cent of the time, searching for some cripple that his moon-shooting tactics have accounted for. It never seems to occur to him that if he would allow a bird to get down within range, that not only he, but others as well, might get a bit of game for their efforts.

In bird season, Cicero takes on another form. It is he who wants to borrow your best dog, because it is too much trouble and expense to feed one of his own. And if you lend him "Old Queen," get ready to borrow another dog for yourself. She will be sore-footed, wire-cut, full of burrs, and a rabbit hound of the first water—that is, if you get her back at all. Frequently you will have to go claim your property, and then learn that two days before the pooch dug out under the woodshed door and has been A.W.O.L. ever since.

It must be the keen competition in hunting that gives us Cicero. I cannot recall that we had him twenty-five years ago. It might be that we did, and because there was so much more hunting area, he was scattered out thinner and went unnoticed. In olden days, when a flock of ducks came into the marsh where I hunted, the blinds would tune up and invite them in to look over the decoys. All hunters kept their necks in while the wily birds made a swing and decided whom they were going to favor. There was no one out on the bank prowling around, building fires, or hunting rabbits. When the birds did stool to some hunter, the other blinds immediately became silent and the occupants stayed discreetly out of sight.

Loud shouting, shooting at bottles, and splashing of duck boats was entirely out of order at such a time. Neither did some optimist arise from his scant concealment along the shore 300 yards distant, and turn loose a barrage of high velocity B.B.'s in the direction of the stooling birds. If he had, I think a jury would have exonerated the man that shot him. It would have been considered justified manslaughter by any judge on the Mississippi River.

Today, unless properly managed, public shooting areas are a shambles. In some instances the number of blinds are restricted, and a waiting list of hunters are on the docket to draw for gunning places on the favored day they may hunt. Usually, too, it is necessary to have a guide. I, like many of my old cronies, do not care for this help, though I know it is probably necessary to keep the overly zealous and inexperienced in check. Somehow it is too much like playing draw poker with a kibitzer hanging over your shoulder to tell you when to bluff, or when to raise the bet. I also like to build my own blind, put out my own decoys, and shoot when I get darn good and ready. Nowadays very many of the guides are Ciceros and urge their hunters to shoot at birds entirely out of range, hoping for a scratch shot to aid in increasing a scanty bag.

In Iowa a few years ago, I saw the opening of duck season on a state-owned marsh. As I remember, there were seven hunters per acre, as near as I could compute their abundance, and most of them were Ciceros. A few old-timers had their own boats, decoys, and blinds, but they did not have a prayer. The lake was full of birds until about twenty minutes before legal shooting time, when the anxious, who could wait no longer, opened up. The sky was full of birds, and I saw as many as 50 shots fired into bunches of mallards by John Highshots, without even as much as a feather being knocked out of their midst.

The crowning performance of the day, so far as I was concerned, was when a poor lone young pintail was scratched down from the stratosphere. Eight hunters slopped through the marsh eagerly to retrieve the fowl. One large swarthy gent, appearing fresh from Southern Europe, won the race. I had a good look at him, as he wallowed through my decoys, and became entangled in one of the strings. My companion pointed, in horror, to the old '97 model Winchester that he was actually dragging behind him by the muzzle. The hammer was fully cocked, and I presume the piece was loaded. As the gun swung our way covering us, we both went into the bottom of the blind together, nor did we appear again until the squabble of ownership had been settled, and the hunters had departed. Then hurriedly we gathered our decoys, and retreated in the best order that we could.

The long range shooting antics of John Highshot have caused me actual amazement from the standpoint of ballistics. Some of the long kills that I have witnessed did not seem possible, as they were executed at many, many yards beyond the probable killing range of a common full choked gun. It is a revelation to study a large flock of birds through a pair of good binoculars, when some moon-shooter slaps three loads of large shot through the bunch. Frequently two or three of them will show indications of being wounded—a leg will drop, or the bird will wobble. In some rare instances, when head or neck shot, the fowl will fold up in the air and burst wide open from his terrific long fall. It is this chance kill that Cicero hopes for, nor does he give much thought to the havoc he is wreaking upon many other birds. To be honest, I am of the opinion that few new shooters know any better, though many of the old veterans are acquiring this habit. Often one hears the shooters boasting that they "hit the bird," but "he got away."

Up on the Mississippi last fall, I saw a friend of mine that had always been a good hunter, going over into John Highshot's crowd. He was loading his automatic with No. 4 shot in the barrel, the first shell in the magazine held No. 2 shot, and the last one was filled with B.B.'s. He was frank in stating that on occasion he managed to scratch down a high flyer with the big shot. He had many cripples, he confessed, and lost the most of them in the swift river.

Ciceros usually go in for big shot, and such fits in well with their long range activity, and according to the ballistic boys of the Ammunition Companies it is the berries. They say the big stuff maintains a higher velocity over long ranges, and does not fall off so fast as the smaller pellets. However, there is something that has to do with density of pattern that small shot can take care of best. At decent yardage a standard trap load is a killer of any duck that flies. Big shot will kill farther, and through lack of pattern density also cripple a bird at much greater distance.

A friend out in Amarillo, Texas, whom I hunted with in the good old days of live decoys, always shot geese with standard rabbit loads of No. 6 shot. It was his system to hunt on small isolated lakes, where he was the only gunner. With live birds, it was easy to get the honkers within a decent range. The small shot were most deadly. It was rare that a bird fell that was not stone dead. It would be hit repeatedly in the head and neck, and farther back, wings would be broken. Geese were never body hit without coming down, and that sickening sensation of watching a bird glide out of sight over the prairies to become coyote feed, was not experienced.

Lest I digress, and get away from Cicero or John Highshot, let's look at him in the upland shooting game. Twenty years ago, when one put up a covey of birds and marked them down, it was unusual that some other nimrod intercepted them and started hunting out the singles. Today even the dogs will fight when one party of bird hunters meets up with another while afield, and it is not unusual for Cicero, hearing your shots, to hasten over and attempt to kill your birds.

Apparently such poor hunting ethics are the result of our reduced cover and game supply, and the increased hunters afield. In other sports new rules are adopted with the intent of putting that pastime on a higher plane. We probably have an equal advancement in thought along conservation lines—we deplore poor shooting tactics, such as taking "sitting" birds—we talk of law enforcement and are all for it. But our conduct while afield with others sometimes is "haywire."

It is a real pleasure to witness a field trial, or get in on a good old Down South fox hunt. Traditions of these sports are still carried out, and proper ethics continue to be in vogue. At the traps, one does not need to go to the Grand American handicap to see proper consideration given to the shooter at his post. In skeet, there is an equal courteous procedure, and rules of sportsmen govern the game. Any Cicero that treads this sanctified ground does not long endure unless he mends his ways.

It is the contention of this unworthy critic, as Confucius might put it, that most of our "Cicero's" activity is due to ignorance rather than to deliberate intent. I have, as a matter of interest, on occasion, invited a "Cicero" duck shooter into my blind with me. I must confess, that frequently I take one in to get him out of the way, and to have him where I can control his shooting activities and harmful technique. As a rule, I find I have a good fellow with me, and human like anyone else, except that his education along some lines has been sadly neglected. One bank shooter that I took in hand a few years ago developed into a wonderful duck hunter. It is with great difficulty that I can now keep him from engaging other "Ciceros" in mortal combat when one appears on the bank behind our blind.

Many of the bank shooters are boys. These eager youngsters should be given every consideration, and have, in many instances, been crowded out of shooting places by hoggish adults. Through their lack of knowing just what to do about getting a shot at the elusive game, with wishful eyes, they haunt the water's edges, and unless given proper instructions, may develop into chronic Ciceros.

New shooters without a friend to guide them also take up the Cicero procedure. In fact, this bar walking tendency seems to be the first step in hunting by the novice. I remember a shooter I met on the banks of the Mississippi River a couple of years ago. I was attracted to him first because of the noise that I heard emanating from a clump of willows directly below me at the edge of the water. I thought someone was choking a cow.

Looking closer, I saw a hunter. He had on hip boots, a swell hunting coat, and all the finest of ducking raiment. Everything brand new. Offshore some six feet, and half submerged in the swift current, bobbed one lone decoy duck. On the bank were strewn half a dozen ears of corn, those imitation ones—and that hideous racket that I had heard had been made with a very fine ten dollar duck call.

I glanced apprehensively up and down the river. I actually felt sorry for the fellow and was afraid someone would see him and laugh. Maybe it was his new single trigger double with ventilated rib that caught my eye. Anyhow, I liked his looks, and at least he was not running up and down the sandbar gumming up the shooting for others.

It took a little persuading to get the new hunter into my blind. He was anxious to learn and a swell fellow besides. Also he was a very fine shot, even though all his previous gunning had been on a trap-shooting ground. When we parted company, I advised him to hunt at day shooting places with guides, until he learned some of the rudiments of the game, and he did. Today he belongs to a good club and is an enthusiastic and successful hunter.

You of the old school know what I am driving at, when I discuss Cicero and his activities. We no longer stoop after firing the first barrel, to see beneath the cloud of black powder smoke, whether a second shot is needed. Times have changed, and there are many old style things that might well be dispensed with—however, on our ethics we have slipped, and they are something that we should keep. In our zeal to restore game, cover, and favorable environment for our haired and feathered quarry, we have let a new generation of gunners grow up, just like Topsy.

On private holdings, John Highshot is barred, and shooting ethics are observed. Rules governing the taking of game, to the mutual benefit of all concerned, is the practice. I even know of day shooting places where a group of hunters that know each other will rent the entire area for a day. In this way they can exclude the Ciceros that invariably are present to ruin the shooting of everyone. It seems a shame that in this country we must go to private clubs for our hunting. Such smacks too much of European conditions, but with the present supply of game, and the thoughtlessness given to the taking of it, that is about all we have left.

Even today, shooting on public areas is so poor that many of the old-timers have given up in disgust. It is a hard pill to swallow, to have guides and flunkies do your hunting for you—or need shoot where you have the guilty feeling that the birds were just released from a coop. In Europe, prior to this war, only the wealthy could hunt. Tomorrow the same conditions may be present in America.

What can we do about it? Cicero may be the answer. We must take him into our blind and teach him the ethics, whether he wants to or not. Practically all things, from World Wars down to plain family fights, are a result of a lack of respect for other people's rights. We must teach John Highshot what other people's rights are.

In a recent publication by Outdoor Writers Association of America, Nash Buckingham offered the following definition:

"A Bar Walker is a so-and-so who won't stay in his pit, but ruins the shooting by getting out and promenading the sandbars. I hope they all die in agony and that no stone marks their resting place."

Shooters, it is up to you. Do you want to be a Bar Walker—or a John Highshot—or a Cicero?

Fabulous Fish

By WILLIAM J. SCHALDACH

ANY VETERAN FOLLOWER OF SPORT WITH ROD AND REEL WILL tell you that, strangely enough, the trips that went well, with a full creel at day's end are not necessarily those that live on in memory. Often as not something intangible will stir the pulse and bring a warm glow long afterward. It may be a mighty trout or salmon, lost almost at the net; the fleeting glimpse of a broad caudal belonging to a fish that did not take your fly; a fish beautiful in form or coloration, or almost any finny trophy taken under unusual circumstances.

These are fabulous fish. Every angler has his own personal collection, stored away in memory. If listeners raise their eyebrows cynically when tales of them are told, that is understandable. The seasoned angler knows that he has two strikes against him, anyhow, when he goes up to bat; so he can afford to be good-natured. He also knows, better than any non-fisherman, that in the enchanting waters of sea, lake or stream the weirdest things happen. There, indeed, truth is stranger than fiction.

A memory that will live with me forever concerns a deep pool near the head of a backwater, formed by a dam, in a medium-sized mid-Western brook. The fern-covered bank was deeply undercut, forming a shaded pool. Though the water was crystal-clear, the depth was sufficient so that the bottom of the stream could not be seen. A shaft of sunlight struck the sandy, shallow bank opposite the deep hole and illuminated the upper part of the water.

I was a mere kid and, with a home-made fly rod, was walking past this spot to reach the dam, where I intended to fish the swift water below the spillway. A little green frog leaped out from underfoot and splashed noisily into the pool. I saw a huge form stir from the shadowy depths and start upward. Transfixed, I gazed in awe as the shape rose swiftly at the frog, like an arrow to the target. There was a momentary flash as the fish turned. Green, rose, silver and blue; a myriad of black spots; a hooked beak and a wicked eye—that was my impression. Then came a liquid explosion, a disappearing shadow, slowly diminishing ripples and silence.

For some moments I thought it was all a dream, and then I realized that I had seen a tremendous rainbow. Feverishly I caught a small frog, rigged it on my tackle and, with all the stealth I could command, dropped it into the pool. But my method was not nature's, and the old boy wouldn't be fooled. I returned several times that day, and on many days thereafter, trying a variety of baits and lures. I even sneaked up and tossed in live frogs, hoping to see the monster again, but without results. Weeks passed, and I began to doubt that I had ever seen the fish. Perhaps, after all, it was just an illusion. But not being given to such hallucinations, I began to worry about the thing.

Then, one evening, I heard news that cleared up the situation. The local game warden caught a fellow who was spearing, illegally, of course, on this stream. The law-breaker had in his possession quite a bag of trout, and among them was a great, hook-nosed male fish weighing close to nine pounds. He admitted that he had taken it from the pool where I had seen it. The incident cleared up all doubt in my mind. It also demonstrated how close the truth can sometimes come to fantasy!

The popular idea seems to be that the only thing that counts in angling is the taking of a whopper or a heavy creel of fish. While freely admitting that these are valuable considerations at times, I think there are other things which can easily hand the angler a bigger kick. My personal list of thrills contains one which is memorable for its strangeness.

On a day in late May, many years ago, I was fishing for trout in Bear Creek, which is located in western Michigan. At best it was an undependable stream, but once in a while an exceptionally big brook trout would nail the fly—which went a long way toward evening up the dead spots. This time, however, things were exceedingly sour, and I had not stirred a fish in a half mile's wading. A small brook entered the main creek on the left bank, and I idly followed it for a few yards, out of curiosity.

The brook was not over six feet wide in most places, but there were some fair pools and ripples. I stripped line and casually dropped a small wet fly into a likely-looking place, letting it drift downstream toward me. A fish flashed at the lure; I struck and hooked it. As it raced back and forth I had the impression of pure silver flashing in the sunlight. I took it to be a chub or a dace and flipped it up on the bank in disgust.

But something about the fish's contour, as it flopped on the grass, looked wrong for a chub. The tail was square and the head strongly resembled that of a brook trout. A hasty examination showed it to be just that—a brook trout about eight inches in length. It was a plump, shapely little fish, identical with any of a thousand others, except for one thing: it *lacked color of any kind*. It glinted like burnished silver in the sunlight. On its back there were very faint impressions of the vermiculated markings characteristic of the brook trout. They were even more indistinct than in the case of the sea-run brookie, or "salter," which loses most of its color while in salt water.

Greatly interested now, I worked upstream for a half mile, casting into all sorts of likely-looking places. Before exhausting the fishable spots I had taken four more of these unusual specimens, the largest of which was 12 inches long. That night I stopped at the fish hatchery and asked for an explanation. I was told that the fish were true albinos—a very rare occurrence. Since that time I have fished many waters in widely separated parts of the country, but have never encountered further examples of these "ghost" trout. Nor have I heard of anyone else who has.

A great deal of emphasis is placed on subtlety in angling: the lightly cast fly, the delicate approach, finesse in tactics. Volumes are written on the subject, and they are eagerly read by the perfectionists. Theory is a desirable thing, and I have no quarrel with it. But I sometimes wonder if occasionally we do not allow supersophistication to clutter up our fishing. It is desperately easy to follow rules to such an extent that we overlook the obvious. We know, for example, that trout are found only in such-and-such places, at certain times of the day or season. We have been reading and hearing it for years; why bother, then, to investigate further? My own feeling is that "it ain't necessarily so."

In a small Connecticut town where I once lived, there were several enthusiastic trout fishermen. Near by, a couple of streams furnished fair fishing, and they were well patronized. To reach any of them it was necessary to cross a tiny trickle of a brook, flowing through the center of the town. It came down from a hill edging a cemetery and flowed under the main highway, over which rumbled thousands of cars. In great haste to get out of town, no one ever paid any attention to this little stream. It was just too tiny and public to hold trout. I should know, because I was one of the fishermen.

Then, one day, a fellow from out of town spotted the trickle, rigged up his rod and dropped a night-crawler into the culvert leading under the road from the upstream side. He couldn't have known anything about the way of trout, of course, or he never would have thought of anything so unorthodox. The line traveled a few feet and stopped. In a minute the fisherman started to retrieve his line. It seemed to be snagged on something; then it felt wiggly and rubbery. What took place after that is not recorded, but shortly thereafter a huge brook trout lay on the bank!

In just no time at all the news spread over town. The scales at the local grocery store showed the weight of the squaretail to be better than four pounds! That's what started me writing bits of fantastic information on my cuff for future reference. When it comes to fishing, I'll believe anything!

Sometimes it isn't the fish itself that gives the angler his big moment, but rather the type of fight a particular finny battler puts up. We all know that certain fish, like individual humans, are pugnacious and argumentative. Others can't be bothered with a struggle and give in easily. Then, too, circumstances have a lot to do with it. One of the most thrilling encounters, in fresh-water fishing, of which I have any knowledge was related to me by my friend John Taylor Arms, the eminent etcher. He is an enthusiastic and expert salmon and trout fisherman, and for years has fished the early runs in New Brunswick, when his limited time would permit.

On one of these trips he rose and hooked what appeared to be a large salmon. He was fishing from a canoe, and as the salmon at once started downstream the guide followed. The first run seemed interminable, and before the fish halted about a mile of river had been covered. Arms was put ashore to play the quarry, but in a few moments a new downstream run had started and line began to disappear from the reel at an alarming rate. Angler and guide hopped back into the canoe with alacrity and started off downstream again, with the salmon leading a hot pace. This performance was repeated a half dozen times.

The minutes and miles began to click off alarmingly, but the hooked fish showed no sign of tiring. The conclusion of both fisherman and guide was that this galloping captive could be nothing short of a 30-pounder. After the fifth attempt to play the salmon from shore and bring it to gaff, without even a hint of success, they were sure that here was a Cain's River record fish. Since the salmon had not even showed above the surface, there was no accurate way of gauging its size. As time went by, estimates of the fish's size grew larger and larger.

At long last the salmon stopped in a deep pool to sulk. Arms got out again and started the fish, which this time made no attempt at further running. After a few feeble rushes, the salmon gave up and was beached. It was a fish weighing only 16½ pounds; yet the fight had lasted 2½ hours and the distance covered was 8½ miles!

How come? Well, when the salmon rose it missed the fly, and the leader, by a twist of fate, made a loop around the strong caudal fin. This loop held, and the salmon was practically a free fish, able to keep its mouth closed and to use all of its fins in a desperate fight. Since a very light rod was being used, there was no stopping the salmon until it was ready to quit. And that, I submit, was just about a battle to end all battles!

While on the subject of reactions in individual fish it might be a good time to take a peek at the fisherman, with the same thought in mind. Have you ever noticed how different fellows act when out with rod and reel? Some are sober, businesslike and in deadly earnest about everything they do. Others are light-hearted, boisterous and gay, taking nothing seriously. Vic was the former, and his brother Carl the latter. They visited me one time at a house which I had taken for the summer on a well-known Catskill trout stream.

Vic was a dry-fly fisherman of intense convictions. He tied his own flies and fished only as the book says. Carl, on the other hand, was a non-conformist. He used any sort of tackle, and flies, spinners or worms were all the same to him. As an angler he just didn't rank with his brother; he was clumsy, careless and unskillful and, as a result, seldom made notable catches. But he did have a lot of fun.

The brothers started out one morning in opposite directions to fish different parts of the river. Vic was garbed in waders, fishing vest and leather-bound creel. He carried an expensive hand-made fly rod, and his pockets were crammed with aluminum cases filled with beautiful dry flies. Carl had on rubber boots and an old weather-beaten gunning coat. He trailed an ancient steel rod from the crook of his arm, and in one pocket a tobacco tin of angleworms could be seen.

It was a fine, soft day, with a gentle southwest breeze blowing. The May-flies were hatching up in great shape, and the water was clear as crystal. Under such conditions my bet would have been laid on Vic to win hands down.

But when evening came and the boys returned, my wife and I received a terrible shock. Vic had four or five small browns and rainbows in his creel. Not one of them measured over 12 inches. Carl calmly reached into the capacious hollow of his gunning-coat pocket and began hauling out fish. One after another, he placed them on the table—pounders, two-pounders and over. Then, without emotion, he tugged and hauled on the tail of something. After some little effort, a huge old brownie popped out and smacked down on the table.

It was, as they say in movie circles, colossal. Everybody gasped—that is, everybody but Carl. He didn't see anything to get excited about. Caught it on a worm, in a fairly shallow run, in bright sunlight. Fight? Naw—just hauled it out. Not bad fishin' up this way at that.

We never did know what that trout weighed, because Carl had caught it early in the morning, cleaned it on the stream to save weight and carried it all day in his coat pocket. As a result, it had dried out like a kipper. At that, it tipped the scales at just under five pounds! All of which proves—well, is it necessary to prove anything?

Didn't someone once make a remark to the effect that unheard melodies are the sweetest? Well, screwy as it may sound, I think the author of that had something. And there is a direct application to fishing. Some of my best memories of fabulous fishing center around Lockwoods—a long, beautiful pool on the Beaverkill. Though it happened twenty years ago, I can still see the picture clearly. And the high spot is not, as you might suppose, the capture of a whopper. On the contrary, the memory that continues with me concerns fish that were taken by others, and trout that I could not take.

It was mid-June, and a fine hatch of yellow May-flies danced tantalizingly over the surface of the water. A large number of big brown trout had moved into the pool, and late in the afternoon they were usually in a taking mood. The melodious note of rippling water was frequently accented by a liquid "glunk" as a brownie swirled and clamped his jaws down on a succulent insect. It was a time to stir the vitals of a fly-fisher. There were many anglers on the stream, working studiously all the important pools from the Junction to Baxters, well down on the river.

But Lockwoods was the most favored spot; in a couple of days four brown trout of exceptional size had been landed there. Each weighed more than four pounds. They were all taken on very light dry-fly tackle. Anything heavier than a 3x leader would fail to interest these much-fished-for and highly sophisticated trout. Most of the boys used rods weighing less than four ounces. Under these circumstances, when a trout was hooked the fight was long and the outcome most uncertain.

I said that four big brown were landed. How many were hooked and lost is something of which I did not keep a record. But the wails and hard-luck stories heard at the hotel, at the end of the day, were eloquent!

In a week's steady fishing I caught many trout, some of which weighed two pounds or more. It was one of the best trips I had ever had on the old river. But what I really wanted had steadily eluded me—the scalp of one of the old dogs out there in the purling waters, rising consistently with that fascinating "glunk," rolling over and showing his broad side spotted with black and red. Time and again I rose and hooked heavy fish. Often they would go under a rocky ledge and cut the leader. Or the hook would pull out. Sometimes the trout would break loose with a mighty leap.

Once success was almost mine. I rose a huge brown at the edge of a current, not twenty feet from me. I could see every detail of him as he sucked in the fly and rolled leisurely into the current. I struck, felt the weight of a solidly hooked fish, saw the line cut a V through the water as the little 3½-ounce rod bowed into an arc. A 50-foot run terminated in a smashing break as a magnificent brown came out two feet above the surface. This was it!

The tackle held, and as the fish dashed down to the tail of the pool I splashed through the shallow water, following and giving line grudgingly. For many minutes the big fellow was on; twice more I saw him and knew that he was better than a five-pounder. Then, when victory seemed close, the fly popped out of his mouth and snapped through the air at me contemptuously. The big trout flipped his tail and swam out of sight forever. I can still see his powerful fins boring into the current as he worked back to the sheltering waters of his home pool. This will always be one of my big moments in angling—the trout I did not catch!

Like all mortals, the angler has his trials and tribulations. But there are always the lighter moments, and these have a way of shining through the darkest clouds. A sense of humor is as much a part of the fisherman's equipment as his rod and reel. I have always liked the quaint story told to me by my friend Ted Townsend, game warden of Westchester County, New York.

Ted and several helpers were seining carp from one of the watershed reservoirs, where these coarse fish had become so plentiful as to menace the supply of desirable food and game fish. It was hard work, and the men were well tuckered out toward the end of the afternoon. As they were bringing in the last seineful of squirming, brassy-colored carp an expensive limousine drove up and stopped. A very elegantly attired old lady got out, adjusted her lorgnette, peered at the flopping captives and exclaimed: "My, what lovely fish! What are they?"

Ted removed his cap, bowed gallantly and replied, "Golden salmon, madam, and an exceptionally fine lot, too."

"Oh, how perfectly romantic!" exclaimed the dowager, bubbling over with delight.

"She drove away happy," Ted told me; "but if I had said that they were carp, it would have spoiled her whole afternoon."

And there you have it. The angler is, indeed, a fabulous man. Listen to him respectfully as he goes about scattering pearls. To the outsider he may seem to be romancing, but his stories are invariably true—in one way or another.

Steve's Mixed Double

By FRED COPELAND

AT UNEXPECTED INTERVALS A YELLOW AND RED PAINTED LEAF let go high up in the maple beside Nood's old brick drugstore. It tumbled with crisp bumping sounds down through the tree, glowing like a Chinese lantern in the brilliant October moonlight. Suddenly the drugstore door opened, revealing the lofty, angular silhouette of Hen Magoon. Behind him came a mellow outflow from six corncob pipes, four hound dogs and Steve Cleveland.

Mr. Mangoon was elated. He stopped on the ancient stone steps and looked down at Steve, whose head came up to his elbow.

"I've been tellin' 'em right along a woodcock whistles with his

266

bill, and not his wings. Fancy Doc Parkhurst runnin' onto that piece in a paper where a feller claimed to have a tame woodcock that sat right still in a cage and whistled!"

The moonlight night crouched down as still as the moment before a July thunderclap. Mr. Magoon tilted his rusty-black derby, emblem of his paperhanger's trade, and looked up into the jeweled mystery of the great maple. White diamond dust was gathering on both the fallen leaves and those still clinging to the limbs.

"There'll be flighters in the morning. You ever see a doodle bird, Steve?"

"Yes, I did—just once. It was up along Moore's brook last summer."

"Ever taken a shot at an old flight woodcock in the alders?"

Steve looked up quickly. He shook his head. Mr. Magoon continued. "Mm-m, tomorrow will be a prime morning for woodcock. It takes a cute, fast gun for 'em. You wait a minute, Steve." Hen Magoon let himself back into the pumpkin-colored glow of the old drugstore, and returned with a delightful smile. "I've got the loan for you of Doc Parkhurst's little double-barrel 16-gauge. Doc's got such a game leg this fall he can't travel. Can you come?"

"Honest, Hen, can I really come?" Steve asked excitedly. "But, Hen, we ain't got a dog. I've heard 'em say you've always got to have a bird dog or you can't get a single woodcock."

"Huh, you don't have to keep from huntin' woodcock just because you ain't got a dog," explained Mr. Magoon as he set off up the village street in the brilliant frosty air. "All you got to do is to find tiny clumps of alders and poplars so small folks with dogs don't pay any attention to 'em. And I'm goin' to tell you if there's a woodcock in one of them tiny clumps you don't need a dog to find him, even if they don't get up till you almost step on their tail-feathers. I'll show you tomorrow."

"What time you want me to come, Hen?" The freckles on Steve's small uplifted face were alert with attention.

Hen took hold of one side of his cavalry mustache and reflected. "Oh, eight is early enough. It's nicer and smellier when the sun gets in the alders. And besides, we ain't got to worry about our covers being gunned out; the dog men will hit for the big swales. I'd a hundred times rather drift from one little patch to another. It ain't so tuckerin', and it's awfully more divertin'."

"Yes!" breathed Steve just as though he understood, only he didn't. "Hen, do—do you suppose I'll get one?"

"Oh, certain, certain! They're a little more curiouser than partridges, but similar. Anyhow, they're nearer when they get up."

In the morning a blade of gold slid through the maples on the East Hill and touched a valley glistening with frost. Tiny columns of smoke from village chimneys reached pale silver stems straight up and burst into yellow blossom where the sun hit them. Far across the valley, thinned by the distance, a rooster crowed out of a chilled throat. Mr. Magoon put his large bony face to a small window-pane and examined his woodshed roof, which had become shingled with powdered diamonds during the night. Above the rooftree hung the flawless sapphire of a New England October sky. Hen Magoon swallowed contentedly.

Just before eight o'clock Steve rapped cautiously at Mr. Magoon's kitchen door. He was panting from hurry. He looked anxiously up at Mr. Magoon when the door opened. Hen was smiling all over his face. It was all right. They were going—his first woodcock hunt, with a real double-barrel 16-gauge. Steve edged to the snapping kitchen range and warmed his hands, stung red by the frosty morning air.

They were going to walk to the cover, for it was a tiny valley where the village lay. Hen knew numerous woodcock parlors around its entire fringe. Often gunners with dogs would go twenty miles, hunt out endless swales and come back with one bird, only to learn that night at Nood's drugstore that Hen Magoon had picked up the limit and never been out of sound of the village clock.

At Doc Parkhurst's cottage they stopped for the gun. Steve stood behind Hen on the great stone doorstep and held his breath. Doc had hobbled to the door and was now looking out with his friendly brown eyes. He didn't say much, but you could see it sobered him to think he couldn't go. He studied with a queer expression the half of Steve's freckled face peering anxiously around Hen's elbow. Then Doc reached over in the hall corner and held out a trim, racy little 16-gauge with the tiniest of engraved hammers and mottled twin Damascus tubes.

"We shan't let a single scratch get on it," said Hen by way of thanks.

"I know," nodded Doc easily, then reached out something to Steve.

A whole box of 16-gauge shells factory-loaded with No. 9 shot— a special load for the fast little gun. Steve held the box in both hands; he was speechless.

"He won't never forget it, Doc," said Hen.

"It's his first try at woodcock?"

Hen nodded.

Doc Parkhurst's brown eyes were swimming with eagerness to go, or, perhaps, with the memory of that far-away first day of his own in the black alders. Smiling them success, he slowly closed the door.

Steve managed to stuff six shells in each pants pocket, and Hen stowed the rest in his tattered hunting coat. He was still wearing his rusty derby, the badge of his calling, and his wrists came out a long way from his coat sleeves. He filled a corncob pipe and fired it with slow pressure. It smelt strangely sweet in the still air. Then they started along the narrow dirt sidewalk.

Shortly the white cottages of the village pinched out. There were a few narrow meadows before they came to a small wooden bridge where a trout brook jingled down out of a gently rising pasture. They bent double and crawled through a pair of bars to the glistening whiskers of pasture grass.

Almost at hand, on rising land, a little stand of alders crept secretly around a series of leaking springs where the dark soil was cut up by cow tracks. The audacity of that tiny woodcock cover! Only Hen knew about it. Pitched, as it should be, on a gentle northwest slope, it was an invitation to any woodcock as far away as Labrador.

Hen led off up the open pasture beside a water-trickle now sealed with thin isinglass covers. The sun, when they reached the cover fringe, was slanting yellow bars through the alders, still clinging to their curled, blackened leaves.

"This is their kitchen," nodded Hen, stuffing his corncob in a side pocket. "And one of 'em has had breakfast."

"He has?" Steve stared wonderingly into the mottled twilight.

"Them little white spatters is a telltale. Watch out! Cock both hammers. Keep to the left and a little ahead. I wonder if it's a native or a flighter. He's goin' to let go awful sudden. You'll have to shoot quick."

They inched like shadows into the first alder stems. Steve's face was so tense and white that his freckles fairly twinkled.

"Sh-h!" cautioned Hen. "By jinks! I can see him! It ain't once in a coon's age you can see one on the ground. He's right in front of that stump straight ahead!"

Steve became motionless, searching the curled alder leaves about the stump. Out of mystery a wild little form suddenly caught his eye.

The woodcock squatted there like a tiny duck, an exquisite pattern of brown and black and cream.

"Watch out now! He's got some of the crookedest and awfulest springs hitched to his dew-claws. He'll fly crazier'n a June bumble-bee when he gets started."

"What'll I do, Hen?" Steve was trembling.

"Keep your gun clear of branches, and shoot quick."

Steve's eyes opened wider and wider. It was unbelievable that that alert woodcock would let them creep up so close.

"He thinks we don't see him," Hen started to whisper.

"*Whe-e-e-t! Wheet! Wheet Wheet!*"

The woodcock boiled straight up, and then twisted like a tiny ghost among the alder tops.

"Quick, Steve!"

Steve jerked up the little 16-gauge. The muzzle sawed anxiously among the branches. A shadowy wing-flip cut across the muzzle. An alder stem bumped the barrels.

Wham!

A shower of twigs rattled down like rain. Hen plunged out of the alders and stood watching in the pasture, bent and motionless. The woodcock was humming like a hornet along the open lands.

"He's an old flighter. Gosh! I wonder if he's going clear to South America. No, he's swingin' down. He's going into them witch-hazel bushes under the ledge."

"I thought I got him." Steve hurried up to Hen's side.

"No, he wasn't even skeered, Steve. They're a good deal more troublesome and awkwarder to get at then a partridge. We better go right over where he dropped in."

They hurried over the swelling crown of the pasture. Suddenly the bird's new lair was revealed at the bottom of the far slope, where a ledge pushed out behind a thin grove of poplars.

"He may flush wilder this time, and he may stick tighter—I never seen such curious critters. I guess it's why they're so all-fired inter-estin'," panted Hen, hoofing eagerly down the slope. "We better circle and head him back to the alder clump."

On the west side they picked up an old wood road which entered the grove. It led back to the ledge pocket.

"This is the most woodcocky place I know of. Be ready any minute," said Hen, balancing his way on grass tufts across a swampy place.

The gray face of the ledge looked down on them. At its foot was a fringe of large bushes. Tiny, delicate blossoms of pale yellow starred the tips of the bare, dark twigs—the last of fall. It was witch-hazel. A strange, silent mystery brooded about the place. Vivid against the gray ledge, one single flare of crimson, still clinging to a lone maple limb, told that anything could happen in this secret pocket.

A sudden, unseen rustling broke out on the forest floor in front. They caught a glimpse of something gray—bristling. It ran scolding like an old woman. A mammoth ruffed grouse burst out of a swirl of maple leaves.

"Steve!" Mr. Magoon's gun was half raised. "Steve, shoot!"

The boy's gun hopped up like a flash. With it came a break-taking sound—a rollicking whistle rose out of the witch-hazel. There, at the same instant, ahead of the guns was that rare upland miracle—a humming grouse and a buzzing woodcock.

"Watch out, Steve!"

Wham!

The rushing grouse plunged downward.

Wham!

A dodging woodcock pitched sidewise among the witch-hazel branches. Mr. Magoon came galloping over to Steve. He placed a great bony paw down on Steve's small shoulder and half shook, half patted it. The blood was coming back into Steve's face. He was still speechless. But Hen Magoon's throat was working behind the ends of his cavalry mustache, which were twitching up and down.

"My gosh, Steve! It ain't liable to happen again in a lifetime. A mixed double! Jee-mi-ma! There's old gunners eighty years and more never had it happen to 'em!"

"Hen, I guess—I guess it was just—just luck. I don't remember aiming a mite."

"No, you pointed. Gol darn it! That's the only way you can stop partridge and woodcock. Jinks! That double was a daisy! It's goin' to be awful when I tell 'em in Nood's drugstore tonight."

They picked up the woodcock first in the witch-hazel. Then the partridge from a tangle of tobacco-brown ferns. Steve held them both by the feet in one hand and fed his eyes on the startling beauty of their markings.

"Jinks!" broke out Hen. "It ain't only a leetle past ten, but I've got to celebrate. Let's squat over there where the sun burns in amongst the ferns by that little spruce."

Mr. Magoon knelt down at the spruce and began working with

wrinkled brow in the tail of his tattered hunting jacket. He finally untangled a round, flat object done up in a newspaper. When the wrapping came off, Steve took his eyes off the partridge and woodcock. Hen was holding in his hands a whole apple pie.

"It's a leetle early, but I guess we better." Mr. Magoon opened a jackknife and cut one line across the pie.

He presented an entire half to Steve. Steve took it eagerly in both hands like a slice of watermelon and buried his teeth in the oozing apple-filled crust. Mr. Magoon's mustache ends rose to his ears as a large section of the pie went out of sight.

"See them legs," said Mr. Magoon, nodding at the woodcock. "Rough as an old Plymouth Rock hen's. That's one way to tell a flighter. If they was smooth and light-colored like a chorus girl's wrist, it would be a native, which was raised right here in our heathen valley."

Mr. Magoon took another bite and cast an eye on the partridge. "He's an old drummer. Look at that big topknot and that wild black bar on his tail. And see them little gray heart-shaped spots on his rump feathers. Cuter'n any valentine."

Steve looked. It was true—just like a valentine.

"You know," Hen said as he examined regretfully the small remnant of his pie, "you know when old Doc Parkhurst hears about this, I wouldn't be surprised if he gave you that little 16-gauge."

"Honest?" Steve's eyes were wide open.

"I'll bet he will. Sometime, anyhow. This pie has perked me up amazin'. Let's brush out another old doodle bird."

Bob Hines.

"Pothole Guys, Friz Out"

By GORDON MACQUARRIE

THE PRESIDENT OF THE OLD DUCK HUNTERS ASSOCIATION, INC., hauled up in front of my house in the newest, gaudiest automobile which had to that date, turned west off Lake drive onto East Lexington boulevard.

It seemed that even the gray squirrels among the boulevard beeches were impressed by the streamlined vehicle, if not by the inelegant driver, Hizzoner himself, in a flannel shirt and battered brown hat.

I saw him coming for two blocks for I had been expecting him. The village hall and police station are his landmarks. He made a horseshoe turn around the end of the boulevard, slid into the curb and yelled for all to hear:

"The minute I saw the jail I knew where to find you!"

Leaf raking brethren of the chase leaned on their implements and yipped. The Old Man freed himself from his imposing machine and studied a Schnauzer dog which had arrived with a band of kids to investigate the new automotive device. Anent the dog, Mister President demanded:

"Is that a dog or a bundle of oakum?" He is congenitally allergic to all but the hunting breeds.

In due course he came inside. He'd driven the dealer's model super-duper up from the factory and was stopping on the way by pre-arrangement to rescue me from the city's toils.

"Going through Chicago," he explained, "every cop on Michigan avenue made the same mental note as I drove by—'roughly dressed man in brand new auto.' If the police come, my identification papers are in the glove compartment."

He had climbed into his old hunting clothes for comfort in the long drive.

Later in the evening we loaded the car with decoys, shell boxes, duffel bags and in the early morning while the household slept the Old Duck Hunters Association crept away.

The elements had descended. Streets were semi-granite with frozen sleet.

"Just what the doctor ordered," Mister President exulted. "If it's freezing down here, it's frozen up there."

Daylight came on the feet of snails but long before then the Old Man bade me halt on the slippery road. With the tire gauge in one hand and a flashlight in the other he let 10 pounds of air out of each tire. After that we got along faster.

At Portage, Wis., the President was happier than ever, for snow was falling. We had breakfast and went on. North of Tomah the sleet was gone from the road and dry snow was whipping across the concrete. We re-inflated the tires and pushed on. At Chippewa Falls, crossing the big bridge, visibility up and down the Chippewa river was 200 yards.

Hizzoner nodded in the seat beside me. He was asleep and snoring at Spooner. The snow and the wind increased. The footing for tires was perfect, thanks to the built-up highway over which dry flakes rolled in sheets. Mister President awoke at Minong while a man by the name of Andy Gorud filled the tank.

"Is this it, Andy?" the Old Man asked. For answer Andy took us to his back porch and exhibited a possession limit of snow-sprinkled redheads. Andy said indeed this was it, but if the weather kept up it might drive every duck out of the country before morning.

"Bosh!" said Mister President. "Only the shallow lakes and potholes will freeze. The ducks'll have to wet their feet in big water tomorrow morning."

Such a man, that Andy. Once he walked two miles in the rain with a heavy jack to hoist us up and put on our chains.

The snow kept up. At Gordon we turned off. The Old Man was wide awake now.

"She's a good un," he said, watching the county trunk. "Come so quick they haven't got all the snow fences up. If you see a drift back up and give 'er tarpaper."

Tarpaper was required in several places. I complimented him on the power under the hood of his newest contraption but he was not enthusiastic—"They're all too low, no good in a two-rut road. They're making them so low pretty soon you can use a gopher hole for a garage."

It grew dark. The driving flakes stabbed at the windshield. By the time I was ready to turn off the county trunk onto the town road the Old Man had demanded the driver's seat. He knew that the in-road would be well filled with snow. I protested but he said I could drive "the day you learn your driving brains are in the seat of your pants."

There were a few spots on that narrow road between the jack pines where we barely got over the rises. The car was pushing snow 12 inches deep when we stopped at the top of the last hill.

We went ahead and got a fire going. When I got to the cabin with the first load the fireplace was roaring and he was coaxing the kitchen range to life. By the time I had hauled in the last of the gear and shoveled the snow off the stoop he had water hot enough for tea. While we ate supper the temperature slid from 28 to 24.

We hauled in wood, broke out blankets and took a hooded motor from the shed down through the snow to the lake. We took a boat off its winter roost and set it handy by the edge of the tossing lake. We brought down guns and decoys, put them in the boat and covered everything with a canvas tarp. Then there was time to size up the night.

It was a daisy. There was snow halfway to the knees on the beach. The flashlight's circle revealed a black, tossing lake. From the hill at our backs the wind screamed down through the pine trees.

"How'd you like to be a field mouse on a night like this?" Hizzoner reflected.

We went back up the hill. The last thing Mister President did was study the thermometer. I heard him say, "She's dropped to 22 and it's only 8 o'clock." After that the fireplace crackled, the wind cried, the blankets felt awfully good ...

In the morning there wasn't a breath of wind. Of course he was up before me, useful and belligerent. Everything was ready, including the country smoked bacon. I started to open the door to inspect the thermometer and he announced, "Fifteen about half an hour ago."

I studied him jealously as I have often. There he was, 30 years older than I, tough as a goat, alert as a weasel. He'd just finished an exhausting business trip. Forty-eight hours before he had been 600 miles from this place. He ate six eggs to my four, eyeing me with the indulgent authority a bird dog man feels for a new pup.

"The hell with the dishes and put on all the clothes you've got," he directed.

The lake in the darkness held an ominous quiet, like a creature which had threshed itself to exhaustion. We flung off the tarp with one flip to keep snow off gear, slid in the boat, screwed on the motor and roared out.

We were afloat on blackness, rimmed with the faint white of snow on the shores. Mister President huddled in the bow in the copious brown mackinaw, its collar inches above his ears. He fished in pockets and drew on mittens and when his hands were warmed he fished again and presently a match glowed over the bowl of his crooked little pipe. I saw that he was grinning, so throttled the motor and yelled, "What's the joke?"

"No joke," he came back. "Just a morning for the books."

The run to this place requires about 30 minutes. Dim landmarks on shore were illuminated just enough by the snow. We cut wide around the shallow point bar and went south for the shallow end of the lake. The Old Man has bet that he can, blindfold, land an outboard within 100 yards of the shallow bay point from our beach. There are no takers.

A little daylight was making as I cut the speed and turned toward the shore. The President said, "Go back down the shore further from the blind. The boat'll stand out against the snow like a silo." We beached 200 yards from the point.

There was plenty of time. When the Old Man is master of ceremonies you get up early enough to savor the taste of morning. And what a morning! Just once in a coon's age do the elements conspire with latitude to douse North Wisconsin with snow of mid-winter depth in October. It is a very lovely thing. We toted up the gear to the blind. I was impatient to get out in the shallows in my waders and spread decoys. The Old Man detained me.

"I suppose," he said, "that when a man quits liking this it's time to bury him."

He was determined to size up the morning, and he did size it up. Between hauls on the blackened brier he continued, "Once before I saw this point just as pretty. Back in 1919. Just about the same depth of snow, same old lake black as ink, trees ag'in the sky ..."

I had paused to honor his rhapsody, so he snorted, "Get them boosters out there, dang yuh, while I rebuild the blind!"

Rebuild it he did, pausing now and then in the growing light to tell me where to place the next decoy. In the blind I found he had the rough bench swept off, the blind repaired and a thermos of coffee at hand. He sat on the right side of the bench and both our guns, his automatic and my double, were held away from the snowy wall of the blind by forked sticks. It was unmercifully cold for sitting. He explained his thesis for the day—

"The potholes chilled over in the night. The ice crep' out from shore. The ducks huddled up, getting closer and closer as the ice reached for 'em. First good daylight they'll look around at each other and say, 'Let's go. This place is getting too crowded'."

"You don't suppose they've all left the country?" I ventured. There was scorn in his reply.

"The best ducks stay 'til the last dog's hung."

A burst of bluebills went over and planed into the lake, far out.

"They were up awfully high for cold weather ducks," I said. "I'm afraid if they move they'll go a long ways today—if there are any left around."

"They'll be lower," he said.

A pair dropped in from in back of us. It was apparent they'd come in from any quarter in the absence of wind. I reached for the gun and slid out a toe to kick my shellbox. The Old Man put a mittened hand on my right knee. I could feel his fingers squeeze through leather and wool. Following his eyes I saw what he saw.

They were at the left, about a hundred ducks, an embroidery of ducks, skeined out in a long line with a knot at the head. We crouched down and the Old Man whispered:

"Pothole guys, friz out. Might be from Minnesota. Maybe Ontario. They'll swing and size 'er up and the whole dang bundle will——."

Swi-i-i-ish!

While we had watched the mid-lake flock fifty or so had slid into the decoys, bluebills everyone. The President from his corner eyed me and whispered, "Flyin' high did you say? No, don't shoot! We're gonna have fun."

The mid-lake flock swung in, decoyed by their confident cousins. The President of the Old Duck Hunters grinned like a school boy. He was on his knees in the trampled snow, close against the front wall of the blind. So was I and he was laughing at me. Fifty ducks sat in the decoys, another hundred were coming in, and the Old Man said to me:

"Hold out your hand so I can see if you're steady."

At the moment that the landed birds were flailing out the incomers were tobogganing in with their wing flaps down. The Old Man arose and shouted:

"Hello, kids!"

His deliberateness was maddening. I emptied the double before he brought up his automatic. I reloaded and fired again and he still had a shell to go. He spent it expertly on a drake.

Then the ducks were gone and I was trying to stuff a round brass match safe into the breech and the Old Man was collapsed on the bench, laughing.

"Up high for cold weather ducks!" he howled.

There were seven down, two far out, and as I raced back for the boat Mister President heckled, "Wish I had that East Lexington boulevard Snootzer here and I'd learn him to be a dog!"

As I rowed out for the pick-up he shouted across the water, "Do you get a bottle of turpentine with every Snootzer you buy?"

As he had predicted, it was a day for the books. The clouds pressed down. They leaned against the earth. No snow fell but you knew it might any minute. There were not just clouds but layers of clouds, and ramparts and bastions and lumps of clouds in between the layers.

We sat and drank coffee. We let bluebills sit among the decoys. That was after Hizzoner decreed, "No more 'bills. Pick the redheads if you can. If you miss a mallard I'll kill yuh."

The quick dark day sped by. To have killed a hundred diving ducks apiece would have been child's play. Canvasback, whistlers, mergansers, redheads, and bluebills by the hundreds trouped over the hundred-year old decoys which are the sole property of the Old Duck Hunters Association.

"I'd give a lot for a brace of mallards to color up the bag," he said.

The Lady Who Waits for Mister President likes mallards.

Be assured, mallards were present, as well as those dusky wise men, black ducks. They would swing in high over the open water and look it over. They did not care for any part of our point blind in the snow.

"Wise guys," Mister President said. "They see the point and two dark objects against the snow in the blind, and one of the objects wiggling all over the place. That'll be you."

We went back to the boat and fetched the white tarpaulin. He threw it over the top of the blind and propped up the front of it with cut poles. The tarp erased us from above and seven laboring mallards swung closer. Before throwing off the tarp, Mister President whispered: "Slow down sos'te to nail 'em."

Back went the tarp. I missed a climber, then crumpled him. Hizzoner collected three. He just spattered them. Because these were for the Lady Who Waits.

We picked up and hauled out, raising rafted diving ducks in the long run back.

We hoisted the boat onto its winter trestles, upside down, to let it drain and dry. We put the gear beneath it and slung the tarp over it. We went up the hill and stirred the fires.

I got supper. I worried about the super-duper on the hilltop at the road's end but he said he had drained it. I lugged in more wood and heaped up the fireplace.

He said in the morning we might have to break ice to get out from shore. He said, "we might not see much more than whistlers." He said to steep the tea good. He said not to forget to climb down the well and open the bleeder on the pump "because she's going to really drop tonight." He said he thought he'd "take a little nap 'fore supper." And finally he said:

"Draw them mallards will yuh, son? She likes 'em drawed."

First Covey

By J. AUSTELL SMALL

I SAW JUDY WHEN SHE HIT THE COTTONTAIL'S TRAIL. SHE WAS excited. The little cream-colored, black-spotted setter sniffed twice, snorted, and was off through the twisted grapevine snarl with a bold note of challenge.

I could hear Tom's voice. It was harsh, commanding, a little desperate. Tom wanted to know what the double so-and-so little Judy meant by running "that kind" of a rabbit!

He stopped her finally. I didn't mean to eavesdrop on the little drama that followed. But when an opportunity such as this presents itself, a man can't help but listen. We've all been through that stage. Not a one of us who loves a good setter or pointer hasn't pleaded with a young, inexperienced hopeful not to make a jackass of itself before friends.

"Look, Judy," Tom was saying. "You've got to settle down, old girl. It's time you were catching on to what we're after. It's quail, Judy. Quail. Bzzzzzzzzzzzzz!" Tom pursed his lips and made a buzzing sound. He flapped his hands. "Got it now, girl? Quail!" Tom buzzed again for good measure. "Not rabbits, by gosh!"

I was about to turn away with a grin when Bill Moore came in sight, tramping through the scrub oak, looking for his dog, Queenie. I tried to head Bill off before he got to Tom. But he was going too fast.

"What'd she hit?" Bill asked tactlessly. "A rabbit?"

"A what? Ahh—of course not! She must have been on a pretty cold trail. Lost it here in the brambles. It's too cold, I think, for any dog to follow."

"Maybe they moseyed out into the flats. Queenie may have them pinned down solid out there now," Bill suggested.

"She might have hit the trail after they rested up and began feeding again, at that," Tom agreed. "Don't think she'd ever have worked it out this far back."

I smiled inwardly. We headed toward the flats.

Queenie came trotting up from behind. She hadn't been in the flats at all. Bill got her lined out across a field blanketed in knee-high crab grass. Tom and Judy leveled off to the left, made for a fence line that ran toward a brushy creek.

Across the field, hardly a hundred yards from the creek, Queenie hit solid. We called Tom, but he waved us on.

"Judy's working on birds over here!" he yelled.

Queenie's a good dog, all right. Steady. She works fast but thorough. And she's not too eager. The setter made a pretty sight there in the tall grass, standing stiff and motionless in the best of field trial style.

The birds were up in a roar, scattering wildly and heading for the creek. We had to shoot against a dark background of ragged pin oak trees.

I heard Bill's gun let go as I swung with a flaring bird and squeezed the trigger. Two bobs lost momentum, slammed against the swaying grass. We didn't shoot again. The buzzing specks were by now indistinguishable against a background of drab oak.

"First today!" I said. I felt pretty good about nailing that bird. "Now if we could just keep that up!"

"I won't," Bill said flatly. "Never do." He eyed me quizzically. "You neither!"

"Well, in this dad-burned old brushy country, how could you expect a man to—"

"Aw, shut up!" Bill said.

Quail can lose themselves after they've been scattered quicker than mischievous kids in a holiday crowd. We only downed one more bird out of that bevy. The creek was a jungle of brambles, brush piles, thickets, and natural hiding places. The one Bill got was dropped in a tunnel through the heavy growth.

"Now if you could just do that with your twenty—" Bill began.

"It'll do anything that old blunderbuss of yours will," I said, adding "almost" under my breath.

"It's too early in the morning for fish stories," Bill chuckled.

We walked over toward Tom. Judy was working out ahead of him. She seemed excited. They were less than a hundred yards from the creek. I heard Tom caution, "Easy, Judy!"

Suddenly, the air was full of birds.

We couldn't see the dog completely, but the tip of her tail showed all the time. She had run into a covey head on, not even pausing until quail erupted all around her.

"As nice a case of running through a covey as I ever saw," Bill said. "Let's go see what Tom will tell us about it."

Tom was scolding the dog as we walked up. "Blamed pot-licker!" he was growling. "Why don't you slow down!" He shook the dog by her collar and cuffed her ears a little.

"What happened?" Bill asked from a distance.

We heard the grass rattle as Tom turned his dog loose and scooted her out ahead.

"Blamed birds flushed wild," he informed us. "They're sure jumpy today. Maybe we can pick up a couple along the creek. They stopped at that ragged-topped grass beside the bank."

Bill looked at me and winked.

"Judy'll nail them," Tom said confidently. "She's getting the drift of things already, and this is only her fourth trip out. You watch Judy now!"

Bill purposely waved Queenie to the right of where the quail settled. And then we watched Judy.

She blustered across the short mesquite grass, stopped at the creek bank, sniffed, snorted once, and let out a ringing bawl. It sounded almost like the excited bay of a hound.

Tom flushed uncomfortably.

"Dogged if it doesn't sound like she's trailing a rabbit!" Bill said. He shoved a side grin at me.

"Oh, no—it isn't a rabbit!" Tom said quickly. "It's those quail. She's just—well a little excited, that's all."

Grass crackled as some animal left hurriedly. A big swamp rabbit slapped the ground with his back feet and scurried into the brush.

"This year's crop of quail are sure heavy on their feet aren't they, Joe" Bill turned to me with deep humor in his eyes.

Judy followed the rabbit with a couple of quick barks. And Tom followed Judy. After fifty yards of hard running and shouting, Tom's remarks became gradually more uncomplimentary.

He was across the creek and about a hundred yards away when he caught her. We saw Tom lead Judy into a thicket. Then we heard the dog yelp in pain. "Shuddup, dog-gone ya!" Tom said guardedly.

He was trying to whip his dog without our knowing about it.

Judy looked sheepish when she followed him back.

"Blamed young dogs are over-anxious," Tom said. "They'll follow anything for a few yards. But Judy always quits when she sees it isn't quail. I—look at her now!"

The little dog had picked up the scent of quail all right. Judy looked right good as she parted the ragged grass, followed up the scent with remarkable speed.

Tom's face was flushed with happiness. He said "Steady! Easy now, Judy!" over and over until it sounded like an old phonograph playing on a dented record.

The birds flushed. All around the dog. She jumped involuntarily, looked around and about. Judy was puzzled. Tom sighed heavily.

"Put this check cord on her," Bill advised, handing Tom a long rope. "It's the only way, sometimes, to slow down a young, eager dog."

Tom tied the rope around Judy's neck.

By this time we were feeling a little sorry for Tom. His antics with a young hopeful hand reminded us of days past and we had derived no little amount of satanic delight in ribbing him. But when a man looks as "dragged through the shinery brush" as Tom did now, you've got to feel a little sympathetic. That's why Bill offered him the rope.

Queenie came down on a honey of a covey across the creek. Judy was a few yards behind her. The young dog continued to advance inquisitively.

"Hold it, Judy!" Tom yelled. He raced forward to step on the trailing rope. But he needn't have. As the young dog came up to Queenie and started to pass her, the older setter turned and nipped Judy soundly. The young dog jumped back, whined and looked puzzled.

Tom finally grasped the rope and quavered, "Steady, Judy!"

Encouraged by his nearness, the young dog started forward again, this time in a wide circle around Queenie. Tom jerked her back hard. She stayed put then. Bill nodded his approval.

Tom wouldn't shoot. He just held on to his dog and kept saying "Steady!" to her.

Bill got a neat double. I missed an easy straightaway and then winged another as it fought to gain a break in the treeline.

I looked at Bill's double.

"Accident, eh?" I belittled.

"Accident!" Bill's eyebrows slid upward. "Skill, my boy," he replied. "Plain skill," He smiled provokingly. "You see, with a twelve—"

"With a bazooka throwing that much shot," I snorted, "it isn't skill—you just can't help hitting something!"

We headed back toward the car.

Queenie and Judy were working neck to neck through the high grass, freckled with patches of scrub oak. It didn't look like good quail cover.

But they were there. Both dogs struck scent at the same time. Judy worked forward quickly. Queenie took it a little more carefully.

Judy came down then. She hesitated first, shivered slightly, and froze into as pretty a point as a man will ever see.

Tom's mouth sagged open. He stood like a statue for a full five seconds. Queenie backed the point beautifully. It made a pretty picture.

When Queenie backed, Tom knew for sure that it was quail now and not another field mouse, grass bird or some such trifle that Judy had found. He sprang into action. The young dog had already started creeping forward. She was trembling all over. She was whining slightly too.

"Steady, Judy!" Tom called, running toward her. "Easy now, girl!"

There was deep pleading, barefaced begging in Tom's voice.

They couldn't be far away. The only spot of grass deep enough to cover them was directly in front of Judy now as she continued to creep forward.

Tom died a thousand deaths from the time he started running forward until he finally grasped the check-cord in sweaty hands. A couple more steps and the birds would surely have flushed.

Tom sighed audibly. The dog was still straining forward against the rope, nose twitching, trembling slightly. Tom jerked her back, talked to her commandingly. She finally held it. And when the little dog made up her mind to hold, she held. It was beautiful to see. It was witnessing the birth of a bird dog.

Tom wiped a moist forehead and looked at us with a wry grin. We grinned back at him and nodded. It was as much as to say: "Well, it looks like you've got a bird dog now, all right!"

We were walking toward the car slowly. Tom was up ahead, working out a stretch of Johnson grass with his dog.

"Why is it that a man will lie, excuse, defend, and even brag on a young dog that doesn't even know what a quail is?" I asked Bill.

"Because it's his dog," Bill answered simply. "Every man sees something in his own dog that nobody else sees. In his eyes that bungling, rabbit-running, mouse-pointing youngster of today may be the staunch, perfect-styled state champion of tomorrow. After all, that muddling, too-eager pup is his very own. That's the way you get, once you own a bird dog."

Nantucket Blues

By FRANK VINING SMITH

AXEL WAS SEASICK. IT REALLY WASN'T MUCH WONDER THAT HE was curled up miserably to leeward and had lost all interest in the trip as my cutter *Mandalay* made long sweeping plunges into the green and white-capped seas which swept up against a strong ebb tide just north of Muskeget Channel. These seas, though really moderate, must have looked like mountains to this big North Dakota lad and I could see that he craved a sight of his level plains.

"Cheer up, Axel," I said, as I gave the wheel a twist to luff the speeding boat over a green hill; "cheer up, the worst will soon be over. It'll be smoother down by Cross Rip. This tide, across the wind, makes the sea pile up here."

Axel groaned. We had nicknamed him "Axel," though his real name was Alexander, for no particular reason save that the name seemed to fit. Anyone with so many wheels in his head must have an axle somewhere, the Doctor reasoned, and so Doc and I had called him "Axel" and the name stuck.

We were headed for Nantucket to try for bluefish. They were rumored to have struck in off the Island, and a wire from my friend in the Nantucket Bank urged us to sail across and give them a whirl.

Hawes Shoal buoy drew up abeam, and the sea moderated a little. "How about running a line?" the Doctor suggested. "I see a few gulls inshore. We might pick up a fish."

"Try it if you like," I replied, "but we're moving too fast for trolling, and I want to get across before the tide turns." I dashed the water from my glasses, peering ahead for a sight of Cross Rip lightship.

All this was before the war had laid its ban on cruising, when the coming and going of small boats was controlled only by the desires of their owners, a gypsy existence that now seems so far away.

Axel perked up a bit as the Doctor rigged a line, paid out about a hundred feet and handed it to the seasick one.

"There, my boy, hang on to that and catch us a fish."

"Do they hit hard?"

"You'll know if you get one on," Doc said with a wide grin. "They are a little bigger than your crappies and bluegills, and a lot more active."

Axel sat up, a bit more interested in life, as he watched the line cutting through the creamy waves to lift out and stretch far astern. A gull swooped down in an effortless curve to investigate, and then sheered away in a swooping, soaring lift.

Cross Rip Lightship drew abeam, rolling gently; the sea became smoother, and at last the low line of Nantucket lifted above the horizon, the pencil of the water tower marking the town.

Mandalay, with sails hard pressed like an ivory carving, with water tearing along her lee rail and spray arching from her bows, laid a course for the jetties. Astern, the dinghy pulled hard on its tow rope, yanking this way and that in a smother of spray, like a naughty child dragged along by a determined parent.

"God, this is living," said the Doctor, gazing up at the fleecy clouds driving in from the south. "This sort of thing blows the cobwebs from your rafters, hey, Axel?"

"That's right. It's fine as long as the boat stays put and doesn't jump around too damn much. Back there a ways I longed for my little gray home in the west. I'd just as soon ride an outlaw horse as this thing. Where are all your fish?"

"No use, I guess we're going too fast. The jetty is right ahead; may as well haul in."

That evening, as we lay at anchor in the calm harbor sheltered by the picturesque old whaling town, with its clustered houses rising to the spires on the hill, we were well content, with a good dinner beneath our belts, the shipmate stove making a genial warmth and the cabin lights glistening on bottle and glasses reflected in the mahogany table.

Our friend the banker had come aboard for dinner and now, the dishes finished and the cabin cleaned up, we were nestled snugly among the cushions on the transoms discussing the chances for the morrow.

"I hope we can strike some blues," said Doc.

"Well, you can never tell. Ed Coffin came in with his cat boat this afternoon. He'd caught four or five off Long Point shoal. Tom and Joe, the boys we are going out with, are good men, and their *Nelly B.* is a good boat. If fish are here, they'll find them."

I shook my head. "I haven't caught a blue for two seasons. They're temperamental fish and you can never depend on 'em, that is, of late years; I wonder where they go in those years when they don't show up?"

"I guess nobody knows. There have been reports of big schools on the Brazil and Portuguese coasts, but I wouldn't think they'd migrate that far."

"I've an idea," said Doc, "that the big catches of menhaden by commercial fishermen has a lot to do with it. It stands to reason that if their food is scarce, the fish will be scarce too. Stripers will always be here unless netted out; their food is much more varied but blues depend on surface fish, menhaden and spurling." He relighted his cigar, sipped his drink, and gazed across at Axel.

"That's some rod you've got there, feller. Do you figure to catch a blue on that?"

Axel looked up from the light steel casting rod he was wiping and grinned cheerfully. "Sure, if they bite. I've caught bass and pike on it out in Wisconsin."

"How big?"

"Oh, pike up to twelve pounds. How big do bluefish come?"

"Not twelve pounds," said the Nantucketer, "that is, I never caught one that big. About five to eight pounds, I should say."

Axel looked scornful.

"I've always maintained," Doc said, "that salt water fish, pound for pound, are a damn sight more active than fresh water fish. It stands to reason that fish that are on the go all the time, and being forever chased by larger fish, develop more strength than pond fish which have a limited range and fewer natural enemies."

"Just the same," said the banker, "I'll settle for a trout any day." He glanced at the clock. "How about setting me ashore, Cap? I'm due at a lodge meeting tonight."

"What time do we start in the morning?" I asked as I left him at the wharf.

"About six-thirty. The tide's right about eight. I'll see you at the fisherman's dock."

The sun was well up as we slid through the jetties, and laid a course northeast, with the big converted six-cylinder Packard engine sending the thirty-six foot *Nelly B.* along at a steady ten knots. Clouds of terns rose from the seaweed-covered rocks as we passed, and the shores, hazy in the August sunlight, faded astern. In the big, open cockpit we rigged our rods and gear, watching the lighthouse on the point enlarge from a dot to a tall white tower against the sky. Skirting the reef, with our lines trailing out over the quarter into the breaking rip over the shoal, we stemmed the east-bound tide and hoped for the best.

"This is whaling country, Axel," said Doc. "One's liable to bite any minute now!"

Axel grinned and hung on to his line expectantly. But nothing happened. Up the rip, down the rip, changing from feathers to eelskins and then to shiny tin squid with pork rind. No soap!

Twelve o'clock came, and lunch. The sea was smooth, so even Axel fell on the food mightily.

"This ain't buyin' shoes for the baby," said Tom. "What say, Joe? How about S'conset and try the edge of Bass Rip?"

"Sure, let's try her," said his partner, opening up the engine. "They ain't here, that's sure."

We slid through the rip where gravel bottom could be plainly seen six feet down, and opened up again heading down past Sankaty Light and the bathing beach gay with umbrellas and summer bathers. Off shore the mutter of growling breakers came from the rips, and

I could, in my mind's eye, picture the savage fury of those waters when winter gales hurled in the thundering combers which came all the way from the coast of Spain; the graveyard of many noble ships in the old days, with Rose and Crown Shoal twenty miles to the east and bars and shallows scattered between like a devil's puzzle.

Skirting Bass Rip was another fruitless quest. Gulls were working, and once we saw a slick and for a moment thrilled at a smell like watermelon—a sure sign of blues. But for some reason they wouldn't take and we swung away to the south, almost skirting the beach in a deep slue, or channel, which led around the south side of the Island where the shore rose in steep bluffs to form Tom Nevers' Head. I always wondered who Tom Nevers was. There must be a story there if one could dig it out of the old records.

Joe climbed the ratlines to the cross trees, locked his legs around a shroud, and scanned the horizon as the boat rolled over the long ground swell. Axel didn't enjoy the motion.

"Head a little off shore Tom. I see some gulls," Joe shouted down a few minutes later.

We stood expectantly as the shore moved slowly past. Axel, by our advice, had not rigged his casting rod but held a hand line, as did I. The banker stuck to a hand line too, as he felt we should get some fish for the boys. They had refused any pay for taking us along.

The engine purred and we moved silently and smoothly as in a dream. A hail came from aloft, "Fish! On the port bow! White bellies as fur as you can see!"

"Jees!" said Axel, and his arm whipped straight out. "I got a bite! Mother of mine, I got *something!*" He began to haul madly, and far astern a gleaming shape came out, savage head shaking, and somersaulted back with a splash.

"Keep him coming!" yelled Tom, and grabbed a coil of line with a gleaming tin squid on. "Don't give him an inch of slack!" Whirling the squid about his head in a hissing circle, he sent it sailing fifty feet from the boat and began to haul. My line came to life with a heavy savage tug, and I dropped my hands low and put my back into a swift hand-over-hand pull against the fierce resistance at the other end. I thought of early days in Buzzards Bay when as a boy I had sailed a cat boat through breaking schools of bluefish, running two lines, sometimes three. Those were the days!

The line chafed my fingers as I let it slip through against a particularly savage rush. A heavy fish. Much heavier than we used to catch in the Bay. Doc's reel screamed and his rod bent. Out of the tail of my eye I saw Tom nonchalantly flip aboard a big blue and slap it between his oilskinned legs to tear out the hook. He booted the fish out of the way, hove his line and squirted out a huge stream of tobacco juice, all seemingly at the same instant. Everything happened at once. Axel with a mighty heave, swung a thrashing snapping bluefish against me, and fell upon him to disengage the hook.

"Look out, Axel!" I yelled. "DON'T DO THAT!"—Too late. He dropped the fish and a trickle of blood stained his fingers.

"Let me see it," said Tom, dropping his line and putting his foot on it. "Not too bad; you could have lost a finger. Those babies are mean." He picked up the fish freeing the hook with a swift twist. "I should have warned you. There's some bandage down in the cabin on the port rack."

Doc inspected the damage. "Only a shallow cut, clean as a knife. Rinse it overside in salt water, and tie a rag on it," he said as he gave his full attention to his fish.

Mine was still on and I brought him to the boat with the line hissing through the water as the blue shook his bulldog jaw, surging from side to side in the transparent green water. I reached out and lifted him in a wide swing to thud on the cockpit floor, a heavy fish, all of nine pounds. His teeth snapped savagely. I could hear them grate on the hook and as I got him back of the gills and wrenched the feather from his jaw he spewed out a silvery stream of small fish, some of them almost whole.

The boat turned in a slow circle, our lines went out again, and Tom threw six solid blues into the fish bin under the seats. He had accounted for two of them.

"Where's the one I caught? How much did he weigh?" Axel wanted to know.

"We don't weigh 'em when they're biting like that," grunted Tom. "I'd guess about eight pounds. These are big fish, big as they come."

The school must have been large, for it was an almost continuous performance for one exciting half hour when they tapered off, and then quit altogether. The boat was a shambles, and so were we, with blood, scales and gurry bestowed impartially and our hands were sore from the hardbraided lines.

Axel sat down and groaned, inspecting his cut hand. "By gosh!" he said. "I'd like to catch one of those babies on my casting rod!"

Tom looked dubiously at the outfit. "Dunno why not. Put her over. It won't last long enough to bother us or I miss my guess."

"Head her down to west'd, Tom," said Joe, who through all this commotion had remained aloft watching the school. "I think they went that way."

Axel hurriedly rigged a feather on his casting rod which was equipped with a trolling reel full of six-thread cuttyhunk, eased out his line, and gazed grimly astern. Nothing happened for a long time, then Doc hung a fish and landed him after a pumping battle. Then the banker got a small one, but still no strike as far as Axel was concerned.

"I guess they've quit," said Tom. " 'Bout time we was heading for home, anyway. Hell of a long way to go and we've caught us a real mess of fish."

Axel looked sober and started to reel in.

"Keep your line out. We'll make a slow turn in towards the beach," Tom told him.

The boat started to swing, when Axel's reel screeched like a diving plane and his rod bent to the limit, jerking furiously as we hurriedly got in our lines to give him room. I could see my feather wiggling through the water when there was a lightning glimpse of a fish. The feather disappeared with a heavy surge that split the skin on my already water-softened forefinger, and I landed a blue that had struck within fifteen feet of the boat!

With the clutch out, the boat drifted, while Axel went to work on his fish. I've never seen a blue fight harder. Perhaps the light tackle had something to do with it. He used all the tricks in the book and even leaped like a salmon with long surging jumps shaking his head savagely, with gills extended and mouth agape. He ran under the bow, but Tom gave her a quick reverse and shot clear.

I must admit that Axel did a swell job on that fish. But the fight could have only one ending and soon the blue began to tire. His rushes lost power, and at the end of twenty long minutes Tom emerged from the cabin with a sturdy gaff and spit judiciously as he sized up the situation.

"He's all through. Bring him in slow and keep him on top."

We all lined the rail and gasped. That fish looked as big as a school tuna and we held our breath as Tom reached with the gaff. A quick motion, a heave, and the fish was in the cockpit as we pounded Axel on the back and overwhelmed him with congratulations.

Axel grinned sheepishly but I could see he was as proud as punch and he couldn't take his eyes off that long rangy blue devil.

"Tom," he said, "I can't begin to tell you how much I appreciate the chance to catch that fish. I shall always remember today."

"That's all right. You've done a good job and I'm glad for you. That fish will go better'n ten pounds. Wait a minute, I'll get the scales and see ... by Judas Priest! Twelve pounds, two ounces! Mister, you'll never catch a bigger one. You sure had beginner's luck!"

Axel squatted down to inspect his fish fondly while I thought how nice it would be to be a beginner again. That first big fish!

Surrender to Youth

By NASH BUCKINGHAM

At Home—Christmas Time

M Y DEAR NOELLY *—

In sending you this patched and smelly rucksack, my treasured hunting knife and a few other "Possibles" as the Mountain Men used to call such odds and ends of personal equipment, I'm thinking that such a veteran conglomeration may come in handy, now that you're beginning to ramble on your own, out-of-doors. You see, I call you "Noelly," rather than the more grown up "Noel," because, to me, you're still the chubby, apple-cheeked youngster who romped under your Daddy's feet and mine when we spun yarns and hefted our rifles and shotguns amidst endangered lamps and bric-a-brac. It's a wonder we haven't acquired permanent squints. And those tall, cold concoctions he used to dish up; what were they called—"Flying Trapezes"? Well named they were, lad! One or two of those and you sure flew through the air with the greatest of ease. Anyhow, Boy, you'd best

* See footnote on page 74.

inherit these "Possibles" while there's a chance of their being as helpful to you as they have been to me.

Your slender young shoulders are squaring. Mine may begin to sag before long but not if I can help it. My use of that word "may" shows, however, that I'm not admitting, by a darn sight, being "washed up," as today's saying goes. Your outlook on life is eagerly restive, your eyes strong with youth's keen vision straining for new horizons. You'll hear and read a lot about "last frontiers," Noelly. But maybe by the time you're able to really begin trying to look "in back of beyond," there'll be airship rockets to Mars and you can load into a covered wagon from where you land. Or maybe a conscience-stricken America will rebuild or salvage some wilderness miraculously spared. I hope you and other woods rookies can have high sky lines to quest, and drink from undefiled streams. I'm not one to sell my country short, Boy, but I've just read something that troubles me. I've thought the same thing but couldn't put it into words. A man wrote—"if personal character is on a low level, then there comes a time when no refinement of social planning and no expenditure of public wealth, however great, will create a good social order. In my opinion, life in America is approaching that point." I'm just quoting that because you're getting plenty old enough to understand what it means, and there may come a time when you'll have to make some grave decisions and back them up in the manner prescribed by War. And War, Noelly, can get extremely back to nature and down to the brassiest of tacks. But getting back to that word "may," while I don't have to shoot in glasses, something tells me that it won't be long now. There's still plenty of kick in the old horse, though. I'll probably pop away at many a quail or duck and snap a fly into some bass or salmon. That is I hope to, because, as your Daddy moans, our greatest fear is that we'll check out in between gunning seasons. What I mean is, that I'm getting inclined to be overly willing to look back. While you? You're looking forward, or, better, as we dog handlers say, "you're broadening your casts."

Packing the old kit bag tugged some heartstrings, I'll admit. Some day you'll understand what we silly old out-of-door sentimentalists feel about such plunder. It isn't the junk so much as what it has meant to a man. I've had this rucksack since I came out of college nearly thirty-five years ago, when your Daddy was a youngster with "stummick ache" from eating green apples. It's almost like parting from a favorite old bird dog; something I hope you'll never have to do. I don't mean because of death, but because of—well, because circumstances make it necessary—put it that way—and with a grin. To keep up your courage you say to him—"Don't worry, Old Scout, you're going to a good home with someone who'll care for you as deeply as I do—there'll be quail bevies no end, and plenty of rabbits." Noelly, I hope you heavy your sack with many a rab. I don't want you to grow up one of those hypercritical (you're a trifle young for that crack but your Daddy will explain) guys who forgets he was ever a boy. The kind who doesn't savvy the all-around fun a boy and his dog can chase up together.

This old pack and I went west to punch cattle on a Rocky Mountain ranch. It used to take me two long days teaming and sometimes longer to make our place from the railroad. Great years those, Noelly. Wandering both slopes from the Canadian border southward. Some of those "Possibles" are a lot older than the rucksack. No telling how many times its drawstrings have been replaced. You can see for yourself how it's been cobbled on. "Man-sewing," the women folks call it. But it's stout. I've used mountain sheep, goat, moose, elk, deer and steer whang. But the best lacing is made from the oiled and rolled spinal cords of the fresh water sturgeon. Boy, are they stout and long-lasting?

I've packed this bag from ocean to ocean, and where it hasn't gone with me my dear old hunting partner, Hal Howard took it, God rest his fine soul. Clean across from New Brunswick's bogs and salmon water to innermost and uppermost Alaska, British Columbia and on down into vivid Old Mexico. Since Hal passed on I've never slipped out of the pack and put on the beans and "tay" without somehow seeing the old boy squatting opposite munching his chuck. Ours were the days of the 45-70 and 30-40, iron sights, long heavy bullets and a sound stalk that socked 'em where they belonged. Oh! I'm not saying these moderns don't make long shots with their highfalutin bullets and powerful telescopes. We just had to take up a lot of slack with more hard work, that's all. But we got the meat and I recall no crippled trophies to amount to anything.

Boy, we've sure packed some fine fresh liver and tenderloins back to camps in this old grub-toter. I can smell it frying right now, kinder strong-like if the grease was inclined to age a bit, and even with spuds and a red onion in competition. It has filled our bellies with hot victuals after many a tough day and half a night's scramble over bruising, snow-clad rim rocks and down-timber. Its medicine kit has healed many a trail jab for man or beast. It has burned out a long and honorable line of tea buckets and fry pans. Emptied and stuffed with ferns or browse it has pillowed me when only saddle blankets and a push-log made campfire contact. It always goes along on quail or duck and goose hunts. I'll bet you can dig feathers from its seams right now. You can shoot from it, with ease. I've even swum with it on my back. In a tight place I'd say to myself, "Well, you're not alone, you've got the old sack." It's an ally that'll stick by you, boy! A real friend! Remember that. And now, just a little something about the other odds and ends.

This hunting knife? My dear Mother had a favorite uncle, Noelly. He sailed the seven seas in the King's "Navee," and his hobby was collecting swords and weapons from all countries at ports of call. He gave Mother a pair of these Chinese dirks when I was just a tot. As I recall her story of them they were a present to Great-Uncle Tommy from some mandarin. So you can get an idea how old this soft steel, hand-forged frog-sticker may be. Its mate was lost and so was the ivory sheath to this one. So it has been with me longer than the ruck-sack. It takes an ideal cutting edge, but the temper isn't so hot. You have to keep up with it pretty close—that's what the hone is for. It has helped dress practically every species of North American big game, and sliced enough steaks, bacon and bread to keep half the country off relief rolls. You'll find a flint and steel in the sheath's side pocket. Get yourself some punk and grass straw or a hover of lint and some rag with powder rubbed into it and learn to spark 'em ablaze. That arrowhead I picked up on the Laramie plains of Wyoming, the same morning I found the buffalo skull. I was sneaking some teal I saw pitch into a plains trickle, and stumbled over something. I examined the sharp, black point and began to dig. Before long I uncovered a mammoth "buffler" head, in fact the whole carcass was there, or rather skeleton. I forgot the teal and finally worried off the mud and cleaned the trophy up pretty well. This same rucksack backpacked it to the ranch. And before I forget it, if you don't know how to sharpen an ax or this hunting knife, why go to some butcher or grinder and get yourself taught. One of the most pathetic of all half-baked alleged outdoorsmen is the chap who don't know the first principles of edging up his most important tools.

At our old E-Bar-X ranch there used to come an early heavy snow. When it had melted off, the weather invariably faired into a run of sparkling, winey days and frosty nights. Then was when we figured on getting in most of our winter meat, and old John Dunlap and I usually rustled the assignment. John was a card, and a trump one, too. Born of seafaring folk down Taunton way. But the Civil War fouled his compass and he dragged anchor west. Turned his hand to black-smithing and prospecting until mountains lured him to a homestead away back in our valley. At well past sixty John's was a still powerful frame and a clean, keen, kindly mind. Somewhere, I've got a pair of silver mounted spurs old "Jawn" turned out for me in the ranch smithy.

Well, John and I'd clap the diamond hitch on a light pack and with a couple of extra nags, usually old "Blue" and "Sailor," hit for that big country in between Sheep Peak and Lost Solar. There was a monstrous draw in between the heads of Ripple and Fawn cricks that we particularly favored. We'd throw a quick snug camp an hour of the sun, picket the ponies and separate for a look around afoot. Sleeping bags weren't much in use those times so we used a big double tarp and some thick Navajo blankets. And would they keep you snug atop a jag of spruce feathers! The first night we'd grub on sow-belly and beans because we disliked shooting up the country while getting the lay of things. I can see old John now, sitting tailor fashion by the embers while doing his dishes—he was a great hand to keep a clean camp. That's another thing you'd best remember, too, Buddy. Keep a clean camp; it helps out in later everyday life, sort of "habit-forming" if you get what I mean. Then we'd build up the blaze and lay back while John smoked a couple of pipes. He loved to talk about his young days in staid New England; about tall ships and high seas; and if you'd ever been there as I had you could smell the clam flats and fresh sweet marsh grasses and feel the sting of cutting east winds. The last thing John used to do before we rolled in was to slip his stubby, ivory-sighted carbine under his alongside bedding and shove his boots down under the tarp. Then he'd sit up and wrap a big bandanna around his shiny bald head. His dry wood for next morning's touch-off went under the cover, too, for John just naturally believed in preparedness and labor saving. Those are good camp rules, too, Noelly. Of course we always camped close to water but bedded down just beyond the reach of blow-down trees in case of a storm. Long before the pine squirrels turned on their alarms, John and I would be outside for some hot Java and a crust. He'd have his route spotted, and I mine, so we'd be off through the frosted elk weeds and begin stalking the timber edges around the parks. What we liked best to hear was a bull elk bugling the evening before. When we'd killed, we did just a quick job of butchering and went on back to camp. Figuring we had the panniers full, we'd pack up and horse to the first load, then to the next and so on back to the ranch. I have watched and helped a lot of meat skinners and carvers in my time, but John was the best I ever saw. He had a skinning outfit of two knives he'd made himself out of files. John told me he "got learned" by the buffalo hunters, and the way he could walk around a carcass and lift the hide after a few slashes and rips, was a work of art in venery. Old Bill Gibson who did the ranch tanning used to say that fleshing and graining skins behind John was a pleasure. But John always said (and here's another thing you can remember, Noelly) that after you'd learned the proper cuts even that wouldn't do you much good unless you worked with sharp tools. John's knives and ax were razor sharp, and kept that way, too. Those were great old days, Buddy. To ride out on some hog-back away up eleven or twelve thousand feet, and look out across a world of blue shadows, sun-shot with dark spruce belts and wide ribands of deep lemoned aspens. Or to stalk silently through the lower ridges after sundown and see deer feeding out and up the hillsides like so many cattle. Heigh-ho!

The old rucksack reminds me, too, of Arthur Pringle and his gorgeous moose country spreading far and wide off "Baldy" and crisscrossed with grilse and salmon pools of Sevogle and Miramichi waters. A wonderful man, Arthur Pringle. He'd lost a fine son in France and the blow shook him to his heels. I remember one day he and I had boiled the kettle and were munching sandwiches on a little shrubby point overlooking the lower end of Nash Lake. A fat beaver was having the time of his life playing on his slippery slide just across from us. There were snow flurries but a brilliant sun broke through and routed them. The beaver went off home up the lake. Arthur stirred his "tay" and told me about his lad and how he had so hoped Donald would be spared to take over things. You could tell from the shadows in his fine eyes that he bled inwardly. But, like many another Canadian father, he gave without a whimper for God and Country and for King. That afternoon we sat back to back with the summit of old Baldy and searched a miniature world far below with our binoculars. The packs had gotten a mite heavy after that steep climb. Then Arthur spotted a big bull splashing across some beaver water. We slipped out of harness and lit out down to timber line. There was just a rime of light across Baldy when we finished butchering and hung the heavy cuts onto sprung trees until we could return with the horses. Then we had to reclimb Baldy, get under the packs and hit for home. The shack looked good about midnight.

One afternoon, Noelly, I knocked a yearling bull elk two hundred feet down a snowy sidehill. It was one of the most spectacular falls

I ever saw. I did a thorough job of butchering and hung the meat until I could get back for it several days later. When Sam and I rode into the spruce opening where I'd skinned out the bull, it was deep dusk. I said, "Sam, someone's been here since I was; look how that carcass has been dragged through the snow." I'd hardly spoken when out of a bush at my elbow jumped two grotesque, croaking dwarfs! Scared? Boy, we were so frightened we couldn't move or speak. Our Visitors proved to be two gigantic eagles so gorged with meat they couldn't get air borne. I never did hear Sam cuss any better and it was all I could do to keep him from laying them out with a club. He would have, too, if his eye hadn't happened to catch sight of their nest, on top of a tall dead pine down in a burn just over the gulch. That was the night I probably ate more meat than at any other one sitting. Minnie Frost sliced ropes of succulent tenderloin into thick filets and grilled 'em rare. With spuds and cornbread and choke-cherry wine Sam and I did a noble job. Another time, I got down the best sheep I ever took. I managed to get the caped skull into and on top of this sack and tried a short cut around the ledge and down to my horse, far below. I came to a slide not over forty feet wide but so straight up and down it was shuddery. Turning back meant a two-mile detour and bumping some black timber in the dark. It took me ten minutes to screw up courage for the tackle. Just as I made the last stomach-turning step the slope underfoot caved and down I plunged. At the first bounce that sheep head slipped and a horn point caught a rock just in time to hold me long enough to claw a hand and foot hold and roll over once to a shelf of rock. And there I lay until my "tummy" settled. Do you wonder I feel close to this old side-kick of a pack?

You'll find a battered Army mess kit in the pack, Noelly. There are two or three extra knives, forks and spoons with the original tools. Maybe my chatting along with you about the mess kit smacks of mere sentiment; but, by the time you're as old as your Daddy, and have bucked Life's line as hard as he has, you'll find sentiment an amiable companion due a warm spot in your "Possibles" sack. And that web snap-pocket that holds two clips of .45 auto cartridges is the mess kit's matey. The latter was issue stuff back in '16 when Uncle Sam decided Pancho Villa had become too annoying. Shortly there-after, the Kaiser knocked a chip off History's shoulder and started a fine free-for-all.

My younger brother came home to say good-by, and, meanwhile, I'd been using the mess kit on goose and duck shooting ventures. In order to reach France faster, Henry transferred to another outfit and had to surrender his sergeant's status. He walked aboard the transport a "buck" private. I don't know why, but I asked him to pack that old mess kit along, just for luck. Nor can I explain, Noelly, the deep, tender silence that came over two brothers who had been mighty close, when the time came to—well—perhaps call Life a day. Henry got knocked pretty well to pieces, Noelly, like your Daddy did, but he lugged this piece of junk along home with a lieutenant's trappings, a field promotion for gallantry, and no end of souvenirs "Francaises" for the nieces and nephews. That .45 pocket clip was his, too, and makes a grand belt holder for hunting licenses, medicine gadgets, or fish hooks. Peace and war make strange bedfellows! Like bird nests in cannon mouths, or flower pots out of French 75 cases. And was I glad to see that old shot up, gassed doughboy? As glad as I used to be back in the stone age of professional football when we'd go down under punts together.

So back went the mess kit into my pack, Noelly. How deeply Henry and I enjoyed the duck hunt we made that first winter he was home from the hospital. Our honored father had passed on and willed me his certificate in a great wildfowling club. The Boy and I shot together at our favorite family stand—the head of Long Pond. Shrapnel and gas hadn't left him overly strong, and how he drank in every breath of that glorious day. When snack time came, we waded ashore and broiled ham and eggs over a bed of coals. He related war experiences, and remember, your Daddy was doing his bit right over there while this mess kit was being packed around by an engineer of the Blue Ridge gang. So, in a way, it's just changing homes.

But I recall one day when lack of this pack and the mess kit played the wild with your Daddy and me. We were improving our conservational calibers by gunning ducks in an Arkansas pin-oak flat. Figuring the flight would be fast and our "limits" soon acquired, we left the pack at home and waded far out into the overflowed forest. But ducks, as Horace puts it, were "scaice," and by noon, with a four-thirty A.M. breakfast behind us, the pangs of appetite gnawed upon and reproached us bitterly. So, there we sat, bowling over an occasional mallard and sustaining each other by guesses as to what toothsome dish would best satisfy the moment's craving. Starting with continental offerings, we had worked our way through practically every worthwhile American restaurant down to New Orleans, and were all but drooling at the mouth, when Clarence LaCotts arrived with a papersack full of roast pork sandwiches. Your Daddy said—

"Like the Prodigal Son, I saw Clarence while he was yet a great way off and ran to him and fell on my knees."

Many a good hunter has dipped his fingers in this old mess kit's stews. It last fed Ira Richards and "Dick" Bishop in that same mallard woods where your parent and I so narrowly escaped starvation. I told Ira and Dick how one meal from the kit reminded me of another story. The gunning season previous, I shot with a party of men who had their wives along—including a very lovely Chicago debutante. And a bully good sport that youngster was, too. One icy forenoon, after a midnight breakfast, she, too, waxed "hongry." So, I waded ashore, set some Java to dripping and rummaged a can of hot tamales into the pan. The youngster had never seen a hot tamale, and she sniffed the red-peppered, corn-husked concoction with visible trepidation. But one bite, and did she tear into them?

Her expression had me remembering a long ago afternoon at our old ranch when I came in with a mess of big trout to clean and hand to Grandma Carpenter, the cook. Grandma's pet, a bright-eyed, precocious grandchild and close pal of mine, went along to watch the operation. Kneeling and working fast, with the five-year-old alongside like a pert wren, I became conscious of someone else standing over me. Looking up, I discovered a very aloof and high-nosed Boston woman, who, with her husband, had stopped off at the ranch to study rural characters and atmosphere for a book she was writing. One glance assured me, however, that trout cleaning offended not only her olfactory and pictorial senses of atmosphere, but, in fact, her very being. Just then little Edna piped up at her—

"Do you know what THEM is, lady?"

"W-h-a-a-a-t?"

"Them's guts, lady—fish guts."

Tableau.

So, Noelly, let's hope the mess kit endures and that someday you and I and your Daddy will have a duck shoot together and while we two old fellows wheeze and lounge against a log, you can rustle up what my sweet lady always refers to as a mess of "Buckingham U-g-h-s'." And maybe, out of the fire's haze will emerge reminders of what good men like your Daddy and Henry went through with that you might live to carry on—and have a darned old tin fry platter. Don't ever low rate a mess kit, Boy. Nobody has ever yet produced a satisfactory explanation as to what causes wars. And what's more, after they arrive, a lot of guys like your Daddy and Henry extract considerable secret enjoyment from them. For why do we have

Memorial days? Why do we walk among monuments raised to countless believers in and upholders of our now imperiled Liberty? Nobody in particular hunts up a War, Noelly, but write off a lot of this radio crooning by craven idealists that they "hate war." That sort of clap-trap gets votes, too. The story of the "Three Little Pigs" is the best answer to all that sort of chatter. Just build your house of brick, and, when War comes to your door, Noelly—you may get a break. But the boys will all pack mess kits, just the same.

I can see you smile, Noelly, as you prowl through the jumbled contents you're examining. As years go by you'll replace them one by one with fancies of your own. You can carry a sight of useful stuff this way. But the two things I want most of all for you to have along, Boy, are your ideals and your independence. Make them your shield and sword, and when the going gets toughest why, damn it, keep 'em up with your guard and your God and lam back at the enemy. Sometimes that enemy is just yourself, and at others he can slip up on you with all the pictured disguises of the Big Bad Wolf. The habit of eternal vigilance out-of-doors, Noelly, will help teach you to take nature apart.

Jot this down, too, in your memory book. If you like to fight, for fun or otherwise (a failing of your Daddy's and mine), don't ever figure that you will skip taking some punishment. You'll get yours all right enough. We all do, from life and the rest of the ants running around loose in it. But let me tell you this much, definitely. The hurt of the hardest battering, or the stiffest, rocking punches you may be called upon to absorb, are as nothing compared to the shame of knowing you turned up afraid to risk taking them. Hell, Boy, even a clean knockout is just a jarring bump and flash of light, and then they tell you how it happened. And even while you're stopping punches why remember that the other guy has a chin and a belly, so make it your business to keep firing away. Maybe he is worse off than you are. Maybe he can't take it. I tell you, lad, the only thing the floor is good for is to get up off it when you have to stick. Keep your head and take a "nine count," but get up. I remember one piece of advice good old Patsy Hogan gave me years ago, just whispered admonition as we waited to be called out to the center of the ring for instructions. "Kid," he gurgled, "hit d' Ref'ree, hit d' ring posts, hit d' water buckets, but f' Pete's sake, hit sump'n."

Noelly, you won't find a compass among all these "Possibles." Mine got lost. You can get lost in life though, just like men do in the wilds. Sometimes its sky is so overcast that every crick mouth and drawhead looks bafflingly the same. Just blind alleys every way you turn. That's the time to keep cool and sit down for some steady thinking. But any compass isn't worth a farthing unless you learn to use one correctly. A compass, after all, is just mechanical presence-of-mind out-of-doors. And while I'm on the subject of compasses, study your stars and planets and where they hang out all hours of the night, winter and summer. The Mountain Men had no compasses, but could they navigate? Nor were they astronomers, except by eyes or ears. They journeyed by the sun in daytime, and if they didn't know the stars by name, they knew them by sight. And they swore and steered by them. They got to be old friends and once they clapped an eye on a certain twinkler, the route was as good as won. And in tramping the out-of-doors, I want you to learn to "read sign." Trails, creek bottoms and gully sides are clew-bearers, so keep your eyes on the ground aplenty. Watch the bushes for browse lines. Hawks and owls are invariably up to something, and changes in the wind have meanings all their own. Learn the trees and wild-flowers by name; not to know is like being a stranger at the feast. And if you ever doubt your MAKER'S sense of justice, remember HE gave animals their wonderful sense of smell and hearing, and to birds their supersight.

Unpacking and repacking the old rucksack, I came onto the little dog-eared, all-but-worn-out tract of St. John. I started to keep it, but something said, "No, send it on with its comrades to Noelly, and tell him why you do so." Well, I'm a more or less doggy old sinner, good as was my raising in the Church. I'm afraid we backsliders are worse off than most. I've lived among rough fellows a lot, but some years ago I began to notice that around campfires or long, snowed-in winter evenings the he-men who stood out as most worthwhile in memory knew their Bibles and took delight and not shame in studying the Word in His sight. Then an experience in faith came to me through an old negro who believed that prayer during a hunting ordeal we endured brought us out alive. Ever since that night the Gospel of St. John has had a home in this rucksack. So, let it abide now, with you. It's a grand compass, when you're fixing to lose your wits, or worse, your "guts."

About all a fellow like I am can do is believe in ONE CAMP and its COMMANDER. It isn't just a hunch, or nigger superstition. It is deep conviction. Writing this, there may come a day when you'll have to back me up with this old rucksack and the Gospel of St. John. I may be lucky enough to crash Gabe's Gate and wangle an interview with Saint Peter. About all I could claim is what I've been trying to tell you here, Noelly. Everything would hinge on whether I was telling the TRUTH. Peter might say, "How can you prove it?" And, standing first on one foot and then the other, I'd probably reply, "Well, suh, I sho' lef my Witness in an old pack bag I gave to a young fellow named Noel Sheldon." And Saint Peter would tell Gabriel, "Check on that, Gabe." So, if you lose the rucksack, much less the Gospel of St. John, why, Boy, I'll be in one Hell of a fix.

Merry Christmas, Noelly, good luck, and God bless you all.

No Holes Barred!

By JIM BERRYMAN

WITH ALL THE FUSS, FANFARE, AND FORMALITY OF THE PERRY Matches in the air and everybody who is, or is not, anybody doing his own private nostalgic nugget of remembering, I am overcome with an unquenchable urge to unlimber a few match memoirs of my own.

The powder-burning carnivals I'm retrospecting upon are brought to mind by the revival of the Nationals all right ... but not because there is any connection or any remote suspicion of similarity ... but because there is such a trackless vale of difference!

I'm thinking back to the monthly, sometimes weekly, pistol and rifle matches which are staged in Southwestern communities without benefit of NRA or War Department blessings. Nor have I ever heard of the Marines swarming ashore at the last moment, blazing their way through waist-high cactus, to have the team names inscribed on the good old battered tin tequilla dipper. There are no titles at stake— well, yes, there are, too. The winner might be the All-bore Champion of Gullible Gulch for the Week-of-April-31st, or until the next "card-pluggin' party" takes place.

Like nearly all other functions in Arizona, New Mexico, and Texas, there is a decided atmosphere of informality attending these hinter- land matches...no qualification rounds, no regional representations, no eliminations...except the five lousy shots you fire! In fact, the only questions asked are, "Have you got a buck fer yur entrance fee?" and "Be you acquainted with th' rules we're a-shootin' by, stranger?"

An Eastern tenderfoot has quite a flock of inhibitions to cram down the nearest gopher hole when he competes in or spectates at one of these affairs...they're plenty homespun—or I should say faded-blue-denim. But there's something doggoned real American about 'em! The rankest total stranger can ride a sweat-streaked, desert-beaten pony into the "tournament grounds," receive a wel- come from the host of the day, and he's in...in on the shoot, the round or two of "friendly-fluid" following, and the man-sized meal at twilight time.

While there are no iron clad rules governing these cattle-country target jousts, they all follow a more or less standard pattern. They are a distinct byproduct of remote living. I've never come across one in the suburban areas of any western cities such as El Paso, Albu- querque, Phoenix, and the like. "The suburban area" of a plains city can include anything up to a hundred-mile radius. The larger popu- lation centers all have rifle and pistol clubs, practically all of them affiliated with the NRA, and many of them boast excellent outdoor ranges, and luxuriously modernized clubhouses done in the mission and dobe styles. It is surprising to learn how large their membership lists have grown in the past few years. Many hundreds of cattlemen, their ranch foremen, wranglers, and punchers maintain membership just to have a "home corral" during their infrequent visits to "big town"...and to have a travel-weary copy of *The American Rifle- man* pulled out of a canyon letter carrier's time-worn saddle bag once a month.

As far as I could learn from some old-timers, the Saturday after- noon "powder clubs" go way back to the days long before the introduction of fancy, organized club shoots of today. One leather- skinned old boy from up in the Red Rock section was able to slant

me back to the early '80's. He said: "Wa-al, Ah kin recollec' as how
my dad uster oil an' clean up his Winchester an' his Colt, tie a sackful
of silver cartwheels inside his belt, an' ride over to th' ol' Flyin'
Heart or th' Crazy K to do a flock o' shootin' an' bettin'. Ah was
jest gittin' long-legged enough then t' git m' feet down beside a
pinto's belly 'stead o' stickin' out like extra fenders, an I uster puzzle
m'self as t' whether the ol' man took part in them shootin' matches
'cause they was so restful after shootin' all week at lions, cayoots,
an' Injuns... or whether he was jest a-testin' himself an' warmin'
up fer th' Saturday night faro an' monte games in Socorro. Fer as
Ah kin r'member, they didn't have these purty, printed targets y'all
got now ... they made marks on a board or on th' side of a shed ...
one o' the' fav'rites, though, was 'fencin' th' X.' They'd take a hot
iron or a stick with some black wheel grease an' mark a whole durn
herd o' X's. Th' idee was t' put a hole in each of th' fo' notches of
th' X, then drap that fi'th slub right dead-center o' th' crossed bars."

"Y'know, son," the old man continued, "as yuh git a lot o' miles
o' livin' behind yuh, some o' th' things in th' purplish haze o' yur
early days 'pears awful kinda good, an' Ah remembers thet to a hardly
trailbroke colt like me, my dad an' them fellers he rode with, was
mighty durn good shots. Mebbe they jest plain had t'be if they
wanted to go on livin' an' makin' a livin'!"

He stopped reminiscing long enough to shift his cud and take an
offhand shot at a large green prickly pear blade about twelve feet
away ... it was a clean bull. Then he reached down and picked up
my Winchester Model 70 Hornet. He examined it carefully, squinted
through the Lyman receiver sight which all but disappeared from view
as a bushy brow curtained it, then turned to me and resumed:

"Young feller," he said, "they didn't have no such guns as this
sixty years ago! Guess it's a danged good thing they didn't! Th'
way they could shoot, they might a-kilt off everybody in th' whole
durn West! ... Now, don't git me wrong ... Ah ain't sayin' yuh
yearlin's today cain't shoot, but it's jest that yuh got such good
rifles t'shoot with! Yep! an' lookit th' fine stuff yuh got t'shoot outen
'em!"

The faded blue eyes turned away from me ... they looked past me,
past the far horizon ... past a half century-plus of firearms progress.

"The first rifle I remember seein' was an old Sharps carbine. It
was a breech-loading single shot my dad carried through th' Civil
War. He rode with Jube Early an' later with th' Fi'th Virginny

Cavalry, an' he uster admit it himself thet he was a durn good horse-man an' a helluva good rifleman."

He gave just a perceptible shake of his grizzled head, patted the stock of the Hornet, handed it to me and returned to the present.

"Go on down there, boy, they're startin' in t' fire th' practice shots."

I asked him if he didn't want to sign up and take a crack at the cash. He half nodded and answered:

"Ah'll be down when they git aroun' to th' pistol shootin'...cain't take part in th' rifle shoot...my ol' Krag's gone t'pasture, but Ah'll be in thar with this hyah Colt, an' tell th' boss-man not t'figger me a time fer practice...Ah only got five shells!"

The best way to describe one of these Western matches in the modern manner is to pick a typical set-to. The time is late February, the setting is...let's call it...the Rolling-O Ranch, high up near the head of Greenwater Creek in Castle Canyon...Bill Bellamy, owner, is hosting for the good folk of the canyon...and anybody else within walking or riding distance...in honor of his only son, Bill, Jr., just "fresh out of th' Navy" and three years of commanding a destroyer in Pacific actions.

Three precisely penciled announcements of the gala event have been "posted" in near-by (twenty-two miles away) Castle Station: at the Post Office, Bailey's "Trading Post" and Sorrell's Saddle Shop.

If ever there was such a thing as a blanket invitation, this was it. All a contestant needed was the desire, a dollar, some means of transportation, thirst or hunger...or both.

Happily, I fulfilled all five of these requirements—as did my better nine-tenths, "The Lady Known as Lou,"...that automatically made us competitors! There were no entry blanks to fill out, no formal eligibility declarations to be submitted for approval...nothing to do except put in an appearance at the appointed time and place with some sort of "shootin' iron" and an extended right hand. This par-ticular "shoot" was a mere six or seven miles from our "beddin' down spot," so just a comfortable saddle distance away.

The designated day dawned fair and fit, as do most Southwestern late winter days, and "Lady Lou" routed me from my sack at the ungodly hour of seven. Trail-packing was not nearly as difficult as planning an eastern picnic. No food for the two-legged wayfarers ...only a few carrots and apples for the trusty steeds (a pair of fine quarter horse mares), my Winchester 70 Hornet, Lou's H&R Single-Action Target Revolver, two boxes of Westerns for her and an old leather tobacco pouch filled with 46 grain Hornets for me, one movie camera, four packs of cigarettes, and that precious old pipe of mine which Lou says smells foul even in "the great open spaces."

The sprawling ranch house of the Rolling-O outfit nestles snugly against the north wall of a canyon. The main patio gives on a small corral which in turn fades into the fenced-in big corral down by an irrigated meadow. This lush green spot is the grazing heaven for the Bellamy string of horses and the impromptu shooting range when occasion demands. Ideal for this because it extends level about 200 yards and is walled on the south by a forty-foot bank flanking Greenwater Creek and its leaning cottonwood trees. When a shoot is staged, the "O" horses are turned out to the lower level where they stand craning their pretty necks across the four-rail gate until the first firing pin falls. Then, with a tumult of frantic whinnying and flailing hooves, they take off for secluded corners... all except the half dozen or so gunwise mounts who hopefully await gun-toting riders and sniffing lion hounds.

By the time the contestants begin to arrive, "the range" has been all set up by Bill's hands. All staked out for distance, shooting mats (horse blankets stuffed with straw), spotting scopes (two pairs of regulation Navy B&L binoculars), judges' bench (an old feed trough inverted with a plank across) and the targets, scores of them... and real NRA jobs... are mounted and ready in stacks. There is a long wooden frame beside the judges' exalted rendezvous to hold the entrants' fowling pieces... a saw-horse-supported table for the handguns.

The rifle frame and the pistol table are focal points of rapt attention at these "parties." They are referred to by many colloquial sobriquets: "The Blockhouse," "The Armory," and "The Supreme Court." A religiously observed "eleventh commandment" of the West is Never Lay A Finger to 'Nother Man's Gun 'Thout Him Grantin' P'mission! But there is no rule which says you can't crawl under the table or stand on your head to get a better look at some other chap's firearm if it happens to pique your curiosity. However, if the owner picks up his own piece, hands it to you and says: "Here y'are, pardner, look down 'er... topside and inside!" then you have carte blanche to practically dissemble the mechanism on the spot. It is a rare desert or canyon man who is not boundlessly happy to show you his gun... and everything about it. He has surging pride in it whether it's a spanking new Remington 720 .30-'06, or a forty-year-old converted '03 Springfield.

"The Supreme Court" bench, a few minutes before festivities commence, is loaded down with a veritable museum collection of firing pieces. There are no restrictions on what a man shoots with in a match of this kind. So, the table is racked with all makes, all lengths, weights, and all calibers. I'll admit tho' the dominating weapon is the lever-action type...in .25-20, .25-35, .30-30, and .32 Special. Some are factory new...and garbed...after a quarter of a century; others have had harder lives, have been home stocked, rechambered, rebarreled. There is always a sizable delegation of .22's in various makes and models, and no "Blockhouse" is complete without its contingent of the ever-increasingly popular .270. Krags, Mausers, and Springfield Sporters show in minority factions. Only two foreign-made rifles did I come across in my travels...which speaks well for the American rifleman's faith in American gunmakers' products. And out here, a man learns guns by using them—every day!

There are some few "customs of the country" which are inviolable. All arms are submitted to the judges...*unloaded!* There are always four classes of competition...no more, no less. Rifle for Men, Rifle for Women...the same duo for handguns. The entry fee for each class is one dollar—folding type or clinking! Entrants take their practice rounds and their competitive rounds in the order in which they enrolled...and...WINNER TAKES ALL!!

Now, getting into the personnel department is a most interesting side of these matches. The Rolling-O's Homecoming Shoot had a participating list which just couldn't happen any place but in America...and probably no place in America but in the Southwest! Several ranch owners, two oil well operators, eighteen or twenty cowhands and wranglers, three ranch cooks, four or five "drifters" from God-knows-where, a commander and a lieutenant commander on terminal leave, a saddle maker and his helper, a Mexican sheepherder, two state irrigation-ditch workers, a county highway engineer, a game warden and his pretty wife, a recently discharged turret-gunner sergeant from the Fifteenth Air Force, half a dozen dudes from near-by guest ranches, a politician, a pair of bartenders, a flabby Hollywood lesser-light director and his shapely starlet-protege, a meat-packer's agent from Topeka, and your faithful reporter, aided and abetted by his guardian...the Lady known as Lou.

It would be very gratifying to say truthfully that I won hands down...but Lou will read this, poor patient gal, as will perhaps a dozen of my fellow competitors in that meet, so I'll confess that I ran third...or rather, brag that I ran third! I've never shot four better ones before or since in my plinking career...all of them deep in the black and could have been smothered by a quarter—the fifth one was a "normal" for me, but still on the paper! The AAF gunner took first honors—and the dough.

I'd rather not go into the details of the pistol tourney. Anyway, they were short on pistol targets and I thought it was a generous gesture to leave one unmarked for the next shooter.

When the echo of the last shot had ebbed dimly into the farthest hill, and not until then, the corks started blooping from the big Bellamy jugs. Steaks began to sizzle atop the stone stoves. Bubbling crocks of molasses-and-pork-seasoned beans appeared, huge pitchers of cold milk, and half-gallon pots of coffee were toted from the main cookhouse. Cornbread, sweating butter from every pore, and crunchy cinnamon rolls fought for parking space on the hastily erected tables.

The alpaca-lined leather jacket which had looked so silly rolled up and tied behind the saddle in the heat of the day, began to feel mighty comfy as the thermometer's mercury kept pace with the lowering sun. But it was heart-warming—and tummy-warming—to sit there rubbing elbows, swapping yarns, and spilling scalding coffee with a bunch of regular guys an' gals you'd probably never see again...and never forget that you'd known!

Oh! About Lou?...you wanted to know how she made out?...Well, maybe you've heard what a model husband I am...but I have been for a long time...it's not just because she copped top honors in that day's "Ladies' Pistol" with her little H&R, and then borrowed my Hornet to snag "Rifle for Dames" also!

Ways of the Wild Ones

By FRANK DUFRESNE

F LYING ACROSS ONE OF THE NUMEROUS SALT-WATER CHANNELS IN southeast Alaska, we saw a bald eagle hover for a moment, then plunge completely out of sight in the green waters. When the huge bird showed at the surface, its talons were fast in a very heavy fish, and in the furious struggle that ensued the eagle was dragged hither and yon in a half-submerged condition for several minutes. Gradually the eagle subdued the fish, and as we drew rapidly nearer in the plane we saw it start for shore towing its kill, using its great wings like a pair of sweeps.

We banked the plane in a tight spiral dive that brought us down within fifty feet. For the first time the eagle became aware of us. Instantly the bedraggled bird released its cumbersome tow and with astonishing ease lifted its soaking wet body from the water and flew away, pursued, as it probably reasoned, by an even larger bird of prey.

In this same heavily timbered section of the Territory it is a common occurrence for loggers to see deer come bounding into their presence and remain almost within ax-handle length for several hours at a time. The reason, of course, is timber wolves. Between the two enemies the small Sitka deer evidently accepts man as the lesser of two evils, and at the same time recognizes man's mastery of the wolf.

One morning the crew on a floating wanigan watched a doe, hotly pursued by five timber wolves, come sailing out of the salal brush. It plunged into the bay and swam straight for the wanigan, where its efforts to climb aboard were rewarded with assistance from the loggers. For the rest of the summer this doe remained close to the clearing, making occasional trips out to the wanigan to call on its particular friend, the camp cook. It seemed to thrive on a diet of flapjacks and chewing tobacco.

Among the game birds of Alaska there is none bolder nor more liked by the old-time sourdoughs than the male willow ptarmigan. In the springtime when russet-colored feathers replace the white winter hackles and a fiery red comb adorns each shoe-button eye it becomes a truculent fellow indeed. Its challenging cackle, "Come here! Come here!" is the bravest music on the tundra. For its demure brown-penciled mate it lays claim to a half acre, fighting off intruders with reckless ferocity.

Once I watched a gangling sandhill crane stalk onto one of these preëmpted half acres and begin the preliminary stiff hops and wing flappings of its mating dance. Immediately it was attacked by a knee-high ptarmigan. The crane stopped midway of its terpsichorean antics to stab its long bill angrily at the little intruder, whereupon the ptarmigan cackled in the manner of a Bronx cheer as it flew to a nearby niggerhead.

Then the crane started its dance again. Immediately the ptarmigan was upon it with buffeting wings and abusive tongue. The crane stopped dancing. It stood for a long time like a tall statue before going into its routine again, and for a third time the bantam-sized warrior noisily interfered. This was too much for the crane. It strode away in comical dignity, while the ptarmigan sailed in circles above its head daring it to "Come here! Come here!" But the ptarmigan, for all its cocky ways, knows when it is outgunned.

On a whistling cold winter day in the Far North where the largest tree growths are waist-high willows a flock of these hardy game birds zipped past me like a fusillade of snowballs and flashed out of sight in a willow patch. Seeking the cause for this unusual behavior, I swung around just in time to see a straggler explode into a cloud of white feathers forty feet in the air. Not until then did I glimpse a slim gyrfalcon zooming upward from its kill.

With streamlined flight beautiful and deadly this meteor among birds "peeled off" again to snatch the falling ptarmigan off the brush tops and bear it away across a ridge. Moving into the willows, I found the survivors of the flock half buried in the snow, crouching motionless under the slight protection of brush.

Most of the time it is not hard to understand the ways of the wild ones. Their moves are, for the most part, a logical blending of reason and instinct. But not always. Why, for instance, will a caribou burn up the landscape to place mileage between itself and man, then, like as not, come trotting back to within a hundred feet? Curiosity, perhaps, for they will often rear up on their hind feet for a better look on such occasions.

Or take a wolverine. This skunk-shaped member of the weasel tribe rarely attains a weight of thirty-five pounds, yet when a female wolverine is escorting her cream-colored cub through the forest she seems to think she can whip the world single-handed. Trappers who have witnessed this odd sight wonder why. "It's a good thing the Lord didn't make 'em any bigger," said one old-timer.

What phlegmatic quality has a moose that will allow it to browse contentedly in the lily-pads while the wing-tip of your airplane is almost close enough to part the hair on its back? Try this stunt on a brown bear, and you'll have a fight on your hands. As you buzz by at a hundred-feet elevation the bear will be filling the air with vicious swipes. There is something about an airplane which never fails to excite them to the highest pitch, but nobody seems to know why. "If you know what a bear is going to do next, you know more than the bear does about it," remarked a guide of long experience.

Why did a huge grizzly saunter into a road camp last summer and poke her nose into a tent where four young truck drivers were taking a noon siesta? Said one of the boys: "I woke up to see a bear's head big as a wheelbarrow inside the tent. Before I could do anything about it—I couldn't even open my mouth at the time—the head disappeared. The other guys never would have believed me if they hadn't see the fresh tracks big as dinner plates in front of the tent."

When the salmon run is on in Admiralty Island's many streams—

a spectacle in itself—there occurs with it one of the most striking concentrations of brown and grizzly bears on the continent. There are, to quote C. Hart Merriam, four kinds of grizzlies on this island in addition to a brown bear nearly coal-black in color. When this assortment of bears, totaling more than a thousand individuals, makes its midsummer trek to the salmon streams, it's a sight no observer can ever forget.

Absorbed in their fishing operations, the bears lose much of their usual wariness, so that if you move quietly against the wind and remain under the backdrop of deep-green evergreens bordering these streams you may be privileged to see twenty or more grizzlies and brownies in a single day. You'll see sour-faced old giants monopolizing favorite pools near which no other bear will dare to go. You'll see mothers teaching cubs the knack of catching salmon—always with the teeth. Contrary to most story-books, you'll not see any attempts to bat fish out on the banks with their paws.

Down at Naha Falls near Ketchikan, where numerous black bears perform for visiting town folks all through the salmon spawning season, there is one animal that excites more interest than any of the others. Sometime in its early life this bear suffered the misfortune of a broken lower jaw. It hangs uselessly down like a lolling tongue, and if ever a bear would be expected to swat fish out of the water with its paws this poor fellow is a likely candidate. But he doesn't do it that way. Instead he will herd a salmon out into the shallows and fall on it, pinning it to the gravel bottom with his chest. Having proceeded to squeeze most of the life out of the salmon, the bear will then poke it into his mouth far enough for the throat muscles to engage it, like tamping a load down a muzzle-loader shotgun. Onlookers' sympathies go out to this broken-jawed bruin; but there isn't a fatter bear at the falls.

The ursine family seems to have more human traits than most of the wild ones. We look to the black bears to give us comedy; to the brownies and grizzlies for examples of sagacity and courage. For the most part, they have no quarrel with man. They will bluff their way out of a tight corner if they can, or they'll attack with unbridled rage when they think it is the only way.

The man who walks between a mother grizzly and her cubs certainly doesn't mean to do it—not if he's in his right mind—but the grizzly draws no other interpretation than that you are trying to snatch one of her babies. Her actions at such time are, to coin a phrase, mother instinctive. She'll fight an army to get that cub ahead of her again where she can boost it along out of danger by frequent cuffs on the rump.

A year or two ago a trail builder near Juneau donated a rubber boot to an irate female grizzly. A split second after making a prodigious leap up the side of a tree—a leap to which he can point with pride—the grizzly nailed him by the heel. In the ensuing tug-of-war the boot was stripped off his leg. "Either that, or she'd have pulled my leg out by the roots," said the victim ruefully. "I know doggone well my arms weren't letting go of that tree!"

On another occasion a hunter came out of the hills following an unsuccessful morning's hunt, and after eating his lunch stretched out on a sand-bar for a sleep. A soft movement in the sand awakened him. As his eyes opened he saw a truly magnificent brown bear standing ten feet away, regarding him with keen curiosity. It shuffled around him in a complete circle, then ambled leisurely off into the timber.

Let it be recorded that this hunter was grateful enough to return the favor. Maybe the bear had, temporarily at least, impressed upon him a lesson in the "live-and-let-live" school of thought. Anyway, he shouldered his rifle and started for home.

In the ways of the wild ones there are clear-cut examples of tragedy and comedy. There are hate, fear, curiosity, affection. And there is ample evidence of ability to reason when something better than instinct is needed.

Reconversion of a Hunter

By BERT POPOWSKI

ABOUT A YEAR AGO I MET THE MEANEST MAN IN THE WORLD. He had a cabinet full of the finest products of the gunmakers' art and lavishly extolled the virtues of every one of them. While we were talking, his fifteen-year-old son came in and hung over our shoulders, his soul in his eyes as he watched us heft and swing that choice assortment of shooting irons. I waited and waited for that youngster to get in on the fine man-talk. Finally, I could stand it no longer.

"Which one of these is yours?" I demanded.

"He's too young to have a gun of his own," said the man, who—with apologies to all owners of that grand old name—we shall call Bill Jones. "I'm going to buy him a gun of his own when he's twenty-one."

I glared at him and I was wholehearted about it. Just as soon as I possibly could, I got out of there, for I hated his guts from that moment. And all through the following hunting season I avoided him for, though he had access to some of the choicest hunting areas in his native state, he was too stingy to share it with his own flesh and blood.

About a week later young Bill came over to see my John about some Boy Scout doings. John and I were hustling about, getting ready for an afternoon with the squirrels. It was a technicolor autumn day and I was in a hurry, but the yearning on young Bill's face did things to me. I gave John the eye and he followed me to my den.

"Why don't you ask him to go along?" I suggested. "He looks like he might be pretty good company."

"Gee, could I, Dad?" he said. "Bill's a grand fellow but he's never gone hunting and he'd like to so much I'm ashamed to talk in front of him about the good times we've had together."

Well, I had an awful time getting out of town that afternoon. The glory that overspread that youngster's face when John invited him along was positively indecent.

That afternoon stands out in my mind as one of the finest hunts I've ever enjoyed, and I didn't fire a shot, at game, that is. We drove out about a dozen miles to where the river makes a big loop, almost doubling back on itself. There was some underbrush in the stand of timber, but not much. Mostly it was oak, beech, and elm with a sprinkling of walnut and hickory. The leaves were half on and half off and the ground was covered with a crunchy carpet of them.

We drove right down to the river bank and John started to get out his .22 repeater, while I uncased a 20 gauge shotgun.

"You know, we ought to check that rifle for zero," I suggested.

John opened his mouth to remonstrate, for we'd just done that the previous week. But he thought better of it and we set up a piece of board at the edge of the water, pasted a one-inch sticker on it, and flopped down on our bellies.

"The upper left-hand corner," I suggested, and John put one about an inch high. "Two more," I added. The three made a neat triangle that wouldn't show under a dime, but I shook my head and reached for the gun. Aiming at the lower left-hand corner, I got the next three just edging the paper sticker. I unloaded the rifle and handed it to Bill, while John and I went down to look the target over.

"It would be a good idea if we set the cross hairs to hit right on the button at about fifty yards," I said. "Bill ought to be able to hit a couple at that range and you can hold over if you get longer shots."

For the next half hour Bill did the shooting. Of course, he yanked 'em off and got nervous as a treed cat, but John and I ignored that and kept him at it. Finally, on the fourth sticker, he got three shots in a triangle about the size of a quarter, all nicely spaced about his aiming point. He looked pleased.

"That's a nice group, Bill," I said. "Now, let John take three shots at the same aiming point and see if it's any better."

John took plenty of time with those aiming shots and his triangle was well inside Bill's. In fact, the three bullet holes came precious close to touching each other.

About the aiming point I drew the rough outline of a squirrel's head, indicating the eye in its proper relation to the rest of the skull.

"Six shots, six squirrels," chuckled John.

"Bill, I want you to look at this," I said. "This rifle is plenty accurate to kill a squirrel with every shot if you hold it steady and squeeze your shot off. But you'll have to cut that squirrel's head in quarters with the cross hairs to do it."

"You mean I can shoot at squirrels?" he said. "I thought you'd just let me shoot at sticks and stuff." His face wore the most delighted expression I've ever seen. My own eyes smarted as I led the way, imagining the gnawing hunger for hunting that must have lived with him for months and years.

"John, I want you to use this rifle as a single shot to be on the safe side. Each of you take a box of cartridges and put it in your pocket, and I don't want you to separate at any time. He's the boss, Bill. You do exactly as he tells you." I turned back to the car.

There I picked up my 20 gauge, filled the magazine, dropped a half-dozen spare loads in my pocket and trailed the boys by fifty yards. It was a bit early for the afternoon feeding session, so I anticipated slow going for a while.

I was wrong. Within ten minutes I saw John hand the rifle to Bill and stand at his elbow. That bushy-tail was wary and they jockeyed around for five minutes before Bill raised the rifle, rested it against the gnarled trunk of an elm and sought his target with the cross hairs. A minute ticked by, then another, and still no shot came.

Finally, the whiplash of that shot woke long rolling echoes through the timber. I saw Bill start forward, then hold and come back as John spoke to him. Three pairs of eyes sought eagerly for falling game and of the three I think I was the most anxious. Just as I'd given it up as a miss I saw the squirrel plummet down and fall limp beside the gnarled roots.

John held the rifle while he sent Bill to retrieve that bushytail.

Bill's yell of delight must have scared every squirrel within a half mile. I didn't blame him; I felt like yelling myself. I've never seen a lone squirrel that gave three hunters so much satisfaction.

"Bill, a hunter has to know other things besides shooting. When you yelled that way, you probably robbed yourself of any other shooting for the next half hour, at least."

"That's what John told me," he confessed. "But I had to yell or bust. Did I do all right on that one?"

"You sure did," said John. Then to me, "That squirrel was on top of a branch about as thick as my wrist and only his head was showing. It was a good shot, a swell shot!"

"Is that rifle loaded?" I asked as he set it against a tree.

"Yes, but the firing pin is set down."

"Unload it and let Bill do it all himself this time," I said.

"No, it's John's shot next," Bill said.

"Unh-uh. Not after that war whoop. You sweat it out."

Well, that's the way it started. Before the day was over, John and Bill and I had two more squirrel hunts under our belts, and Bill had popped off a cottontail that hesitated a bit too long. That, too, was a dead-center head shot. Then and there I decided that Bill was ready for the next step in his training.

We ate our lunch under a huge oak that sat back some ten yards from the river bank and, when only crumbs remained, I salvaged the waxed paper in which the sandwiches had been wrapped, picked up our four squirrels and one cottontail and took them down to the water's edge.

"Bill, bring me that hunting knife in the car panel."

Both boys came to the water's edge while I dipped all of our game in the water to settle the loose hairs and then laid them out on a piece of driftwood. Bill looked askance at me.

"Every good hunter ought to know how to dress out his game. Even if he intends to give it away he ought to dress it out; then he knows it won't be wasted. I'm going to show you how on one squirrel, then I want you to do the rest."

Picking up a squirrel, I lifted a pinch of skin off the middle of its back and slit it across. Matching one hand against the other, I turned the halves of that squirrel pelt inside out, cut off the four feet at the ankles, the tail at the root, and beheaded it. John held the nude carcass by the hind legs while I split it at the crotch, sheared off the ribs at their point of attachment to the backbone, and flung the offal to midstream. Laying the dressed carcass on a piece of waxed paper, I offered the knife to Bill.

"Be careful of that knife," I warned. "It's razor sharp."

Bill fumbled around a bit, it's true, but by the time he reached the cottontail rabbit he did an acceptable job. We wrapped the lot in waxed paper, then rolled it up in newspaper and headed for home.

There was one more lesson and then young Bill's training was complete. Of course, he would learn for years, but the fundamentals of safety, consideration for the other fellow, and proper care and use of firearms and game were properly instilled in him. He had to be introduced to the shotgun and its use on moving game. I'd cheerfully contributed the rifle ammunition, but in view of the shell shortage I hesitated a bit and finally appealed to John.

"His dad shoots a 20 gauge and he ought to be able to get some shells from him," John said.

"From that skinflint? Not a chance!"

But a week later, just as we were about to shove off for a combined crow-and-cottontail hunt, Bill came up with a box of the precious loads. They were a mongrel mixture—some black shells that I hadn't seen in fifteen years and a motley assortment of shot sizes. I grinned as Bill proudly presented them for my inspection.

"Where'd you get them?" I asked, to get him talking.

"A neighbor hunter came over and said he was going to throw them away," he admitted. "Said they were old and he had plenty of new ones. They'll be all right, won't they?"

"Of course, they will!" I said. "Besides, John got a new hunting coat and with it we got another box of shells that you can have." John blinked at this sudden share-the-wealth move, but he was a gentleman about it.

The wind was uneasy with that restlessness of late fall days and uncertain weather. The leaves scudded and whiplashed back and forth across the roadway and the grasses bent low one moment, only to spring erect with little effect from the vagrant wind the next.

The two wildcats in the back seat had quit helling around about the time I pulled off on a road that wandered down to the river. And, when I stepped from the car with my shotgun ready, I found both of them right behind me with ready guns.

"Scram out of here," I ordered. "Do you think I'm gonna birddog for you? Drop down to the river bottom and get up your own game. And we'll meet at that big elm tree across the draw at high noon. Get goin'."

In the meantime I scouted along the river flats for the crow roost I suspected was there and about four miles downstream I finally found it, complete with all sign and large enough to indicate a sizable flock.

At noon the boys showed up with seven squirrels and four cotton-tails. Bill didn't wait a minute after he absorbed the quarter of apple pie that concluded our lunch. He picked up the game and some news-papers and started right for the river bank to dress 'em out.

"You don't have to help me, John," I heard him say. "I'm so glad to have this chance to get out that I'll be glad to do them."

"Don't be silly," John said. "I guess I'm entitled to my share of the fun of cleaning them." Bless his understanding heart!

We loafed around for an hour or so, then climbed in the car, and drove down near the crow roost. We didn't have many shells to spend but the experience would be something for Bill, giving him an opportunity to try his skill on wing shots with no great harm done if cripples resulted.

As I recall it we killed forty-nine crows in that abbreviated melee, and walked out of there without an unspent load to our name. The boys joined me on the front seat for the trip home, for the wind had turned cold and the soughing heater was an item of equipment not to be lightly discounted.

Young Bill took those squirrels and rabbits home with him. His father came over to see me a couple of nights later. The old boy came in with fire in his eye, but he went out as meek as a lamb.

Now, the two Bills form one of the better-known father-and-son combinations. They hunt together at every opportunity and I've even heard Old Bill refuse a hunt so he and the boy could take a long-planned jaunt after quail. I hope their luck was good; young Bill deserves it.

The Rejuvenation of Greene

By IRA BRIGHT

HE HESITATED AS HE REACHED THE OFFICE DOOR, TURNED around, and stood holding his black felt hat clutched to his middle. His air was that of one who inquires about an old friend.

"Doctah, whar's dat hamm'less britch-loader whut you' daddy had?"

I turned in my chair and pushed the prescription pad from me. "What do you want with the old gun, Greene? Shoot rabbits?"

The hat changed hands and a ray of sunlight squeezed through a hole in its crown. His manner became a mixture of careful diplomacy and offended dignity.

"N-a-a-w, suh! I know's whar dey's er millyun ducks."

Here he paused to permit this statement to serve as a gentle, but deserved, reproof for my lack of familiarity with his cultivated taste in game. For I had remembered too late that twenty years as caretaker at the club, and as guide and favorite paddler for many of our oldest, most distinguished sportsmen, had led Greene to feel that anything less than deer, turkey, duck and quail were hardly worth a gentleman's notice. A youngster could pursue the rabbit as a part of his early training, but was certain to discard such childish pursuits with the approach of manhood.

In the moments following his words relative to a million ducks I also recalled that the disappearance of game from the club property as the years rolled by represented a loss to the old negro in more than one way. I knew the club had changed from a refuge for sportsmen to a place for Saturday night poker, Sunday picnics and ladies in slacks. And with this change had come a more subtle change in Greene's status.

No longer were his duties manly and honorable, such as paddling for Mr. Will as he jumped ducks, or feeding and caring for the deer dogs. Nor did spring find him with Dr. Smith after turkeys on Big Ridge. Most of his old turkey hunters were long dead, and the turkeys had been gone even longer. It had been years since he had saddled Sadie, the white mule, and driven with the hounds. Sadie and the hounds had departed with the deer.

And now it was necessary to open the club at eight every Saturday night and make all preparations for the weekly dances. On Sundays he provided boat paddlers for men whose idea of a big fishing trip was six or seven not very large bream. On picnic days he brought in a town man to help park the cars and open the beer. He did not spend long hours practicing turkey calling, but he was becoming handy with radio and phonograph of the portable variety.

My gloomy reflections on the changes in Greene's life ceased abruptly as the full force of the meaning of his words sank home. Here was a man who had guided for the best, and he said he had seen a million ducks. If anyone in my acquaintance knew his ducks, Greene did. However, I began an investigation, for even with Greene to vouch for their presence I found it hard to believe in a million ducks.

"Where are you going to hunt ducks, Greene? There hasn't been a mallard in those pin-oak flats at the club in twenty years. Not since the canals were cut."

Here he stooped and placed his hat, hole and all, carefully on the floor, thus freeing his hands for their rôle as conversational assistants. He reseated himself in the old leather chair and went through all the other little preparations which a man makes who is about to become eloquent on a subject near and dear to his heart. At times, as he talked, sorrow for those departed and for days fled by crept into his voice.

"Doctah, back in de times 'fo' de Panic, when yo' daddy wuz so he doan' 'low no nigger but me to tote dat ol' gun er his'n, de rivah riz up an' git 'mongst de pin-oak trees at de haid o' de lake, an' de ducks uses in dar mighty free. Wuzn't no way fo' hit to miss, 'ginst dey wuzn't no high watah."

How well I remembered the tales I used to hear around the stove in Chandler's Drug Store! Tales of wonderful duck shoots in the overflowed pin-oak flats at the head of McIntyre Lake.

"Yas, suh! Mos' all de club use to git ovaflowed when de rivah riz, but hit doan' nevah do us no harm, 'cause de club-house wuz on piles an' my house wuz on 'em. An' de deers an' de turkeys mek hit fo' de ridges, an' de watah sho' doan' git dem!"

I certainly agreed that the cypress piles which supported the floor of his cabin, eight feet above the ground, had often been his salvation. I recalled one spring flood during my boyhood, when my father and I paddled our boat up to Greene's house and stepped easily out on his porch.

"But when dey cut de grudge ditches an' call deyse'f straightin' de rivah, dey's done plumb ruint de bizness."

The cotton-growing Mississippi Delta is crisscrossed by numerous canals, or drainage ditches, designed to combat the evils of spring floods, and particularly to enable the cotton planter to drain and then cultivate new land. Also, many of the larger rivers had had their courses straightened by cutting through bends or turns in their channels. To Greene a dredge-cut drainage canal had always been a "grudge ditch." This nomenclature he shared in common with all his colored brethren.

"Wid de ditches cut, de floodin's 'bout gone an' de folkses 'gun to clear de lan' 'round de club. An' when de big timbah on de Yallerbushah River wuz cut, den de mostes' er de deer went wid it. I ain' seed one sence. An' no sooner dan de mens cut de firs' tree on Big Ridge, ol' man turkey say to hese'f, 'Dis ain' no place foh you!' I ain' seed no turkey signs sence me an' you' daddy an' Mist' Sim cotch de flu in nineteen-seventeen."

He shook his head sadly over this desecration. I fully understood his mood as memory brought to mind descriptions of the great forests of oak and hickory covering the ridges that ran for miles on both banks of the Yalobusha River. Each ridge once had its bountiful quota of deer and turkey.

"Den some er de gent'mens in the club say us gwine mek some money if us clear de ol' Cribbin' Groun' and Holly Ridge an' plant hit in cotton. An' 'foh you kin say, 'Jack Rob'son,' dey had dis nigger a-plowin'!" Greene paused in order that the depth of his degradation might be fully appreciated. To fall from the status of sportsman and guide to that of a plow hand was quite a drop.

"Yaas, suh! Us plant all de ridges in cotton. At de meetin' all de ol' membahs 'posed hit. Mist' Will an' Mist' Sim an' de Judge an' Mist' Jeff nigh th'owed er fit!" A gleam of pride in their fight against the money-lenders shone in Greene's eyes.

"Mist' Jeff, he say, 'Lawd'lmighty! Ain' I got cotton enuff? Whut I needs is turkeys an' deers an' mallets 'nuff ter keep dat lazy nigger Greene so he kin paddle er boat. I didn't jine dis damn club ter git rich!' "

The town clock in the court-house across the square struck ten long, mellow strokes. Greene fished tenderly in his pocket for his old watch—a gift to him from an ex-governor of the state.

"An' de Jedge, he jes' sot dar an' look mad an' chew he lip lak he done de time he miss de big buck. I seed him th'u de do'h, 'cause I sho' lis'nen." Greene chuckled and shook his head in appreciation. Apparently satisfied that the local clock was right, he pocketed his watch. I doubt that it ever occurred to him that his precious watch could be wrong.

"But hit don' mek no diff'ence to de bulk o' de membahs. An' you knows de rest. All de o' membahs is gone. All de ones whut tuk me to de club when I wuz er young buck. De ones whut is left is new membahs. Dey jine foh de swimmin' an' de dancin', I reckons, but hit 'pears to me dat dey do mo' poker playin' dan anything else." The conversation ceased as Greene began what was a fruitless search for tobacco until I handed him mine.

Since my return after ten years' absence, Greene had paid me several purely experimental visits in order to determine just what the young doctor could do with "misery in the j'ints." He had cheerfully and hopefully taken all medicine prescribed for him, although he had more than once intimated that it was difficult to see how I could be a good doctor and appear so young. In none of our discussions, however, had he ever before offered his account of just what had happened to the old club. Just as I was on the verge of insinuating that he had yet to explain the million ducks, he chose to proceed.

"Yas, suh! Dem grudge ditches ruint de bizness, an' hit 'gins to 'pear lak dey sho' gwine fetch hit back!"

Rumors had reached me, and I was not entirely unprepared for this remarkable statement. However, I am glad to say I did not forget to be surprised. During the week before Greene's visit, a farmer patient had casually mentioned that the river, due to some obstruction in its course, had returned to its old habit of flooding the countryside. And the floods were making farming impossible. It seemed that a drainage canal had been cut for twenty miles through some of the adjoining hill counties in an attempt to produce a more rapid run-off of water. The canal ran down into the flat delta land and emptied into the river. Much sand and other silt had been washed into the river bed, and an unintentioned dam across the stream had resulted.

"Dey's done cut er new grudge ditch fum outa de hills, an' hit floods ev'y time dey's er heavy dew rounst Grenada. Dey's done cut dat ditch so hit jine into de rivah an' done plumb filled hit up!"

He paused and leaned back in his chair, obviously wishing to give the impression that the best was yet to come.

"Yaas, suh! Dat grudge ditch done mek er big dam 'cross de Yallerbushah River! When de watah run down de rivah an' hit dat dam, hit spread all ovah de whole country. All dat's left out is dem pin-oak ridges." Greene unfastened his vest, a sure sign he was becoming excited.

" De farmin' ain' nevah been much in dar, but dey's been jes' enuff folkses an' fields an' goin's on to keep de game kilt off or runned off. But now de rivah gits ovah de lan' so free dat dey jes' natcherly cain't be no farmin' did."

Here he stopped long enough to rub his knee and wince. "Dis miz'ry in my j'ints ain' 'low me to go back in dar an' do no lookin' roun'. But dat whole country might git lak hit wuz, jes' growed up to de wild an' er natch'l nest foh deers an' turkeys. An' foh dat matter, my boy Willie say dey's sho' some mallet ducks in dar now."

New pin-oak ridges under water. The ducks should be there!

"All right, I'll be at your house with the old gun and shells at five tomorrow. I don't think a hunt will hurt you—probably do you good."

In the little restaurant known as the Post Office Cafe the familiar faces and warm air were enough to dispel early-morning gloom. And as I drank a preliminary cup of hot black coffee while awaiting Southern baked ham, partly hidden by two country eggs, the doubts of the previous day were replaced by complete assurance that all of Greene's million ducks would certainly materialize.

The old cafe has long been a gathering place for planters who live in town and come by for coffee before an early drive to their plantations. Bits of conversation came to my ears as a gray-haired gentleman discoursed on factors affecting the price of long staple cotton. I looked around for someone to talk ducks with and was about to give it up when two hunters in hip boots clumped in. Soon I was happy in an argument over the merits of small shot for wildfowl. And we did not neglect the old question of soft versus chilled shot for quail. The ham and eggs improved my disposition still further.

A glance at the clock told me it was time to move on. I turned the car north and soon felt the crunch of graveled roads under my tires. On both sides of the road stretched vast cotton plantations. Soft lights in the distance marked log fires on negro-cabin hearths. The wide radiance of the headlights picked out great white patches of unpicked cotton in the fields. Suddenly a lone mule with dark overall-clad rider came into view, and I swerved past, thankful that I had seen them in time.

A few more miles and the club-house loomed large and lonely ahead. I passed around it and stopped in front of a small three-room cabin. Its floor rested on cypress posts that reached fully eight feet above the ground. The door was open; the fire-light sent shadows dancing out over the porch and into the trees. A figure blocked the flow of flickering light.

"Y-a-a-s, suh! I'se erbout to give you up!"

Guiltily I remember the argument in the cafe as I worm out of the car and begin the climb for a brief warming before the logs. While Greene completes his preparations I make conversation with his marital partner of some thirty years. As we talk two small and very black heads appear from beneath the quilt covering the big double bed standing just across the room. And two pairs of black eyes watch me closely. They belong to Samuel and Delilah, who are Greene's grandchildren. No doubt they are wondering if the doctor has come to give them more medicine for chills and fever.

As we hurry the cypress dugout across East Lake an owl hoots over on Holly Ridge. Across, we hold a quick council, and Greene decides to place me in a log blind, paddle over to East Ridge and jump-shoot ducks along the water's edge during his walk home. We instruct Willie, Greene's youngest son, to come for me at eleven o'clock. Surely, with the three of us, we can keep the birds moving even in so large a territory.

Red and gold flame and glow in the east. From their great height cypress trees along the run look down upon the narrow ridge road lined by lesser oaks. Deep shadows lie at our feet. Not far ahead the road vanishes, and we plunge into the undergrowth. The cold morning air is forgotten in the warmth of more strenuous movement. Ahead of me, Willie's back, enormous with a sack of decoys, is my guide. A lone wood duck passes high on whistling wings.

We reach water and begin to wade. Thin ice twinkles along the bank. The cold water reaches higher, and we are relieved when Greene finds his hidden boat pulled well up in a fallen tree-top.

Old stumps and logs hinder progress through the overflow as we twist and force our way. Water standing the year round has killed the timber on a 100-acre lowland, and our boat floats quietly out into the open. A single cypress towers up and up. As our eyes follow its reach into the blue and gold sky we see a long, wide V of mallards crossing high. We move on, and Greene's voice comes softly to my ears. "Doctah, is you col'?"

"Not much."

"Whut logs us gwine use?"

"Take me to that big drift yonder, and I can hide in the grass on it. There's enough grass and weeds growing on those old logs to make a good blind."

"Yas, suh, Willie say dey lights out heah in dis deep watah an' swims into de bank foh de acorns."

Twenty mallards loom in the early light, cup their wings, hover over a thicket not seventy yards away, and settle slowly down. I now believe fully in Greene's ducks.

Soon I am in the blind with gun ready. Two parallel weed-grown logs give uncertain footing, but plenty of cover. Greene paddles quietly off, the old gun by his side. The decoys bob a little in his slight wake. The roar of high-velocity loads begins on Six Mile Lake, and my call goes to work as two drakes beat over the tree-tops. They have heard my hail and perform a wide circle while dropping to a lower level. I carry on conversation with chatter and cluck as they make one more circle. And now—straight in! A clean miss with the first barrel, but the second smashes its bird at the top of the rise.

I have just readjusted myself when a telltale whisper behind me sends a thrill of hope. But the gun swing is checked in time as a wood duck is recognized. These ducks are frequent visitors through the morning, and it is a source of satisfaction to learn how they have increased in numbers.

Two drakes and a hen approach from the rear. It is necessary to turn a bit before shooting, and the decision is made that it is better to take chances now than risk not having them return. The long barrels swing rapidly ahead. A spurt of feathers and a change of pace as the gun leaps to get on a climbing target. Then the sweet satisfaction of a double.

Somewhere on a ridge behind me two squirrels can be heard fighting, and I sit idly on my logs and wonder if Willie is plotting their destruction. Caught thus, I am totally unprepared for the twelve birds that sweep into range from the left. As they pass in front of me I hope they have seen my decoys, but they continue on their way, paying no heed to my plea. Again I am ruefully remembering that eternal vigilance is necessary.

But no time is given in which to regret, for just above the cypress tops to my right mallards are heading my way, and as they pass over the low sun strikes their breasts and all their hidden colors are agleam. The clear, sweet whistle of their wings is in my ears as I decide to shoot. The black tubes of the heavy 12-gauge slip from behind to a spot just ahead of the leading drake. His slender neck goes limp as he hurtles down through the limbs. And I do not mind so much the miss with the second barrel.

An hour passes as I watch the swift flash and swerve of flighting wood ducks. Two pintails arouse my hopes, but do not come within range. The sun is now quite high, and again I am being lulled into a state of unawareness and remind myself that I must keep a sharp eye. But in spite of careful watching, a large drove is almost on me before I see them. As they pass I feel they will not decoy, but intend to drop into the pin-oak trees near by. With wings curved downward, they twist and rock as they filter through the branches. In the bright morning sunlight each detail of their coloring stands out clear and lovely. A beautiful sight!

I drop the call on its string, and at the finish of a side-slip the right barrel centers a drake. The left pulls down a climbing hen.

Eleven o'clock—time to quit if I am to be in the office by two. I think how pleasant it would be to spend the day on the logs and

watch the wildlife in this new lowland. But I resist temptation, stretch
and call Willie. No answer. Several minutes pass, and I call again.
This time a gunshot about two hundred yards away is the answer.
The roar of wings comes across the water, and forty or fifty mallards
are headed my way. Just clearing the trees, they seem easy targets,
and it is only the memory of past lessons in humility that save me
from over-confidence.

The lead bird appears very large and dark. It is a black mallard.
The others are forgotten as I steady myself for the shot, and the old
thrill comes again as the magnificent bird comes curving downward
to splash water over the blind. A grand finish to a great day!

I am still admiring the black duck when a slight gurgle directs my
attention to the decoys, and I see that Willie has returned and is taking
up the blocks and gathering the dead. I am, as ever, amazed at the
silence that is a part of his every motion in the woods or on the
water.

It is good to stretch in the boat, and we enjoy a smoke while
doing it. Everywhere I turn I can see small and large droves of wildfowl moving over the timber. I give thanks to good old Greene for
sharing his secret with me.

The return walk through winter woods is pleasant to stiff limbs.
And especially so when we feel the warmth of feathered bodies
bouncing against chest and back with each step. Contentment reigns
supreme. We do not have a limit, but we have enough. Soon we are
in Greene's front yard and Willie is holding up his three mallards
for inspection. I suddenly remember that I did not hear him shoot
but the one time when he flushed the drove from which I collected
the black duck.

"Willie, how many times did you shoot?"

Disappointment appears on his face. "Well, Cap'n, hit wuz dis way.
I done been behin' er big drove of mallets all dis mawning, an' dey
sho' led me er chase thu dem elbow bushes an' cypress kneeses. I'se
erbout to lose 'em when er old hen fetch er loud hollah an' I eases
de boat ovah dat way. Atter er while I gits close up on 'em—dey sho'
wuz er heap er ducks dar on de watah."

Here he pauses and eyes me just a moment, then goes on.

"But when I'se erbout to shoot, I heahs you callin' dis nigger. An'
de ducks 'gins to git oneasy lak, an' moves erbout dis er way an' dat
er way on de watah, an' I had to shoot whar dey wuzn't many
of 'em."

We have walked down to the lake's edge while Willie is giving his account of the hunt. Through the gold and red leaves of oak and gum trees the sun thrusts long fingers of bright light across the woods road along the opposite bank. A figure in blue denim overalls and canvas shooting coat steps out of the shadows and moves along the road toward the lake. The apparently youthful hunter comes into full view with long, swinging stride. I stand open-mouthed in amazement, for it is Greene! But what a transformation from his former bent and shuffling gait.

I am still doubting my eyes as he steps into the dugout and paddles to us. Clarence, his ten-year-old nephew, has long since ferried the dugout back to pick up his uncle and is very proud of the ducks we can hear him counting on the bottom of the boat.

"Doctah, is you had er good hunt?"

I assure Greene I had a fine time as he collects ducks and gun and steps ashore. I am still puzzled by the absence of his stoop and the return of his old, graceful carriage.

"Greene, you look mighty pert and spry."

"Yas, suh, I feels pretty good."

He puts the ducks down and carefully rests the gun muzzle on a log. Such studied movement can only mean that something is on his mind—something big.

"Yas, suh, I feels pretty good. I'se done walked back ovah on de ridge when I lef' de boat. Ain' been on dat ridge in erbout five years. Sho' is done got wild. I kilt my firstest duck right dar an' raked him in wid my gun barrel."

I see there is nothing to do but wait until he works up to it.

"Yas, suh, hit's near erbout as wild in dar as hit used to be. An' I'se done seed de track er de bigges' buck deer dey is in de world."

He hesitates and watches my face for the effect his words might have. Apparently satisfied, he proceeds.

"Dat deer 'most big as de Skip Crossing buck what yo' daddy kilt. Dey sho' is been things er goin' on in dese woods sence I been down wid de miz'ry in my j'ints. I seed er heap er coon an' mink sign, too."

He turns to Willie. "Boy, whar dem steel traps whut Mist' Sim done give me? If you ain't been so busy a-cotin' an' runnin' wid dem town gals you could er tol' me dese woods is full er varmints." Greene would never admit that anybody but himself could have discovered the deer tracks.

We pack decoys and birds in the car, and I bid Willie farewell. The motor is running, and I have told Greene I will return next week. He stands, hat in hand, all smiles and still looking twenty years younger.

"Doctah, you reckon dem turkeys gwine come back?"

"Greene, I sure hope so. You keep a lookout for them and keep the gun. I know you'll take good care of it."

"Yas, suh, I knowed you gwine let me have dat gun."

I almost released the clutch.

"An', Doctah, see cain't you git us er coon dawg. I sho' believes de night air ain' goin' give me no j'int aches."

"You don't think it'll hurt you, Greene?"

"Naw, suh, Doctah, I feels er heap better. I sho' does!"

As I drive through the club-house gate and look over the cotton fields toward home I am happy in the knowledge that I have lost a patient, but regained a guide and hunting companion.

The Last Day

By COL. HAROLD P. SHELDON

IT WAS A LITTLE MORE THAN TWO MONTHS BEFORE THAT FATEFUL day in December, 1941. Despite the fewness of his years, Young Feller stood a husky six feet; but due to the perversity of those who are charged with the education of the young and who insist upon opening the school year at the very beginning of the shooting season, the lad had never enjoyed a bona fide excursion into the uplands in glowing October. He sat now with his big shoulders hunched over a text book, trying hopelessly to force some trifle of algebraic fact into a head full of boyish fancy. Merely by raising his eyes from the loathsome hieroglyphics before him he could gaze upon the darkly shining beauty of his new over-and-under 12-bore standing there in the cabinet beside the fireplace, ranked with the veteran weapons of his male parent.

There was a fine fire burning, for it was a crisp evening. The

Dark-Haired Lady had gone visiting, leaving her two menfolk to themselves. Perhaps the Captain recalled the days of his youth, when he sat at a desk in a red schoolhouse, a desk that bore the graven initials of three generations of his ancestors.

As he struggled with a bloodless thing known as the binomial theorem there came to his ears the sharp solitary crack of a squirrel rifle from the butternut grove on Enos' Hill, or the double thunder of a shotgun from the copses of birch and alder along the brook. His own precious gun, a stanch single-barrel would be hidden behind the stone wall a quarter of a mile up the road. At four o'clock, if he didn't have to stay after school to complete some dreary passage, he might get an hour of high adventure with the pa'tridges, woodcock and gray squirrels. The hours thus snatched, however, did no more than sharpen the appetite of a boy whose hands were shaped to the feel of a gun and whose eyes were keen to follow the line of a pa'tridge's flight among the scarlet sumacs. Ah, yes, and he could remember the heady smell of black powder and the curious fragrance of the beautiful, deadly toadstools under the pines in Rock Pasture.

He spoke, and the boy could scarcely believe his own ears. "Young Feller, I'm of a good mind to take you along to Tranquillity next week for a solid month of gunning. How'd you like that?"

The boy leaped to his feet, and the expression on his face was that of one who has seen a vision. "Gosh, Dad! Do you mean it?" Then his elation shrank. "Mother'll never let me stay out of school for a whole month."

"Maybe she will, my boy, this time."

The Dark-Haired Lady returned, her eyes bright from the effects of tea and neighborly gossip and her cheeks glowing from the frosty air, and found the plotters ready. Her first cry when she heard the scheme was one of deep dismay. Young Feller felt cold water rising about his feet from the shattered hull of his hopes. His advocate was taking it easy, however, listening with great deference and respect until the lady had enumerated all the objections, which were many and valid.

Then, quite sincerely, the Captain produced his main argument.

"There's another thing—this cursed war," said he. "We're going to get into it. We've got to, and we ought to, and when that finally happens there'll be no more fun then for the 18-year-olds."

The Dark-Haired Lady's troubled gaze met his in understanding. "Can I come along too?" she asked.

"Couldn't do without you," replied the Captain, and he meant it from the bottom of his heart.

Certainly none of the three ever had occasion to regret the decision. The days that followed were without blemish.

For the Dark-Haired Lady there were the long, bright hours spent on some painted hillside where the Captain had thoughtfully placed the car with a fine regard for the landscape and the scenery. The book which she always brought along was seldom, if ever, opened, for nature turned for her the pages of a nobler volume. She made friends with the chipmunks and the chickadees, who know a friend when they see one, and she listened to the soft and anxious voices of the feathered folk migrating southward. Occasionally she would be enthralled by the sight and sound of a flock of wild geese passing overhead. When this happened, the Dark-Haired Lady thought that she could almost understand the wild language of the birds as they bade farewell to the Northland.

But her most poignant moments came as she watched the two tall men striding side by side across a field or down a tapestried wood road. They were so strong and confident, and they were hers. Her heart was like to burst with pride, and she could forget for a moment the menace of the mortal storm gathering beyond these peaceful hills.

Weeks ago, on the evening of their arrival in Tranquillity, the Captain and the Dark-Haired Lady had lingered long before the fire in the big room under the eaves. A soft glow came from the cracks in the ancient stove. Except for their own low voices and the comforting crackle of the fire, the old house was silent. In the next room the Young Feller was deep in the dreams of youth.

Outside the small window-panes a white frost was settling over the countryside. The little owls were exchanging querulous comment upon their small affairs, prudently leaving problems of larger import to be discussed by their greater kinsfolk whose solemn hootings sounded from the distant woods.

The Captain rose to his feet and laid a fresh chunk on the coals. "It's my general idea that the Little Brother is about to have the time of his life, if my plan works as I hope it will," he said. "I aim to take him to the very spot where I shot my first pa'tridge—I won't tell you how long ago that was, Ma'am—and I want to take him to the places where I killed my first woodcock, my first duck and my first squirrel. My prayer is that he'll have the same luck. I want to be there to see it. The poets say that you can't relive your past experiences, but I'll bet a doughnut that the boy will help me do that very thing."

The plan worked well, and Young Feller killed his first woodcock in a patch of white birches within twenty paces of the spot where the Captain, so many years ago, had dropped his first bird with his old single-barrel and a hand-loaded brass shotshell. Then, for a little time, while the Captain smoked a cigarette and watched with pride and approval, the boy studied his prize with a concentrated interest such as his algebra had never received.

That night, again beside the stove, the Captain told his lady about his own reactions.

"By Judas, Ma'am, it worked. It more than worked! Not only did I feel the same elation that I knew when I gathered my first timberdoodle and sat down to admire it, but, do you know, I somehow felt his, too!"

She smiled her gentlest and wisest smile, which was more in her brown eyes than on her lips.

"I'm glad," said she, "and I think you were right about the school, but I do wish he were a better scholar."

"He'll never get a Rhodes scholarship, I guess," the Captain admitted, "but who cares? He's going to make a hell of a good gunner, Ma'am."

The Judge and Uncle Bill Paraday had known the youngster for most of his life. The bluff Doctor had known him for all of it, for it had been his palm that brought the first lusty bellow of protest from the squirming infant.

Now all three accepted him as a gunner and a gentleman. It must be confessed that the Captain's eyes smarted a bit at times as he observed how well and carefully the old boys tended his young sprout. They never laughed at the mistakes he didn't know he had made. Instead they showed him, by their own conduct, the right way to do the trick. But when he missed an easy shot, or fell into a brook, they razzed him as mercilessly as they razzed his dad, and the boy liked it.

They connived to maneuver Young Feller into the most favorable positions for a shot while one or another of them went into the thick stuff to flush the bird. It worked for a time, until the lad saw through the conspiracy.

"No, sir, Judge," he announced firmly one day. "Not this time, please. You stay out and I'll go in. Can't hit a pa'tridge anyway, but you and Dad can."

When the Captain heard that firm pronouncement, his heart expanded to the size of the prize pumpkin at the County Fair.

The Judge grinned and drew the hammers on his faithful double. "All right, son. Go on in then. Danged if you ain't as stubborn as your old man!"

It occurred to the Captain at that point that he had no monopoly on this reliving business. The Young Feller, through the magic of his own enthusiasm, was making an 18-year-old out of everyone of these time-scarred veterans.

Uncle Bill invited the boy to join him on a squirrel-shooting expedition. He did not include the Captain, who had sense enough to find something very imperative that he had to do that day. The Judge took the boy at four o'clock one stormy morning to shoot ducks with him, and again the Captain was left to his own devices, which, by the way, were many.

Young Feller came home that evening wet to the skin, with an ecstatic gleam in his eyes and five big black ducks.

"Wish I had him," said the Judge, speaking from the corner of his mouth to the Captain while the Dark-Haired Lady issued orders to her offspring for a hot bath and dry clothes.

The Captain was content with that.

And now it was the morning of the last day. The long valley lay under a bright and cloudless sky. No breath of air threatened the security of the last of the faded leaves which still clung all forlorn to the parent twigs of the great maples along the roadside. In this magic atmosphere the small familiar sounds from distant farmsteads came clear and distinct to the ear.

If a man paused from his toil to listen for a minute, he could know the nature of the tasks that occupied his neighbors. The rhythmical thuds from down the valley indicated that someone was splitting the summer-cured chunks of firewood. Neighbor Briggs was "topping off" his silo with a thick wad of late-cut clover. The hungry clatter of the whirling blades of the ensilage cutter, followed intermittently by a deep drone of satisfaction as a fresh bundle was tossed into the eager maw of the machine, told the whole story. Other sounds and voices spoke of fall plowing and of similar rural activities being carried on in preparation for the stark months of winter, whose icy legions were already poised for invasion just beyond the northern horizon. There was no time to lose.

Toward midnight the Captain was awakened by some mysterious message that came to him from the sky. When he went to the window in response to the mystical summons he saw long lances of ghostly radiance sweeping across the zenith and recognized them as signals of warning flashed from the polar ice-cap. He went shivering back to bed.

And still Young Feller hadn't shot his first pa'tridge. He had done better than well on woodcock and ducks, but had not yet acquired the knack of that quick, instinctive half snap which alone enables the gunner to drive a load of shot across the bows of a bird that knows how to employ an astonishing combination of speed and evasion. His father's admonition to get farther ahead and not think of anything else had been so often repeated that it had become monotonous.

Young Feller would grin and shake his head ruefully as he ejected the empty cases. He observed carefully as his companion demonstrated the technique, but all this split-second precision was forgotten when the next gray ghost rose and went flickering away through the hazels.

"I can see how you do it, Dad, but I'm darned if I can do it myself. I guess maybe I'm kind of slow-witted or something."

"You are not!" his parent informed him positively. "You just haven't learned how to sing high C. But you will."

The last day began auspiciously, almost too much so for the Captain, who had, when it came to bird shooting and games of chance, a certain superstitious distrust of good beginnings. He thought that to miss the first bird gave the gunner a certain advantage in that it humbled his pride and demolished any overweening self-confidence. So reduced and humiliated, he was then in proper shape to take up Sir Ruff's challenge.

They were alone and together today, for the Judge, Uncle Bill and the Doctor had found several reasons for being in other places on the last day. They'd be around for dinner tonight, but they had a generous notion that the Captain and his boy should have this day to themselves.

The car was placed on the crest of the noble hill which supports a maze of pine, birch and poplar plantations, together with old apple trees, snowball bushes, swamps, runs and corners. This is known to the gunners of Tranquillity as the Grapevine Cover, because of the profusion of vines which overruns the ancient stone walls and rail fences.

The two set out along a hedge, the Captain on one side and Young Feller on the other, leaving the Dark-Haired Lady to her thoughts and the majesty of the great lake and the Adirondacks beyond it. It was pa'tridges or nothing today, for the woodcock had come and gone except for a foolish stranger now and then that, for the sake of worms and larvae, lingered on the rich ground in spite of his better woodcock judgment.

The pair had not proceeded far when, from beneath an apple tree, six pa'tridges took off in multiple thunder. The Captain's little 20-bore clapped twice, and he saw both birds pitch downward.

But the noise and confusion that had galvanized his immediate ancestor had the opposite effect upon his son. He followed a bird, only to abandon it for another, and then a third, and he finally sent a futile charge of sevens after the poorest of all the targets that had been presented so briefly.

His first thought was not of his own failure but of his companion's prowess. "Gosh, Dad, you sure can mow 'em! I don't see how you can pull a trigger as fast as that—much less do any aiming! I can't even think that fast."

"Neither can I," the Captain admitted in all truth and humility.

A bit farther along a pa'tridge got up in front of him and swung to the left. It was a foolish bird, or seemed to be so, for it stayed in the clear, inside the fringe of pines that would have given cover. It wasn't even flying at standard pa'tridge velocity. The gunner clearly observed the bright eye and every detail of the band of jet across the fan. Every night in the year a grouse shooter dreams of an opportunity like this. Once in a season he gets one, and usually does just what our friend proceeded to do on this occasion.

"Did you get him, Dad?"

"No, my boy, I didn't. I'm inclined to believe that with a slingshot it might've been different, but I'm no great shakes with a shotgun. I missed that bird, all clear and in range, with both barrels."

"Don't let it get you down," came the cheery counsel from across the swamp. "Maybe you didn't get far enough ahead!"

"It could be," the Captain acknowledged.

He did better with a single bird that dived out of an apple tree thirty yards ahead. The first barrel fetched a cloud of feathers, and the bird struck far out in the pasture.

"That other one back there just wasn't flying fast enough for you," the boy told him, trotting out to retrieve.

The Captain nodded. "Do you know, I believe you're absolutely right about that. I was set for a fast pitch, and he threw me a floater. However, I shot behind him. Slow or fast, that's the way pa'tridges are missed, and always have been."

He took the bird which Young Feller handed him. "Thank you, sir. Now what say we sit on yonder rail fence and smoke a cigarette and admire the wonders spread before us? One of the best things about a pa'tridge is the bird's love of beauty. Wherever you find one that spot is beautiful. Gunners who are also artists know this. You'll sometimes catch a woodcock without a proper background, but not Mister Pa'tridge. He knows where he belongs—plumb in the center of the picture."

Presently they returned to where the Dark-Haired Lady had lunch laid out for them. This time there was little of the gay jocularity that usually prevailed at these outdoor feasts, for they knew that the few hours that remained to them were few, and the poignant sorrow of anticipated partings was upon them.

Speechless, but not uncommunicative, they sat for long after the meal gazing at the rugged hills. In the forests and fields the carnival colors of autumn had been washed away. Where there had been a flaunting of yellow and scarlet banners were now displayed the colors of repentance: soft gray and sober brown and the somber green of the pines. On every hand there were signs that the land was preparing itself for a time of ice and snow, a time of howling winds and bitter tribulation.

The Captain glanced at his companions and rose to his feet. "Let's break up this Quaker meeting. We've been sitting here like three owls on a limb! Come along, brother. I know of a corner just over yonder where we'll find a woodcock. I call her the Last Day Woodcock, for she's always there. Not the same bird, of course, but one just like her. Manitou manages the affair. I'm telling you, Son, that you'll always find a bird there just before sundown on the last day."

He blushed, for it's difficult for a Yankee to confess his superstitions, even to his own kin. "I have a good notion that there wouldn't be any woodcock there for a man who couldn't appreciate Manitou's gesture."

The Last Day Woodcock was there, just as the Captain had predicted; but when it rose whistling over the birches Young Feller couldn't see it, and the older gunner, after waiting an interminable time, regretfully dropped it.

"I wish you'd—" he began, but he never finished the sentence.

There was a quick impulse, a confusion of flying leaves and an imperious thunder of wings, followed by a single shot and silence.

"I missed that one, too, Dad." The Young Feller's tone was contrite.

The Captain's more experienced ears had noticed the sudden cessation of feathery thunder.

"Stay where you are. I'm coming over."

He made his way through the thicket to where Young Feller stood, disconsolate, with a faint wisp of powder smoke rising from the open gun breech.

"Which way was he going?" he inquired.

Young Feller pointed. "Right over there. But heck, Dad, I didn't hit him. I couldn't even see him!"

"Stand fast!" the Captain ordered.

There were white shot streaks upon the saplings and torn wadding on the ground to guide him. He went forward slowly, his eyes studying the carpet of fallen leaves and debris.

Finally he stopped and called to the boy, "Come here, Young Feller."

The lad came, and his eyes, following the direction of the older man's pointing finger, saw only a litter of twigs, leaves and bark. But as he gazed something happened. A pattern was forming there— a band of jet, darker by far than the black soil itself, then a jewel fashioned from purest topaz. The last expiring tremor of gallant wings confirmed the miracle.

The Captain stood silent, his eyes on Young Feller's face.

"Brother," said he, "you have reached a man's estate. You have shot your first pa'tridge. I picked up mine right over yonder by that black birch. That," he added softly, "was forty years and a great many pa'tridges ago."